Plumbing

Illustrated Dictionary –
A practical A–Z guide

John Thompson

www.harcourt.co.uk

✓ Free online support
✓ Useful weblinks
✓ 24 hour online ordering

01865 888058

Heinemann

From Harcourt

Heinemann Educational Publishers
Halley Court, Jordan Hill, Oxford OX2 8EJ
Part of Harcourt Education

Heinemann is the registered trademark of Harcourt Education Limited

Text © Harcourt Education Ltd, 2007

First published 2007

09 08 07
10 9 8 7 6 5 4 3 2 1

British Library Cataloguing in Publication Data is available from the British Library on request.

10-digit ISBN: 0435402080
13-digit ISBN: 978 0435 40208 2

Edited by Alexander Gray
Designed by HL Studios
Typeset by HL Studios

Original illustrations © Harcourt Education Limited, 2006
Illustrated by HL Studios
Cover design by GD Associates
Printed in the UK by Scotprint
Cover photo: © Harcourt Education/Gareth Boden
Picture research by Liz Alexander

Tel: 01865 888058 www.heinemann.co.uk

Introduction

This book has been designed as an essential reference tool for trainees, apprentices and experienced plumbing and heating professionals, providing quick and clear guidance on key plumbing and heating terms and processes.

The dictionary contains over 1,400 entries, covering the full range of plumbing and heating work activities undertaken in both residential and non-residential properties including:

- plumbing systems installation – above ground sanitary pipework and rainwater systems
- heating systems installation – including references to current environmental legislation targeted at reducing greenhouse gas emissions
- combustion appliance installation – appliances fuelled by oil, gas and solid fuel, including key references to alternative forms of energy usage
- electrical systems installation – electrical work associated with the installation of plumbing and heating systems
- sheet lead installation – sheet lead weatherings to building surfaces.

Each entry in this practical, easy-to-use dictionary, clearly defines the meaning, application and purpose of the term. The many full-colour photographs and illustrations provide further clarity and essential information about complex components and procedures.

Cross-references to other entries in the dictionary are identified in *italics* the first time they appear in a definition aiding your research on a particular subject. Entries that are described by multiple terms such as 'rainwater pipe', 'down-pipe' or 'fall-pipe' are fully cross-referenced.

Particular emphasis has been placed on providing clear, practical interpretations of terms that are used in current legislation and standards such as 'branch discharge pipe' and 'discharge stack'. This should provide invaluable assistance in 'getting to grips' with the relevant standards and legislation.

So, whether you are just starting out on a plumbing career or have been working in the industry for some time, the Plumbing Illustrated Dictionary is your key reference guide; providing a clear, concise and current interpretation of the many terms that are used by the plumbing and heating industry.

John Thompson

Acknowledgements

The author and publisher would like to thank the following individuals and organisations for permission to reproduce photographs:

Getty Images/PhotoDisc page 1 (unit opener); **Ginny Stroud-Lewis** pages 13, 231; **Harcourt Education Ltd/ Gareth Boden** pages 24, 27, 43, 45, 46, 48, 61, 84, 91, 99, 102, 104, 128, 129, 139, 140, 169, 175, 177, 480, 193, 201, 202, 203, 204, 205, 215, 223 (bottom left), 225, 227, 228, 237, 258, 262, 278, 286, 287, 308, 315, 324, 325; **Ingram Publishing / Alamy** page 223 (bottom right); **Kevan Thomas** page 282; **Institute of Plumbing and Heating Engineers** page 147; **Lead Sheet Association** page 1 (bottom right), 158, 159, 162; **Science Photo Library/ Sheila Terry** page 236

Every effort has been made to contact copyright holders of material reproduced in this book. Any omissions will be rectified in subsequent printings if notice is given to the publishers.

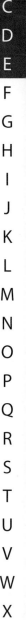

above ground drainage system

A system of pipework used to remove *(foul) black water* or *rainwater* to the drainage system.

above ground sanitary pipework system

A system of pipework conveying the discharge from sanitary appliances.
See *Types of sanitary pipework system*

ABS

This stands for acrylonitrile butadiene styrene, which is a *thermoplastic* material used for waste *discharge pipework*. It has a dull matt surface and will burn if lit.

absolute pressure

The total pressure exerted on a surface. The more usual pressure measured by most gauges is called *gauge pressure* and reflects an adjusted pressure that measures zero at the Earth's surface. Since *atmospheric pressure* at the earth's surface is approximately 1 bar, the absolute pressure is 1 bar higher than gauge pressure at the same location.

So, gauge pressure + atmospheric pressure = absolute pressure

abutment flashing

A weatherproofing material used to seal the join between a roof and a brick wall, such as a garage joining the external brick wall of a house, or a chimney passing through a roof.

▶ Example of an abutment flashing

access point

A position in a sanitary or drainage pipework system at which access can be gained via an *inspection chamber* to undertake maintenance. Access points should be sited at places in a system where blockage is likely to occur, such as bends, branch junctions or changes in gradient. For the purposes of system design, the top of a *stack vent* and the removal of a *trap* can be regarded as access points.

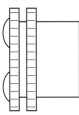

◀ Example of a waste discharge pipe access plug

▲ Example of an inspection chamber

acetylene gas

A gas used in oxyacetylene *welding* and *lead welding*. It is produced when calcium carbide is brought into contact with water. It is a relatively unstable gas and is dissolved in acetone to increase its stability and reduce the risk of explosion; it is therefore often known as dissolved acetylene. Acetylene gas is pressurised in order that it may be stored in cylinders. Cylinders are colour coded a maroon (red) colour in order that they may be easily recognised. The threads to the cylinder are left hand connection. See *Welding equipment*

acid

An acid (often represented by the generic formula AH) is typically a water-soluble, sour-tasting chemical compound. In common usage an acid is any substance that, when dissolved in water, gives a solution with a *pH value* less than 7. Examples of acids in plumbing include active fluxes for pipe-cleaning purposes and drain-cleaning solutions. A further example of a mild acid is when *rainwater* falls through the atmosphere; it collects small amounts of gases such as *carbon dioxide*, leading to a weak mixture known as carbonic acid; the acid content of rainwater may further increase when it travels through material such as peat, further increasing its carbon dioxide content. Water with an acid content is said to be *soft water*, and in certain conditions can cause the corrosion of metals in plumbing and heating systems.

acrylic

A glassy, tough *thermoplastic* material that is vacuum formed by a process of sucking softened acrylic into cast and mould shapes that form the surface of fibreglass baths, shower trays, etc. It is hard-wearing plastic that is tough and relatively resistant to scratching.

A B C D E F G H I J K L M N O P Q R S T U V W X Y Z

active flux

See *Flux*

adhesion

This occurs when substances stick together, for example the surface molecules of water in a container are attracted to each other by *cohesion* and to the sides of the vessel by *adhesion*, and the water forms a thin, slightly curved skin, called a meniscus. Adhesion leads to *capillary action*.

▲ Adhesion of water and formation of meniscus

adjustable spanner

See *Spanners*

adventitious ventilation

This is the air that enters a room through the gaps between floorboards and around doors and windows. Adventitious ventilation is taken into account when determining the amount of natural ventilation air required for correct combustion at *flueless* or *open-flued* combustion appliances.

aerated burner

A *gas burner* in which the gas is mixed with air before emission and ignition.

air admittance valve

A valve that allows air to enter the *discharge pipework* system but not to escape, in order to limit pressure fluctuations in the system. They can be used as an alternative to a *stack vent* in a limited number of properties connected to the *drainage system*. They must not, however, adversely affect the amount of air needed for the *below ground drainage system* to work correctly. *Air admittance* valves can also be used on *branch discharge pipework* as a means of preventing *trap seal loss* with pipework systems that do not meet the requirements laid down in *Building Regulations* or *British Standards Institution* requirements. They should be placed in a position where air is

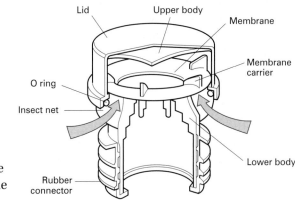

▶ Air admittance valve, showing the internal features

B
C
D
E
F
G
H
I
J
K
L
M
N
O
P
Q
R
S
T
U
V
W
X
Y
Z

A
B
C
D
E
F
G
H
I
J
K
L
M
N
O
P
Q
R
S
T
U
V
W
X
Y
Z

readily available at their inlet, and they are prone to freezing, so they should only be used on the inside of a building.

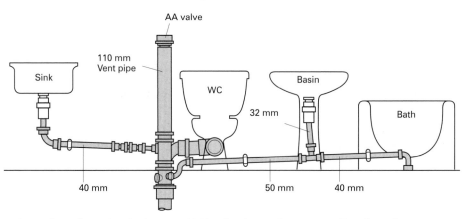

▲ Location of an air admittance (AA) valve in a primary ventilated stack system

air brick
A purpose-designed brick with fixed ventilation openings to allow air to pass through, ensuring there is proper combustion in *open-flued* combustion appliances, and adequate *ventilation* which prevents rot in suspended timber ground floors.

air change
The rate at which the air in a room is completely changed by either *natural ventilation* or *mechanical ventilation*. The rate of air change in a room is dependent on the rate of ventilation to and from the room, that is, cracks/gaps in building components, size of natural air vents, extent that windows are opened and the speed and capacity of any extractor fans in the room. The rate of air change in a room needs to be considered when designing a *central-heating system*. A higher air change will lead to a higher heat load required in the room as there will be a requirement to heat a greater volume of air in the room every hour.

air gap
The vertical distance between an appliance outlet, such as a tap or *warning pipe*, and the highest level that the water can reach in the appliance, which is often known as the *spill-over level*. An air gap is commonly used as a *backflow prevention device* to prevent *back siphonage* and possible water *contamination* occurring in water fittings such as taps.

air lock
The trapping of air in a pipe or fitting, resulting in a reduction or a complete stoppage of the flow of water. Air locks are associated with low-pressure systems, for example water supplied from a *storage cistern* or *gravity circulation* in primary pipework to *hot-water storage vessels*. An air lock is usually formed as a result of bad installation practice, whereby pipework is not laid with sufficient fall to prevent air from escaping from the system during filling.

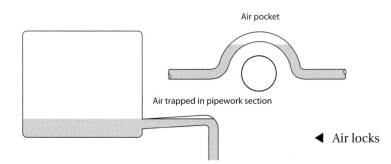

◀ Air locks

air-pressure switch

A safety cut-off device used in fan-flued boilers. If the fan is not operating, the air-pressure switch stops the ignition process from taking place and the boiler fails to safety condition and does not light.

air separator

This device, which is used in *open-vented fully-pumped central-heating* systems, allows the *cold feed* and *vent pipe* to be joined closely together in a desirable pipework configuration, causing turbulence, which removes air, reduces noise and reduces the risk of corrosion.

air tap (air valve)

This is a high point, usually in a *central-heating system*, where air can be bled from the system by manual means, as in the case of a *radiator*.

air tap key

A purpose-made device used with an air tap for letting out air from components such as *radiators*.

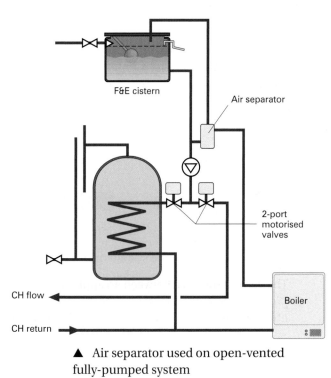

▲ Air separator used on open-vented fully-pumped system

air test

A pressure test applied to plumbing systems to check for leakage. For gas systems, see *tightness testing*. Air tests are not recommended for use on *hot-water, cold-water* and *central-heating system* components, as false readings may often be encountered owing to the fact that air is easily compressed. The test may be used with these system types in areas of the building where leakage could lead to substantial damage to expensive components such as computer suites.

Air tests are commonly carried out on *above ground sanitary pipework* systems and *below ground drainage systems* to check for leakage. With *sanitary pipework* systems the test is carried out as follows:

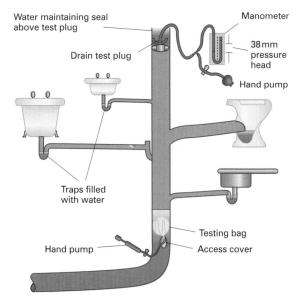

- Seal the system using hollow *drain plugs*. Fix a *test nipple* in the one to be used for the test. An inflatable bag can be used at the base of the stack as an alternative to a hollow drain plug if it is difficult to site.
- Fill the *traps* with water and cover the test plugs with water to make sure they are airtight.
- The *manometer*, rubber hose and hand pump are connected to the drain plug.

▲ Air test on a sanitary pipework system

Air is pumped into the system until a water head of 38 mm is reached on the manometer; the system is left for a test period of three minutes, during which time there should be no loss of pressure.
- Where a pressure drop is identified the system may be checked with *leak detection fluid* to identify the source of leakage.

With *below ground drainage systems* the test procedure is similar:
- Any *gully* traps are filled with water and pipe ends are plugged.
- Air is pumped into the system until a water head of 100 mm is reached on the *manometer*; the system is left for a test period of five minutes.
- During the test period there should not be a greater pressure drop than 25 mm on the gauge.

air vent

A grille which allows the free passage of air at all times, in particular for supplying air to combustion appliances for correct combustion and/or cooling purposes. Approved *air vents* cannot be adjusted or closed. When sited in an exterior or *cavity wall* the inner and outer grilles are connected by a liner which prevents blockage in the cavity. Air vents should be stable and resistant to corrosion. When used with combustion appliances there must be a minimum *free area* of aperture through the grille to meet the air supply requirements.

Labels: Internal grille, Telescopic cavity liner, External grille, Draught diverter (used as required)

▲ Air vent through cavity wall liner

alignment test

This is a test carried out on *drainage systems* to determine whether a drain is properly aligned. There are two tests undertaken:

- Mirror test. A mirror is placed at both ends of a drain and a light shone down the drain; if the drain is in proper alignment then a perfect circle should be shown in one of the mirrors; if an ellipse is shown then this will indicate the extent to which the drain is out of alignment.
- Ball test. A ball slightly less in diameter than the drain is rolled down the pipe; if no obstruction is present the ball should roll freely down the pipe from one end to the other.

alkaline

Any substance that in solution gives a pH of greater than 7, as in the case of lye (potassium hydroxide or sodium hydroxide), baking soda (sodium bicarbonate), and lime (calcium oxide or calcium hydroxide). If *rainwater* which contains dissolved carbon dioxide travels through soils containing limestone or chalk, those alkalis are taken into suspension resulting in *hard water*, which has a pH greater than 7. Alkali waters may result in 'furring' taking place inside plumbing components but do not tend to be as corrosive as water containing *acids*.

Allen keys

L-shaped tools with hexagonal heads of varying diameters designed to fit into socketed screws, allowing loosening and tightening of the screw.

alloy

A metal compound made by combining two or more metals. For example:

- brass is a combination of copper and zinc used for fixings
- bronze is a combination of copper and tin used for decorative purposes and for corrosion-resistant pumps

A B C D E F G H I J K L M N O P Q R S T U V W X Y Z

A
B
C
D
E
F
G
H
I
J
K
L
M
N
O
P
Q
R
S
T
U
V
W
X
Y
Z

- solder is a combination of lead and tin or tin and copper used for electrical connections and as a jointing material
- gunmetal is a combination of copper, tin and zinc used for corrosion-resistant underground fittings.

alternating current (a.c.)

The electrical current supplied to domestic properties, a.c. flows in forwards and backwards cycles (positive to negative). In the UK, domestic alternating current is usually single phase and supplied at 230 volts and a frequency of 50 Hertz (cycles per second).

ambient air temperature

The air temperature surrounding a body.

ammeter

A device used to measure current flow (electrical current) in amperes.

ampere

A measure of electric current. One ampere of current represents one coulomb of electrical charge moving past a specific point in one second.

angle branch

A junction in a main run of pipework where the branch joins the main run of pipe at an angle of less than 90°. An angle branch is sometimes called a splay or Y branch.

angle welded joint

The *lead welding* of two sheets of lead lying at different angles.

annealing

This process reduces the brittleness of metal by gentle heating and cooling, sometimes referred to as 'softening' the metal. Different metals and alloys require different temperatures for annealing.

annular space

The space between pipes or surfaces in close proximity, as in *flue systems* where there is space between the two pipe walls in a *twin-wall* pipe or there is space between a *flue liner* and its surrounding *chimney*.

anode

A positively charged electrode in an electrical circuit. During *electrolytic action (corrosion)* the anode is destroyed by the cathode. The rate of corrosion is dependent on the position of the metals in the *electrochemical series*.

anthracite

A 'hard coal', bright and shiny, smokeless, and generally found deeper in the earth than bituminous coal. It produces no smoke when burnt but may be difficult to light initially.

anti-capillarity groove

A groove cut into building materials preventing *capillary action* taking place, which may result in water entering the building. An anti-capillarity groove may be used where a lead *drip* is used to joint two pieces of sheet metal. The groove prevents water rising under the top piece of lead (overcloak) and prevents entry into the building.

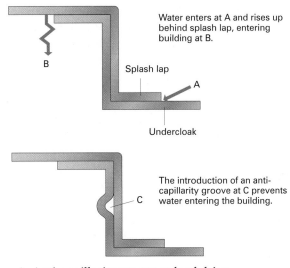

Water enters at A and rises up behind splash lap, entering building at B.

Splash lap

Undercloak

The introduction of an anti-capillarity groove at C prevents water entering the building.

▲ Anti-capillarity groove to lead drips

anti-gravity valve

A type of *non-return valve* that is used in *central-heating systems* to prevent unwanted *gravity circulation* taking place in pumped circuits when the circuit is turned off. Essentially, with certain pipe layouts it is possible for gravity circulation to take place in the circuit when the *motorised valve* is closed or the pump is turned off. The anti-gravity valve is a special type of non-return valve that operates under low circulating pressure, so that when circulation ceases in the circuit, gravity circulation in the pipe in which the anti-gravity valve is sited cannot take place.

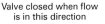
Valve closed when flow is in this direction

Valve open when flow is in this direction

▲ Anti-gravity valve

anti-legionella valve

A special valve connected to the inlet of an *expansion vessel* to ensure that fresh water circulates within it as water is drawn through the system. The valve is designed to minimise the possibility of bacteriological growth on the surface of the expansion vessel diaphragm which may lead to the growth of *legionella bacteria*.

anti-siphon traps

See *Resealing trap*

anti-vac traps

See *Resealing trap*

A
B
C
D
E
F
G
H
I
J
K
L
M
N
O
P
Q
R
S
T
U
V
W
X
Y
Z

anti-vacuum valve

A *valve* that is designed to open to the atmosphere when negative pressure occurs in a section of pipeline (suction pressure). The valve can be used as a *backflow prevention device* to guard against *back siphonage* in a pipeline and prevent system contents under suction pressure from being drawn back into water supply pipework. The anti-vacuum valve can also be used on certain types of *resealing trap* to permit air to enter the trap during operation and prevent the contents of the trap from being siphoned back into the waste discharge pipework, that is, it can be used to guard against *trap seal loss*.

anti-vibration mountings

These are special mountings sited under components, such as pumps, that are used to minimise the transmission of noise and the effects of vibration from the pump to the surface on which it is mounted. Anti-vibration mountings are usually manufactured from a rubber-based matter which acts as a good absorber.

APHC

This is the Association of Plumbing and Heating Contractors, which is the employers' trade association for the plumbing and heating industry in England and Wales. APHC represents the interests of its members to key organisations such as government and provides a range of essential services in support of running an effective plumbing business.

appliance compartment

A non-habitable space or enclosure designed to house combustion appliances.

appliance shut-off valve

A *service valve* fitted on or next to an appliance that is used for the purposes of isolating the appliance, usually for service or maintenance activities.

apron flashing

A type of cover flashing which lays over a roof structure at the point where it meets an abutment in order to weatherproof the building at that point. See *Lead flashing*

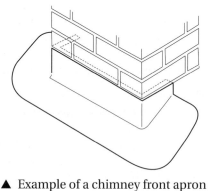

▲ Example of a chimney front apron

arc welding

This is a group of welding processes that use a welding power supply to create an electric arc between an electrode and the base material to melt metals at the welding point. They can use either *direct (d.c.)* or *alternating (a.c.)* current, and consumable or non-consumable *electrodes*. Special eye protection must be worn during the arc welding process to ensure that the eyes are not damaged.

artesian wells

An artesian well is formed by boring through an impervious layer of rock to a lower porous zone containing water. The well is designed so that the mouth is below the water table, forcing the water from the porous layer up and out.

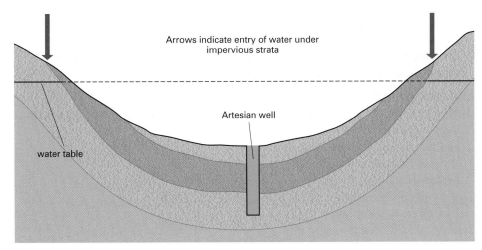

Arrows indicate entry of water under impervious strata

Artesian well

water table

▲ Head of water forces supply out through artesian well

artificial reservoirs

These are formed by damming a river in a low-lying area causing the land to flood, so that the water is preserved for domestic and industrial use.

asbestos

This is a mineral, extracted from rock to form a fibrous material used in products such as cement, fire-resistant boards, floor and ceiling tiles, insulation and roofing. Asbestos causes very serious health problems if the fibres are inhaled; it is not therefore widely used and great care must be taken when working with it in existing properties or removing it from site. Those who work with asbestos are required under Health and Safety legislation to be properly trained, informed and supervised in the work that they undertake.

asbestos cement

A mix of cement and asbestos used to form building components such as cold-water storage tanks, flue pipes and roof coverings. Asbestos cement is not now used owing to its asbestos content. Although not as dangerous as asbestos insulating materials, care should be taken when working with or removing asbestos cement-based materials; so all operatives must have received proper information, instruction and training on how to work safely with the material.

ascending spray bidet

A type of *bidet* which has an ascending spray below the *spill-over level* of the appliance, which presents a high risk of potential contamination to the water supply through *backflow*. Ascending spray bidets are not suitable for connection

A
B
C
D
E
F
G
H
I
J
K
L
M
N
O
P
Q
R
S
T
U
V
W
X
Y
Z

to *supply pipes*; care should also be taken when connecting ascending spray bidets to systems fed from storage; in most cases the hot and cold supplies must come from independent dedicated *distributing pipes* rather than common pipework feeding more than one appliance.

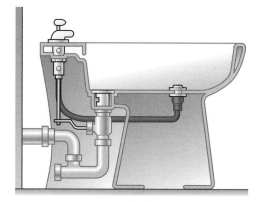

▲ Ascending spray bidet

atmosphere-sensing device (ASD)

A safety control, fitted to appliances such as water heaters and gas fires, to detect oxygen depletion. It is also known as a vitiation-sensing device or as an oxygen-depletion device (ODD). The device has a specially designed pilot which lifts away, cooling the *thermocouple*. The *thermoelectric device* then closes, shutting off the gas supply. Atmosphere-sensing devices are fitted to *flueless* space or water heaters, or *open-flued* appliances, such as gas fires, or *back-boiler* units. In a faulted condition a flueless or open-flued appliance may produce *carbon monoxide* as part of the *products of combustion*; this would eventually result in the oxygen supply to the appliance becoming depleted, in which case the appliance would fail owing to the operation of the atmosphere-sensing device.

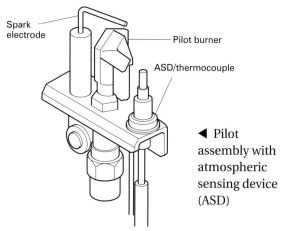

Spark electrode

Pilot burner

ASD/thermocouple

◀ Pilot assembly with atmospheric sensing device (ASD)

atmospheric burner

See *Natural draught burner*

atmospheric corrosion

Corrosion caused by elements and compounds in the air, for example the combination of oxygen and water vapour in the air can attack steel and iron causing rusting. Carbon dioxide, sulphur dioxide and sulphur trioxide are present in the air, especially in industrial areas, and can corrode iron, steel and zinc. In coastal areas, sea salt, which is very corrosive, dissolves into the local atmosphere and attacks iron-based (ferrous) metal. Copper, aluminium and lead do not corrode as easily; they also form a patina or protective barrier on the outer layer, for example copper sulphate.

atmospheric pressure

The *pressure* caused by the weight of the Earth's atmosphere, which varies at different heights above sea level; for example the pressure at sea level is 101.3 kN/m^2 or approximately 1 bar. It is important to take atmospheric pressure into account to avoid creating negative pressure or vacuums in some pipework systems which can lead to problems. Atmospheric pressure is the force that allows *siphonage* to occur to good effect in some plumbing components.

atom

An atom is the smallest part of a chemical element, with a nucleus at the centre containing neutrons (electrically neutral) and protons (positively charged) particles. Negatively charged electrons orbit the nucleus. Atoms contain equal numbers of protons and electrons. Electrons can move out of orbit and on to another atom. The movement of electrons creates electricity.

atomising burner

See *Pressure jet burner*

autogenous welding

A *welding* process to join two pieces of the same metal using heat without the addition of filler metal.

automatic air vent

A device that is primarily installed on a *central-heating* system at a high point so that when air gets trapped in the system, the vent automatically removes the air. They usually work on the principle of a float inside the *valve* rising to close off the vent when there is no air present or falling open to release air if there is an air build-up in the vent.

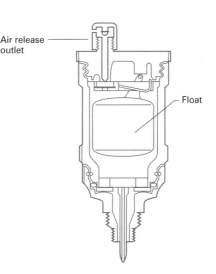

▲ Automatic air vent

automatic bypass valve

A mechanical device used in systems with *motorised valves* or *thermostatic radiator valves (TRVs)*, to ensure a minimum water-flow rate through the boiler if the zone valves or TRVs close and the circulating pressure developed by the pump goes over a pre-set limit. The automatic bypass valve minimises noise in the system and ensures premature failure of the pump and boiler *heat exchanger* does not occur.

▲ Automatic bypass valve

A
B
C
D
E
F
G
H
I
J
K
L
M
N
O
P
Q
R
S
T
U
V
W
X
Y
Z

A
B
C
D
E
F
G
H
I
J
K
L
M
N
O
P
Q
R
S
T
U
V
W
X
Y
Z

automatic changeover valve

This is used on *liquefied petroleum gas* installations fed by gas bottles to automatically change the supply from an empty gas bottle to a full gas bottle without affecting the gas supply to the property.

automatic flow cut-off device

A device which controls the flow of water into a *cistern* supplying *urinals*. The automatic flow cut-off device could be in the form of a *solenoid valve* operated by a *time switch* or *infrared sensor* controlling the flow of water into the cistern; or by means of an *hydraulically operated valve* that senses the use of other sanitary appliances in the toilet/washing area.

automatic flushing cistern

This automatically flushes the contents of the *cistern* feeding a *urinal* at fixed intervals. The time period between flushes is based on the rate of water flow into the cistern. *Water Regulations* lay down the maximum amount of water to be flushed over specific time periods. To ensure that the urinal cistern does not operate when the building is not occupied, an *automatic flow cut-off device* is fitted to the installation to isolate the supply to the cistern when flushing is not required. The operation of the automatic siphon is as follows:

- As the cistern fills, the air inside the dome of the siphon is compressed.
- The increased pressure forces water out of the u-tube which reduces pressure in the dome.
- The pressure reduction in the dome causes siphonic action to take place, flushing the cistern.
- When the cistern has emptied, the water in the upper well is siphoned into the lower well and the process starts again.

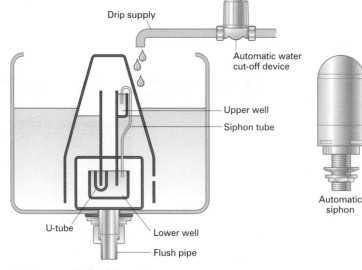

▲ Automatic flushing cistern

automatic valve

A device on a gas-fired *instantaneous water heater* which turns the gas on when a tap is opened and turns the gas off when the tap is closed. Automatic valves usually work on the principle of *differential* pressure, using a *venturi*.

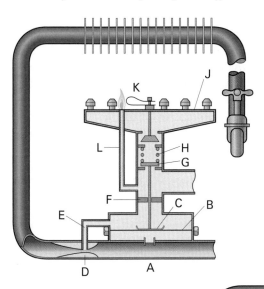

Key to diagram:
A – automatic valve/ diaphragm housing
B – rubber diaphragm
C – bearing plate
D – venturi
E – low-pressure side
F – gland for push rod
G – gas valve
H – gas-valve spring
J – burner
K – flame supervision (bi-metal strip)
L – pilot feed

▲ Operation of an automatic valve

auto-pneumatic pressure vessel

This device is normally used to supply water under pressure to the upper floors of high-rise buildings. The cylinder contains a cushion of air under pressure that is in contact with the water that is to be pressurised; this cushion of air forces water to high level and, as the water is drawn off, the air expands and its pressure falls.

A B C D E F G H I J K L M N O P Q R S T U V W X Y Z

At a pre-determined low level a *float switch* cuts in the pump; the pump will then supply water to the system which will meet the demand and gradually increase the air pressure in the cylinder until at a pre-determined height the high-level switch cuts off the pump. From time to time the air in the vessel will need to be topped-up; this is achieved by an air compressor feeding air into the vessel.

A variation on this system design is to use a high-pressure *expansion vessel* with internal diaphragm set to a fixed charge pressure. High- and low-pressure switches are incorporated into the design to operate the pump. So, on filling, the water in the system compresses the air in the vessel to a point at which the setting on the high-pressure switch is reached which cuts off the pump supplying the system. On water being drawn off, the expansion vessel is capable of supplying a fixed volume of water into the system that has been stored in the vessel by virtue of compression of the air space; on reaching the pressure setting of the low-pressure switch the pump is activated slowly, charging the system to the pressure set on the high-pressure switch, and so on. See *Boosted cold-water system*

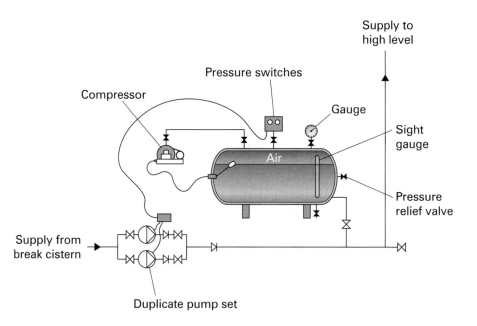

▲ Auto-pneumatic pressure vessel

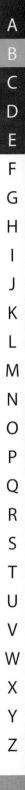

back-boiler

A water-heating boiler which is installed behind a *gas*, *oil* or *solid-fuel fire*, saving wall and floor space.

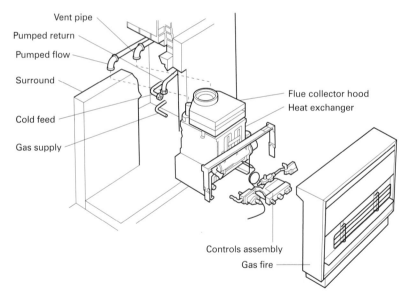

▲ The installation of a gas-fired back-boiler to a fireplace opening

backflow

Water flowing backwards, contrary to its intended direction, caused by *back pressure* or *back siphonage*. For example, water in a hosepipe under certain conditions may flow back through the tap and into the water supply creating water *contamination* and a serious health hazard. There are strict regulations requiring the installation of *backflow prevention* devices to guard against this risk.

A
B
C
D
E
F
G
H
I
J
K
L
M
N
O
P
Q
R
S
T
U
V
W
X
Y
Z

backflow prevention device

A device, fitted in a hot- and cold-water system, to prevent water flowing backwards. The *fluid risk category* for each type of installation is given in the Water Regulations, and the type of device required and the correct positioning of the device is specified. Backflow prevention devices may be *point of use* or *zone protection* devices. Detailed information about the selection and installation of back-flow devices may be found on the following websites.

Department for Environment, Food and Rural Affairs:
http://www.defra.gov.uk/environment/water/industry/wsregs99/guide/section6.htm

Water Regulations Advisory Scheme:
http://www.wras.co.uk, under 'Interpretations and advice'.

background central heating

See *Types of central heating*

back gutter

This is the rear section of the *chimney weathering set* used to weatherproof a *chimney*. It is often *lead welded* owing to its complex shape, however it may also be produced by *lead bossing*.

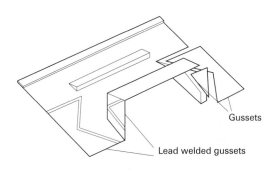

Gussets

Lead welded gussets

▲ Lead-welded back gutter

back inlet gully

A type of *floor gully* that has a connection point to which waste discharge pipework may be connected.

backnut

A nut which is fitted to components, such as *float-operated valves* and *pillar taps*, to keep them securely in place.

backplate elbow

A *brass* or *gunmetal* fitting with integral fixings to which a tap or cooker *bayonet fitting* is connected, providing a rigid fixing for the termination of pipework and the use of components, such as taps or cooker bayonet fittings, without damaging the pipework.

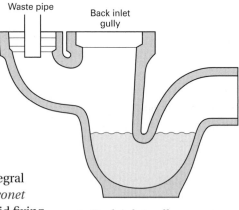

Waste pipe

Back inlet gully

▲ Back inlet gully

back pressure

The flow of water in a contrary direction in a hot- or cold-water system brought about by an increase in pressure in the system. One type of *backflow* is caused when heated water expands in an unvented appliance and flows backwards under increased pressure towards the supply pipe. To avoid this water reaching a tap and contaminating the supply pipe, a single *check valve* needs to be fitted to prevent back pressure causing a backflow.

back siphonage

This is *backflow* caused by *siphonage* of water from an appliance or attachment back into the supply pipe. For example, if a hose is used to fill a tank placed higher than the *mains*, and the supply of mains water is interrupted, the *contaminated* water in the tank and hose may flow back into the mains if the suction pressure of the water in the pipe is below *atmospheric pressure*.

baffle

Usually associated with *combustion* appliances, a baffle is used in a boiler heat exchanger to ensure that the heated flue gases pass across all surfaces of the heat *exchanger* ensuring that maximum heat energy is drawn from those flue gases and so increasing the efficiency of the appliance.

balanced compartment

A non-habitable sealed enclosure designed to house one or more *open-flued* gas appliances. The balanced compartment gains an air supply from a location external to the enclosure and adjacent to the *flue* discharge point. The compartment essentially 'room seals' the appliance and there should therefore be no openings into the compartment (other than those that are purpose-designed for the effective operation of the flue), the door should be self-closing and

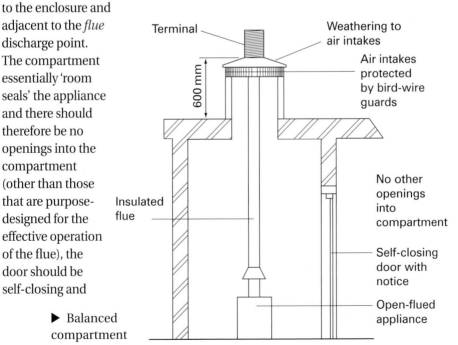

▶ Balanced compartment

Terminal

Weathering to air intakes

Air intakes protected by bird-wire guards

600 mm

Insulated flue

No other openings into compartment

Self-closing door with notice

Open-flued appliance

A
B
C
D
E
F
G
H
I
J
K
L
M
N
O
P
Q
R
S
T
U
V
W
X
Y
Z

have an air tight seal. A notice must be sited on the compartment door advising that it is a balanced compartment and should not be left open during normal boiler operation. The compartment must not be used for general storage purposes.

balanced-flued appliance
See *Room-sealed* flue

balanced pressure
This refers to hot- and cold-water supplies that are at a relatively equal pressure. Balanced supply pressures may be required to ensure that certain types of *mixer taps* and *shower mixer valves* operate correctly. See *Unbalanced pressure*

balancing
The process of ensuring that the correct flow of water is provided to individual *heat emitters* in a *central-heating system*. The water flow to a number of heat emitters in a system needs adjusting by throttling or reducing the flow through the *lockshield radiator valve* in the circuit so that correct flow and return water temperatures are achieved both into and out of the heat emitter. A system that is not correctly balanced will not work effectively in some rooms, not achieving their correct design temperatures.

ball test
See *Alignment test*

ball valve
See *Float-operated valve*

balloon grating
Also known as a bird cage or domical cage, this is a component fitted to the top of a *stack vent* to prevent foreign materials and nesting birds gaining entry to the ventilating pipework.

▲ Balloon grating

bar
A unit for measuring pressure, the bar tends to be used for measuring water and gas pressures and pressures inside cylinders such as oxyacetylene *welding equipment*. One bar is equal to 100 kPa and approximately 10 m head of water.

barrel nipple
See *Spacer nipple*

barrier pipe
Manufactured from cross-linked polythene to British Standard 7291, barrier pipes prevent air permeation and are used for vented and sealed *central-heating systems* to prevent air ingress into the system through the plastic pipework.

base exchange water softener

A unit which softens water using resin or *zeolites* to attract and absorb the calcium and magnesium salts, which cause hardness. The resin should be washed regularly with saline solution (i.e. salt), releasing the magnesium and calcium salts. This is done automatically by the unit via a time clock which is set to operate at specific periods. British Standard BS 6700 applies to the installation of base exchange water softeners, specifying precautions for the prevention of *backflow*. A drinking water supply usually at the kitchen sink is taken off before the water is treated.

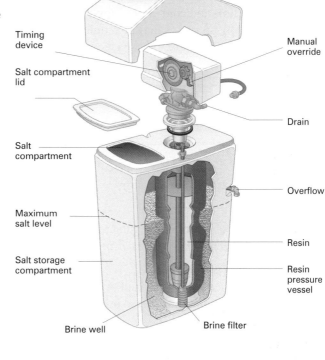

Timing device

Salt compartment lid

Salt compartment

Manual override

Drain

Overflow

Maximum salt level

Salt storage compartment

Resin

Resin pressure vessel

▶ Section through a typical base exchange water softener

Brine well

Brine filter

basin wrench

Sometimes called a basin spanner or basin key, this is a tool available in a number of designs for reaching the *backnuts* and tap connectors of *pillar taps* that are sited in relatively inaccessible spaces.

▶ Basin wrench

bathroom electricity supply zones

Because the bathroom is the highest risk area for electrical hazards in domestic properties it is broken down into a series of zones which present the degree of risk, zone 1 being the greatest. Supplementary *cross-bonding* is used to ensure that proper *earthing* is maintained. The level of supplementary cross-bonding required is dependent on the proximity of plumbing systems and components to electrical components, with bathrooms being the greatest risk. See *Bonding (equipotential bonding)*

A
B
C
D
E
F
G
H
I
J
K
L
M
N
O
P
Q
R
S
T
U
V
W
X
Y
Z

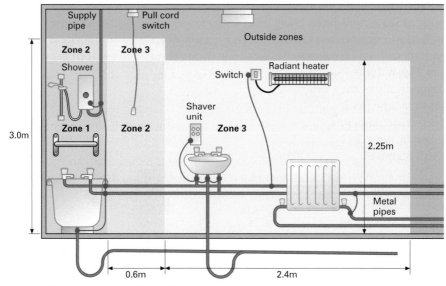

▲ Electrical zones in bathrooms

bay
> One of a number of sections of a flat metallic roof or wall *cladding*, for example the space between a lead *roll* or a *drip* is referred to as a bay.

bayonet fitting (connector)
> The plug-in device at the end of a flexible hose which allows for a quick release, for example a bayonet fitting used on gas cooker connections.

bedding
> The filling material that is used to give support and protection to *below ground drainage pipework*. The bedding material is designed to distribute loads evenly along the pipeline, to provide an even base on which the pipe is rested and to prevent distortion or damage to the pipework due to small ground movement.

bedpan washer
> A device used in hospitals in which bedpans or urine bottles can be emptied or washed.

Belfast sink
> A white, heavy-duty, fireclay sink used in domestic and commercial properties. The Belfast sink has an overflow and usually takes a 1½ inch threaded waste. This sink is usually installed with *bib taps*, but *pillar* or *monobloc* taps may be used in domestic properties.

bell joint
> A type of *bronze*-welded joint used to connect two pieces of copper pipe together. See *Bronze welding*

below ground drainage system

A system of pipework that safely conveys *waste waters* and *rainwater* away from a building to a *sewer* or other point, such as a *septic tank*, for treatment and disposal. Key features of a drainage system are:

- The system must be laid to the correct falls so that the pipework is self-cleansing.
- Access should be provided on long runs of pipework and changes of direction so that any blockages may be readily cleared.
- Pipework must be properly supported so that it does not distort and affect the operation of the system.
- They must be properly ventilated. Incorrectly ventilated drains could lead to pressure build up in the system that could cause *trap seal loss* or the build-up of dangerous gases such as *methane*.
- Ordinarily they shouldn't be run under buildings.

Drains carrying *black (foul) water* must be trapped preventing noxious smells from entering properties or contact with people. *Rainwater* discharged into a *surface-water*-only system need not be trapped. Drainage pipes to new domestic properties are usually plastic; extensions to existing systems may be made in clayware. *Clay pipes* and *cast-iron* pipes (exposed drainpipes) may be used in industrial/commercial properties.

benching

The sloping sides at the bottom of a brick-built *inspection chamber* that are formed to prevent the build-up of solid waste that may lead to blockage, for example faecal matter.

benchmark scheme

A scheme designed to ensure that heating and hot-water appliances are installed and commissioned in line with manufacturer requirements. Installer member companies must be approved to scheme requirements and confirm that they will work to an agreed code of conduct, including the completion of proper commissioning records for appliances that can be used by customers to log the service history of the appliance.

bend

Available in a number of angles to meet specific needs, this component is used to make a change of direction in a pipeline; it may also be available in different bend radiuses. For example, a *long radius bend* is commonly used at the foot of a *discharge stack* to minimise the possible pressure build-up that may take place with a short radius bend leading to *trap seal loss*.

bending machine

This machine, which is used to put bends in pipes, is available in two types: the *hydraulic pipe bender* used for *low-carbon steel* and large diameter copper pipework; and manual benders, which are available as *hand benders* (often known as scissor benders), for bending up to 22 mm diameter copper tube or

A
B
C
D
E
F
G
H
I
J
K
L
M
N
O
P
Q
R
S
T
U
V
W
X
Y
Z

A
B
C
D
E
F
G
H
I
J
K
L
M
N
O
P
Q
R
S
T
U
V
W
X
Y
Z

as *stand benders* for bending up to 42 mm diameter tube. Key parts of the bending machine are:

- Former – this supports the bend while it is being formed.
- Guide (back guide) – this supports the back of the pipe during bending.
- Roller – this permits force to be applied along the guide as the bend progresses.

▲ Hand bender   ▲ Stand bender

bending spring

A spring used for bending copper pipe manually without flattening the pipe. The spring prevents flattening of the pipe and may be applied internally or externally. The pipe is bent around the plumber's knee. Spring bending will not usually be able to achieve as tight a radius bend as a machine, and the copper tube may require *annealing* to stop it rippling during the bending process.

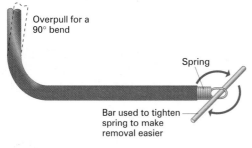

Overpull for a
90° bend

Spring

Bar used to tighten
spring to make
removal easier

▲ Pipe bending with internal spring

bending stick

A *lead working tool* made from boxwood or high-density plastic that is used during the *lead bossing* process. See *Lead working tools*

bib tap

A tap with a horizontal *male thread* at its inlet that typically screws into a *backplate elbow* that is sited above a sink or specialist appliance such as those found in hospitals. A bib tap may also have a hose union connection for the purposes of connecting a hose pipe to it, such as for outdoor use. See *Hose union bib tap*

bidet

A sanitary washing appliance, usually made from vitreous china, which carries a high *fluid risk category*. There are two main types of bidet, *over rim* and *ascending spray*. The ascending-spray bidet cannot be used on *mains* supply and must have piping installed correctly to prevent *contamination* and to meet the requirements of the *Water Regulations*.

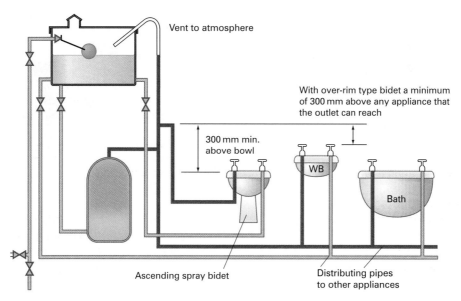

Vent to atmosphere

With over-rim type bidet a minimum of 300 mm above any appliance that the outlet can reach

300 mm min. above bowl

WB

Bath

Ascending spray bidet

Distributing pipes to other appliances

▲ Pipework layout for ascending spray bidet

bill of quantities (B of Q)

A document produced by a *quantity surveyor* by measuring or 'taking off' the quantities of materials from a drawing. The B of Q lists the amounts and costs of all the materials required for a contract and is used to control costs and provide milestones for contractors' payments.

bi-metal strip

A strip made of two metals joined together, such as *brass* and *Invar*, one on each side of the length, that can be used to control the flow of gas into appliances in temperature controls and *flame supervision devices*. The metals have different expansion rates, so one metal expands faster than the other, making the strip bend. This type of gas control does not tend

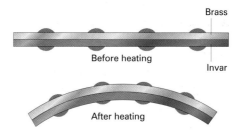

Brass

Before heating

Invar

After heating

▲ A bi-metal strip. The brass expands more than the invar on heating, thus bending the strip

A
B
C
D
E
F
G
H
I
J
K
L
M
N
O
P
Q
R
S
T
U
V
W
X
Y
Z

to be used on modern gas appliances as a flame supervision device, as it does not provide the close control that other devices can provide.

bird cage

See *Balloon grating*

black water

Waste water that contains faecal matter or urine. Also known as foul water.

blowpipe

See *Welding blowpipe*

blowtorch

Also known as a blowlamp, this is used for heating processes such as making soldered *capillary joints* to copper pipework. The blowtorch is usually fuelled by the *liquefied petroleum gas – propane* and may be lighted manually or it may include automatic ignition.

boiler

An appliance fuelled by *gas, oil* or *solid fuel* designed for heating water either for *space heating* or for space heating combined with hot-water supply.

boiler control interlock

This is not a single control device but a group of control devices that may include room and *cylinder thermostats* and *zone valves*. It ensures that the boiler does not operate until there is a demand for heat from one of the circuits in the building.

boiler noise

The noise (also known as 'kettling') from the boiler *heat exchanger*, which may be associated with an incorrect flow rate (usually too low) through the boiler owing to the system not being properly designed or commissioned, which results in a noise being emitted during the heating process which can lead to damage to the heat exchanger. It can also be caused by an incorrect flow rate brought about by the build-up of sediment or sludge; this can be prevented by ensuring proper system design and treating the water in the system with *corrosion inhibitor*. Boiler noise can sometimes sound like a kettle boiling which is why it is sometimes called 'kettling'. See *Kettling*

boiler sizing

This is selecting the required boiler size for a property based on the sum of the heat load from the *heat emitters*, plus the heat requirement to the hot-water circuit (if installed) and any heat lost from pipework supplying the circuits in the building. The nearest boiler size (usually slightly above) is selected to meet the property's heat requirement. It is the boiler output that is the basis for selecting the size of boiler not its *heat input*.

boilers with pump over run thermostats

These are boilers in which the operation of the pump is directly controlled by electrical controls in the boiler, with the controls responding to the activation of the overrun *thermostat*, causing the pump to keep operating for a few minutes after the last circuit has closed, to remove the residual heat from the boiler.

boiling point

This is the temperature at which a liquid boils and changes state to a gas or vapour. Water boils at 100°C when at *atmospheric pressure* (at sea level). For example, if the liquid being heated is below atmospheric pressure then the boiling point of water is lower than 100°C; conversely, if it is above atmospheric pressure then the boiling point will be higher.

bonding (equipotential bonding)

For safety purposes, this is the practice of connecting exposed metalwork together using conductors in the form of earth clamps or clips, keeping all the metalwork at equal *potential*. Cables from the exposed metalwork are connected back to the main earth terminal, usually adjacent to the electrical supply equipment into the property. *Main equipotential bonding* refers to the direct connection of key services such as gas, oil and water pipework to the earthing terminal. Supplementary bonding refers to the connection of exposed metal parts that are remote from the plumbing system or have been separated from the main bonding, for example by the use of plastic fittings. There are specific requirements laid down in BS 7671 that detail the size of bonding conductor that must be used. See *Bathroom electricity supply zones*

▲ Earth bonding to water pipe

A
B
C
D
E
F
G
H
I
J
K
L
M
N
O
P
Q
R
S
T
U
V
W
X
Y
Z

A B C D E F G H I J K L M N O P Q R S T U V W X Y Z

boosted cold-water system

A system of raising cold water in a building to a height above that which the normal *mains* or a pumped supply from a borehole or well can supply. There are three types of system that can be used for doing this:

- Direct boosted system – here the incoming supply is boosted by the use of a pump set to supply all or high-level parts of the building. This system may include a large *header pipe* to contain a reserve of drinking water. The operation of the pumps should be controlled by a high- and low-level switching arrangement in the system to prevent nuisance operation and wearing of the pump. This type of system is unlikely to be accepted by the *water undertaker* (i.e. supplier) owing to its excessive demands on the mains pipework system.

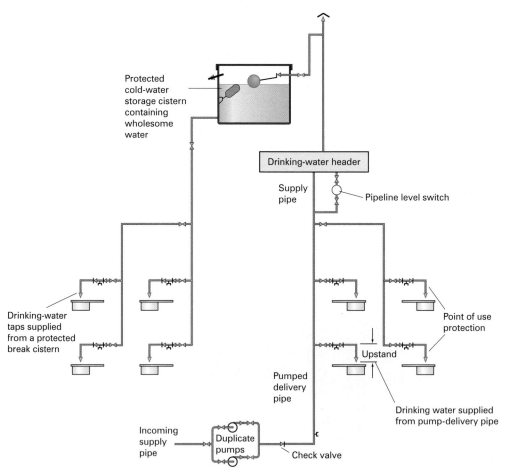

▲ Direct boosted cold-water system with drinking header

- Indirect boosted system – similar to the direct boosted system with the exception that the incoming water is supplied from a *break cistern* sited at low level, usually inside the building. See *Auto-pneumatic pressure vessel*

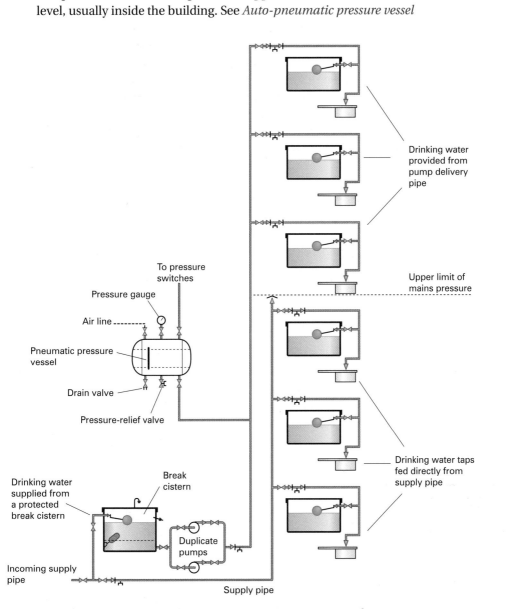

▲ Indirect boosted system with auto-pneumatic pressure vessel

A
B
C
D
E
F
G
H
I
J
K
L
M
N
O
P
Q
R
S
T
U
V
W
X
Y
Z

booster pump

A pump which increases the pressure and velocity of water flow as in the case of boosting the supply pressure to a shower when fed from storage. Booster pumps for shower applications come in single and twin impellor formats, with differing piping arrangements. A booster pump is normally controlled by the operation of a *flow switch*; a pump is also capable of supplying water above the height of a *storage cistern*, in which case a *pressure switch* is used to control the operation of the pump.

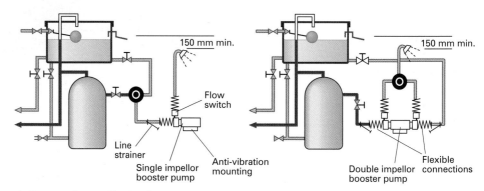

▲ Pumped supplies to showers

borax

A type of flux that can be used for *welding* and *hard soldering*.

boss

A means of connecting a pipe or component to another pipe or component, for example an *immersion heater boss* or *strap-on boss*.

bossing

See *Lead bossing*

bossing mallet

See *Leadworking tools*

bossing stick

See *Leadworking tools*

Boss pipe ring seal   Strap-on boss

▲ Plastic pipe boss and strap-on boss

bottle trap

A trap used where appearance is important, as in the case of free-standing basins; they are neater than *tubular traps*. Bottle traps are easy to install in difficult situations, but should not be used on sinks or waste disposal units as they are easily blocked. See *Trap*

▲ Bottle trap

bottled gas

This is *propane* or *butane liquefied petroleum gas* that is stored in gas bottles and may be used for applications such as soldering fittings through to heating properties.

bowl urinal

A bowl-shaped urinal designed for individual use (rather than communal use), sited at a convenient height above floor level. See *Urinals*

box gutter

A square boxed gutter section at the termination of a flat or pitched roof, sited behind a parapet wall. For waterproofing purposes, the gutter is lined with a metallic material such as sheet lead.

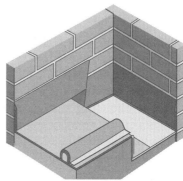

▲ Box gutter section

brackets

These are fixings for supporting pipework, such as copper or plastic clips for supporting copper and plastic pipework in domestic properties. In commercial buildings, clips or brackets need to be stronger, and the types to be used on large contracts may often be manufactured from *brass*.

branch

A branch or tee is the connection of pipework into the main flowing pipework.

branch discharge pipe

A pipe connecting sanitary appliances to a *discharge stack* or a *drain*. See *Types of sanitary pipework system*

branch-forming tool (tee extractor)

A special tool used to form a tee or branch into a main copper pipeline without the use of a fitting. The branch pipe is *hard soldered* to the main pipeline.

◀ Branch forming tool

branch ventilating pipe

A ventilating pipe connected to a *branch discharge pipe* and to the *discharge stack* above the *spill-over level* of the highest fitting served. If the pipe serves a single appliance the minimum size allowed is 25 mm. If the pipe runs further than 15 m or serves more than one appliance, the minimum size allowed is 32 mm. See *Types of sanitary pipework system*

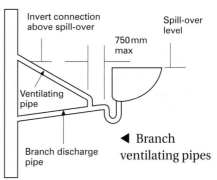

Invert connection above spill-over

Spill-over level

750 mm max

Ventilating pipe

Branch discharge pipe

◀ Branch ventilating pipes

A
B
C
D
E
F
G
H
I
J
K
L
M
N
O
P
Q
R
S
T
U
V
W
X
Y
Z

branched flue system

A common *open-flued* system serving appliances on two or more floors.

brass

An alloy of copper and zinc used in the manufacture of plumbing fittings, for example pipe brackets, stop valves, etc.

brazed joint

This is a type of *hard soldered* joint using *brass* or a similar molten alloy as the soldering material. The hard solder flows between the two surfaces of the metal by *capillary action* and is therefore categorised as a *capillary joint*. This type of joint is much stronger than a standard *soft soldered* joint and requires a higher temperature to make the solder molten; an oxyacetylene *blowpipe* will normally be used for making such joints. A brazed joint should not be confused with *bronze welding* as this is a different process.

break cistern

A water-storage unit for *boosted cold-water supplies* used to overcome problems with reduction in *mains* pressure, and mostly used in the case of high-rise buildings or in situations where there is a very poor incoming water supply pressure. The break cistern must be fully protected (fully-fitting sealed lid, sealed and filtered vent etc.) when supplying water for domestic purposes, for example cooking, drinking etc., in order to protect against the ingress of contaminants.

British Board of Agreement

This is an independent body that tests and approves materials for use in the construction industry, including certain plumbing products, such as *unvented hot-water* cylinders.

British Standards Institution (BSI) kitemark

This symbol indicates that materials and equipment displaying it have been tested and proved to meet the quality standards of the British Standards Institution (BSI), which sets quality standards and standard dimensions for equipment and materials. British Standards also set quality standards for the installation of materials and equipment; these are often called codes of practice. All British Standards start with BS followed by a number, for example BS 6700 is the standard for the design, installation, testing and maintenance of services supplying water for domestic use.

▲ British Standards Institution kitemark

British Thermal Unit (BTU)

An old imperial unit used to measure quantity of heat, defined as the quantity of energy necessary to raise the temperature of 1lb of water by 1°F. Combustion appliances are sometimes given a rating in btu/hr.

bronze

An alloy of copper and tin used in the manufacture of plumbing components and fittings.

A
B
C
D
E
F
G
H
I
J
K
L
M
N
O
P
Q
R
S
T
U
V
W
X
Y
Z

bronze welding

This is a *hard soldered* jointing process made by building up filler material across a gap between copper pipe surfaces. The joint is not now widely used owing to issues with *dezincification* of the filler metal. *Brazing* tends to be used as an alternative hard soldering method.

BSPT

The initials for British Standard Pipe Thread, which is the imperial type of thread commonly in use in pipework systems in the UK, for example pipe threads include ½, ¾, 1 inch etc.

builder's opening

An enclosure constructed for fireplace components such as *back-boilers*.

building control officer

A person employed by the local authority to check that buildings conform to the relevant Regulations, such as access for people with disabilities, conservation, public health and safety. The building control officer checks the initial plans and work in progress at various stages, and issues a certificate of completion when the building work is finished.

Building Notice submission

A Building Notice is submitted to the local authority to gain approval to undertake items of work for which Building Regulations consent is required.

building paper

A type of *underlay* laid between the surfaces of roofing materials and metallic coverings such as sheet lead.

Building Regulations

These lay down the statutory (legal) requirements that must be met when carrying out contruction work (including plumbing and heating installation) in residential and non-residential properties. Advice and guidance on meeting the requirements of the Regulations is detailed in a series of Approved Documents. Copies of the Building Regulations Approved Documents can be freely downloaded from the website of the Department of Communties and Local Government at: www.communities.gov.uk

building services engineer

An engineer who usually designs, or supervises, installation and maintenance work on building services, including water, heating, lighting, electrical, gas, communications and mechanical services such as lifts and escalators. Building services engineers usually work for manufacturers, large construction companies, engineering consultants, architects' practices or local authorities.

building surveyor

A building surveyor conducts structural surveys of buildings, prepares plans and specifications, advises on matters such as conservation and insulation, and may also be involved in legal work and negotiation with local authorities.

A
B
C
D
E
F
G
H
I
J
K
L
M
N
O
P
Q
R
S
T
U
V
W
X
Y
Z

bulk tank

A tank designed for the bulk storage of *liquefied petroleum gas (LPG)*. Key features of the tank are:

- LPG is stored at relatively high pressure in the tank.
- A first stage *regulator* reduces the pressure to approximately 0.7 bar.
- A second stage regulator reduces the pressure down to the normal system supply pressure of 37 mbar.
- An *OPSO/UPSO valve* is fitted in the pipeline to protect against over-pressurisation of the system should the regulator fail, and under-pressurisation of the system should a large leak occur.
- The tank is protected by a pressure-relief valve should the contents of the tank reach an excessive pressure.
- Shut-off valves are incorporated in the pipelines, and the tank includes a contents gauge to identify the quantity of LPG in the tank.
- There are restrictions on where the tank may be sited in relation to the vicinity of buildings.

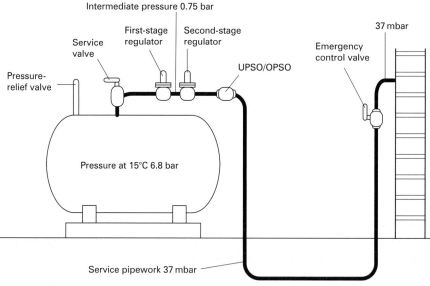

▲ LPG bulk-storage tank

burner

The part of a *combustion* appliance where the fuel is mixed with air and burned to produce heat. See *Gas burner; Pressure jet burner*

burner pressure

Sometimes known as the operating pressure or working pressure of a gas appliance, this is the gas pressure which the appliance requires to work correctly. Some appliances are *range rated* and the burner pressure must be adjusted to suit the specific heat input requirements of the appliance.

bush

A *brass* or *low-carbon steel* fitting designed to connect a larger *female thread* to a reduced *male thread*, and used with threaded pipe connections.

butane gas

A type of *liquefied petroleum gas* supplied in blue colour-coded cylinders, primarily used for gas heating purposes.

butt joint – bronze welding

A type of joint that can be used in *bronze welding*.

butt joint – sheet lead

A welded jointing method used for sheet lead, for example a *lead-welded* front apron would be manufactured using butt joints. The apron is marked and cut between (B) and (D). The sheet lead is worked into position and a *gusset* is cut to fit the gap left in the material. The gusset (which does not overlap the material) is welded to the edges of the metal at (B) and (D).

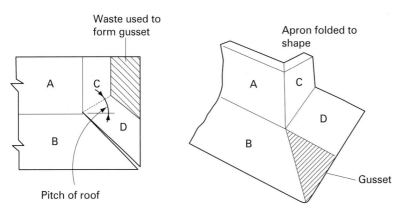

▲ Lead-welded front apron with butt joint

bypass circuit

A circuit which maintains a constant flow of water through a central-heating boiler when key valves in the system begin to close such as *motorised valves* and *thermostatic radiator valves*.

bypass valve

See *Automatic bypass valve*

ABCDEFGHIJKLMNOPQRSTUVWXYZ

ABCDEFGHIJKLMNOPQRSTUVWXYZ

calorific value

The amount of heat energy released when combustible matter (fuel) is burned. The calorific value and amount of heat given off by a specific fuel differs per unit mass from one fuel to another; for example 1 kg of wood gives off less heat than 1 kg of fuel oil owing to the difference in calorific value. The calorific value of solids and liquids is measured in units of MJ/kg whilst gases are measured in units of MJ/m^3.

calorifier

A type of *heat exchanger* used for non-domestic purposes. A calorifier, whilst requiring additional controls, is similar in principle to an *indirect cylinder*.

canopy

A device sited above a *combustion* appliance, such as a *decorative fuel effect gas appliance*, to gather and safely discharge the products of combustion to the atmosphere, or a roof type overhang above a doorway.

capacitor

An electrical device which stores electrical energy and releases it when needed, most commonly in the case of single phase electric motors such as those in circulating pumps in order to provide sufficient power to initially get the pump motor to run.

capacity

This is the quantity of liquid that a plumbing component such as a pipe or a *cistern* can hold either when full or up to a specified point in the component such as the normal operating *water level* or water line.

36

cap flashing

A type of weathering used to protect the top of building components such as parapet walls.

capillarity groove

See *Anti-capillarity groove*

capillary action

The process causing liquids to rise up small gaps between two surfaces of solid material. Liquids can penetrate between two close-fitting surfaces as a result of their *adhesive* and *cohesive* properties. *Capillary action* is put to good effect in plumbing as it is the principle on which the *capillary joint* works. A negative effect of capillary action is the ability for water to be drawn between two closely-fitting surfaces of sheet lead; in this case the sheet leadwork components should be designed so that water penetrating the joint due to capillary action (which cannot be avoided) cannot enter the building.

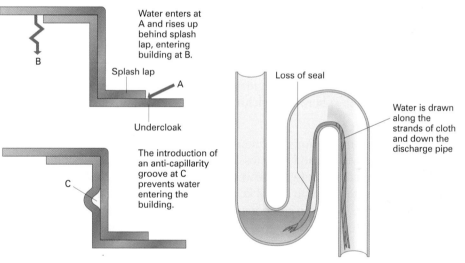

Water enters at A and rises up behind splash lap, entering building at B.

Splash lap

Undercloak

The introduction of an anti-capillarity groove at C prevents water entering the building.

Loss of seal

Water is drawn along the strands of cloth and down the discharge pipe

▲ How to avoid capillary action in sheet lead work

▲ Trap seal loss through capillary action

capillary joint

A type of joint used primarily on copper tubing that may be made by *hard soldering* or *soft soldering*, however the principles are the same. Key stages in the jointing process are:

- The pipe and fittings should be thoroughly cleaned with wire wool or a self-cleaning *flux* in order for the solder to properly adhere to the surfaces of the pipe and fittings to form the joint.
- A flux must be applied to the pipe and fitting; the flux prevents oxidation of the pipe once cleaned and helps the solder to flow to all parts of the joint.

A
B
C
D
E
F
G
H
I
J
K
L
M
N
O
P
Q
R
S
T
U
V
W
X
Y
Z

- Heat is applied to the joint until the solder which is either in the fitting (a *solder ring joint*) or applied from a spool (an *end feed joint*) melts, runs and fills the joint.
- Excess solder should be removed whilst the solder is molten and the fitting left to cool without further movement. Movement during cooling can crack the joint.
- Excess flux should be removed from the fitting on cooling and the system should be thoroughly flushed out to remove any internal flux residues.

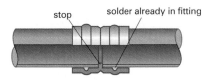

▲ Capillary solder ring joint

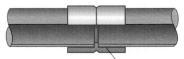

▲ Capillary end feed joint

carbon

A non-metallic element that occurs in all organic compounds and many inorganic compounds. Carbon is combustible and has the interesting ability to bond with itself, as well as with many other elements, for example carbon dioxide in the atmosphere and calcium carbonate (limestone).

carbon dioxide (CO_2)

A colourless, odourless, non-poisonous gas that is a normal part of the atmosphere. It is also a product of fossil fuel combustion and as such it is a greenhouse gas contributing to the warming of the Earth's atmosphere. It can be changed by pressure into a solid known as dry ice and as such can be used in plumbing to freeze water in components so that work can be done on them while still connected to the water supply. See *Greenhouse effect; Pipe freezing equipment*

carbon dioxide indicator

A commissioning instrument used as part of a range of combustion efficiency tests to correctly commission, set up and adjust a combustion appliance. The indicator measures the quantity of *carbon dioxide* (CO_2) in the *products of combustion* emitted from the appliance. In domestic appliances the indicator is usually associated with testing the *combustion efficiency* of oil-fired appliances. The indicator essentially consists of a vessel which contains a gas-absorbing fluid into which a sample of the flue gas products are pumped by a hand bellows. The fluid level in the indicator rises dependent on the amount of CO_2 contained

A
B
C
D
E
F
G
H
I
J
K
L
M
N
O
P
Q
R
S
T
U
V
W
X
Y
Z

in the flue gas sample, so a reading of the percentage CO_2 is provided. The indicator is used as follows:

- It is first zeroed and the probe is inserted into the flue test point and any air is eliminated from the rubber tubing etc. by depressing the hand bellows several times prior to connecting the indicator gauge.
- The plunger is depressed on to the indicator gauge and the hand bellows are depressed 18 times. On compression of the bellows on the 18th occasion the plunger is removed and the indicator now contains the sample of flue gas products.
- The indicator gauge is turned upside down several times to ensure the flue gas products are properly absorbed into the liquid. The percentage CO_2 reading is now taken from the gauge.

The percentage carbon dioxide can then be compared with the flue gas temperature using combustion efficiency charts to determine the combustion efficiency of the appliance.

Electronic *flue gas analysers* are also commonly used as an alternative method of measuring the combustion efficiency of the appliance. Although more expensive in terms of purchase price, the equipment readings tend to be more accurate and the test period is shorter.

▲ Carbon dioxide indicator

carbon monoxide (CO)

A colourless, odourless, highly-toxic gas which can be produced as a result of *incomplete combustion* of fuel-burning appliances. When we breathe in air, oxygen transfers from our lungs and attaches to haemoglobin in our blood to be carried round the body. This process is essential to life. Carbon monoxide attaches to haemoglobin more easily and blocks the oxygen uptake causing poisoning and, often, death. A concentration of only 0.4 per cent of carbon monoxide in the air can be fatal within a few minutes. The following table shows the effects of carbon monoxide on adults, with the saturation of carbon monoxide in the haemoglobin shown as a percentage.

A
B
C
D
E
F
G
H
I
J
K
L
M
N
O
P
Q
R
S
T
U
V
W
X
Y
Z

% CO	Symptom
0 to 10%	No obvious symptons
10 to 20%	Tightness across the forehead, yawning
20 to 30%	Flushed skin, headache, breathlessness and palpitation on exertion, slight dizziness
30 to 40%	Severe headache, dizziness, nausea, weakness of the knees, irritability, impaired judgement, possible collapse
40 to 50%	Symptoms as above with increased respiration and pulse rate, collapse on exertion
50 to 60%	Loss of consciousness, coma
60 to 70%	Coma, weakened heart and respiration
70 or more	Respiration failure and death

▲ Effects of carbon monoxide intake on adults

carburising flame

An oxyacetylene flame which has an excess of acetylene. A carburising flame is used in some types of *welding* processes.

cast iron

A heavy, brittle, long-lasting *ferrous metal* containing iron and 2–4% carbon.

cast sheet lead

This is used mainly on historic monuments, primarily for flat roof purposes. Specialist firms produce small quantities of cast sheet lead, as required, by pouring molten lead over a bed of casting sand.

catalyst

A substance which speeds up a chemical reaction but remains unchanged at the end of the reaction.

catchment space

A space below a *flue spigot* to a combustion appliance fitted to a *chimney* and designed to collect any soot, rubble or debris that falls down the flue.

catchpit

A box-shaped receiver designed to contain fluids. A catchpit may be used as a method of secondary containment in the event that an oil tank ruptures, to prevent the heating oil contaminating the surrounding earth or reaching a water course.

cathode

A negatively charged electrode. See *Anode*

cathodic protection

The use of a sacrificial metal to protect plumbing components from *electrolytic action (corrosion)*, as in the case of hot-water vessels. A *sacrificial anode* made of magnesium which is low in the *electromotive series* may be placed in the hot-water vessel, *cistern* or tank, or on a pipeline. The electrolytic corrosion will corrode the sacrificial anode in preference to the hot-water vessel.

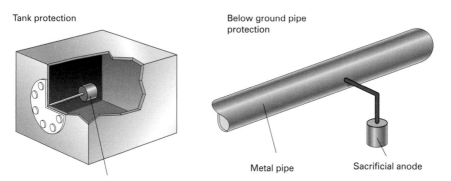

Tank protection

Below ground pipe protection

Metal pipe   Sacrificial anode

▲ Cathodic protection using a sacrificial anode

caulked joints

A method of jointing *cast-iron* pipes which are partially filled with a compacted yarn (gaskin). Molten lead is then poured into the remainder of the pipe socket using a ladle and left to cool. On cooling, the lead is further compacted into the joint using a caulking tool. Molten lead must not be used if the joint is wet or when jointing is taking place outdoors in damp environments. An alternative is to use lead wool in preference to molten lead. Proprietary cast-iron joints tend to be used on most jobs, but lead-caulked joints may still be required to be made on sanitary pipework for historic or listed buildings.

cavitation

A form of water turbulence that may cause erosion of metallic plumbing components. As water flows through a pipe the turbulence in the pipe tends to lead to the production of air bubbles, the faster the flow of water, the greater the turbulence and hence more air bubbles. As the water passes around bends or through valve seatings a reduction in pressure occurs. If this pressure reduction is too great the air bubbles in the water can collapse with an explosive force leading to the erosion of the bend or valve seat, which may result in leakage. A severe case of cavitation can result in problematic noise occurring in the system. Good system design can eliminate the effects of cavitation.

cavity wall

A wall that is formed by two upright pairs of similar or dissimilar building materials suitably tied together, with a gap formed between them that may be filled with *insulation material*.

A B C D E F G H I J K L M N O P Q R S T U V W X Y Z

CE mark

A symbol placed on appliances and equipment, showing that the product has been tested and proved to conform to European Standards.

▲ CE mark

Celsius (C)

The most commonly used temperature scale, this is the method of identifying different temperature levels of a substance. Celsius has now largely replaced the term centigrade.

central-heating system

A method of heating a building using air or water heated at a central source and circulated around the building. Wet central heating can be used to provide heating for the hot-water supply. See *Types of central heating*

Central-Heating System Specification (CHeSS)

These specifications provide recommendations for the energy efficiency of domestic wet central-heating systems.

centralised hot-water system

A hot-water supply system where stored heated water is kept centrally in the building ready to be supplied to a number of outlets (i.e. more than one).

ceramic discs

A method of controlling water flow in luxury *pillar taps*, ceramic discs are often used in *quarter-turn taps* and *shower mixer valves*. Care must be taken to ensure that the taps are supplied with water at the correct pressure; excessive pressures can result in the discs shattering. Pressure surges caused by the quick on and off operation (improper use) of the tap lever can also lead to shattering of the ceramic discs. See *Water hammer*

ceramics

These are products, such as tiles, earthenware, pottery and china, produced by firing mixtures of clay, sand and other minerals. The individual ingredients are fused by high temperature in a kiln. Some ceramics are produced by curing mixtures of sand, gravel and water with a setting agent. For example, sand, gravel, water and cement forms concrete; and sand, water and cement produces mortar.

cesspool

Also known as a cesspit, this is a watertight underground container used to collect *black water* and *sewage*, as in the case of rural properties that are not connected to the main drainage system. They periodically need pumping out and proper disposal of the contents. See *Septic tank*

chamfering

This involves slightly bevelling or angling the cut edge of a pipe to ensure that the pipe will smoothly slide into a fitting. The end of a plastic waste pipe is first chamfered before fitting into a *push-fit joint*.

change of state

A change in the physical properties of a substance which may be in the form of a solid, a liquid or a gas. For example, water in its natural state is a liquid, but when cooled to 0°C it changes state to a solid (ice), and when heated to 100°C it changes its state from a liquid to a gas (steam).

changeover valve

See *Automatic changeover valve*

channel bend

A type of fitting used in an *inspection chamber* where a branch joins the main drain run, to provide access into the pipe run in the chamber.

chase

A recess, to accommodate pipes or cables, cut into an existing structure.

chase wedge

See *Leadworking tools*

chaser die stock

See *Stocks and dies*

chasing out

Cutting into plaster or blockwork to form a recess.

check valve

A *backflow prevention device* or type of *non-return valve* used to ensure that water can only flow in one direction in a pipeline. The check valve is used to prevent *backflow* in a hot- or cold-water system. Check valves are available as single check valves or double check valves. A double check valve will provide protection against a *fluid risk category* 3 and a single check valve will provide protection against a fluid risk category 2.

▲ Single check valve

chemical safety

Always follow the manufacturer's instructions accurately when using chemicals, as the incorrect use of some chemicals may cause serious illness or death. Most chemical products include a material safety data sheet (MSDS), which outlines the correct procedures for using the chemical and the steps to take if the chemical is spilled, inhaled, swallowed or absorbed through the skin. Under the *Control of Substances Hazardous to Health (COSHH) Regulations*, the use of hazardous chemicals requires a *risk assessment* to be conducted detailing how operatives should safely use the substance.

A
B
C
D
E
F
G
H
I
J
K
L
M
N
O
P
Q
R
S
T
U
V
W
X
Y
Z

A
B
C
D
E
F
G
H
I
J
K
L
M
N
O
P
Q
R
S
T
U
V
W
X
Y
Z

chilling
A gas flame which has been reduced to below its normal ignition temperature. For example, if a flame directly touches a cold surface such as a *heat exchanger*, that surface will be at a far lower temperature than that at which complete combustion occurs and, as a result, *incomplete combustion* will take place, resulting in inefficiency of the appliance and possible production of *carbon monoxide*.

chimney
A structure in a building, which is designed to contain a flue.

chimney back
See *Back gutter*

chimney breast
A projection beyond the normal thickness of a wall that contains a fireplace and flue.

chimney liner
A pipe inserted in a chimney to form a *flue*; the pipe may be formed from rigid or flexible material.

chimney plate
A label fixed in a permanent, secure and accessible position, giving details of the *chimney* or *flue* installation.

chimney pot
A purpose-made unit fitted at the *flue* outlet of a *chimney*.

chimney weathering set
The series of sheet lead components that are fabricated to form the weathering to a chimney stack, including *back gutter*, *apron flashing*, *soakers* and *cover flashing*. A *step and cover flashing* may be used as an alternative to soakers and cover flashings with some roofing materials such as interlocking tiles.

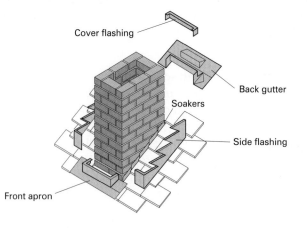

Cover flashing

Back gutter

Soakers

Side flashing

Front apron

▲ Chimney weathering set

chisel

A type of *hand tool* used to cut masonry materials, timber or metal. Plumbers use wood chisels for such jobs as removing surplus wood from timber notches in joists. A wood chisel must be highly sharpened in order for it to effectively cut through the timber; care therefore needs to be taken in its use.

▲ Wood chisel

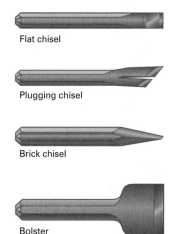

Flat chisel

Plugging chisel

Brick chisel

Bolster

▲ Masonry chisels

Masonry chisels (often known as cold chisels) are available for a variety of different purposes:

- Flat chisel – for cutting through masonry materials such as brick.
- Plugging chisel – for raking the seams out to fit sheet lead.
- Brick chisel – for breaking through solid materials such as concrete or brick.
- Bolster – for cutting bricks or concrete blocks. A flooring chisel is similar in terms of having a wide blade, but it is much thinner and used in lifting tongue and groove floor boards.

Masonry chisels require regular maintenance as the head of the chisel (the point struck by the hammer) must not be allowed to 'mushroom' as flying splinters may result which could penetrate the skin or eyes. *Eye protection* should normally be worn when using a masonry chisel.

chlorination

The treatment of water with chlorine in order to kill any harmful bacteria that may be present. Water supplied through the public mains by a water supplier is commonly treated with chlorine to ensure that it is safe to drink.

circuit

A collection of pipework and fittings in a system, for example a *secondary circuit*.

circuit breakers

Safety devices which interrupt an electrical current in fault situations such as an overload. Miniature circuit breakers (MCBs) break the circuit if excessively high current is detected and can be re-set after operation.

▶ Miniature circuit breaker

A
B
C
D
E
F
G
H
I
J
K
L
M
N
O
P
Q
R
S
T
U
V
W
X
Y
Z

A
B
C
D
E
F
G
H
I
J
K
L
M
N
O
P
Q
R
S
T
U
V
W
X
Y
Z

circulating head

The distance (height) between the centre line of the boiler and the centre of the hot-water storage cylinder, which creates the circulating pressure for *gravity circulation* to take place.

circulating pump

This has an electric motor which drives an impeller, a fluted wheel, which accelerates the flow of water using centrifugal force, and is used to ensure that water reaches all parts of a *central-heating system*. Domestic circulating pumps are fitted with *isolation valves* allowing access for servicing and maintenance.

▲ Domestic circulating pump

circulator

See *Gas circulator*

cistern

A vessel, usually tank-shaped and open at the top, that holds a supply of cold water. The cistern requires a lid to prevent the entry of foreign materials. If the stored water is used for domestic purposes, such as food production or drinking, the lid must be properly sealed and key points of entry or exit, such as *overflow pipes* or *vent pipes*, must be properly sealed and screened. See *Storage cistern; Feed cistern; Feed and expansion cistern; Flushing cistern*

cladding

The weathering or waterproofing layer attached to sections of wall or roof surfaces (usually vertical or near vertical).

claw hammer

See *Hammers*

clay pipes

A type of pipe used on *below ground drainage systems*. Modern clay pipe systems are less susceptible to damage due to ground settlement as they include plain lengths of pipe that are jointed by polypropylene sockets which allow a degree of flexibility. Older clayware systems include pipes with socketed pipe ends that are jointed by a mortar mix.

cleaner's sink

A low-level sink that has a *galvanised* or *brass*-hinged grate on which a bucket may be placed while filling.

cleaning eye

A type of *access point* to a pipework system. *Traps* often include a cleaning eye for the purposes of removing any build-up of deposits.

clerk of works

A person designated as the client's representative to monitor the quality of work performed on construction projects.

clips

Fixing devices used to secure pipework. Clips should provide enough support to prevent accidental damage, displacement of the pipe, or pipe knocking (noise). The recommended spacing for clips on different types of pipe is shown in the table.

Pipe size		Copper		LCS		Plastic pipe	
mm	in	horizontal (m)	vertical (m)	horizontal (m)	vertical (m)	horizontal (m)	vertical (m)
15	½	1.2	1.8	1.8	2.4	0.6	1.2
22	¾	1.8	2.4	2.4	3.0	0.7	1.4
28	1	1.8	2.4	2.4	3.0	0.8	1.5
35	1 ¼	2.4	3.0	2.7	3.0	0.8	1.7
42	1 ½	2.4	3.0	3.0	3.6	0.9	1.8
54	2	2.7	3.0	3.0	3.6	1.0	2.1

▲ Table showing recommended clip spacing for different types of pipework materials

close coupled WC suite

A type of WC suite in which the *flushing cistern* is directly connected to the *WC pan*. See *Water closet*

close coupling

An arrangement for the feed and vent pipework in *open-vented fully pumped systems*, as illustrated by the diagram which shows virtually the whole of the system operating under positive pump pressure. The *vent pipe* is attached before, and within 150 mm of the *cold feed pipe* – at the point of lowest positive pressure in the system. The connections should preferably be formed using an *air separator*. If an air separator is not used, the vent pipe should be taken from the horizontal main flow pipe and the pipe size of the main flow pipe in the vicinity of the vent and cold feed connections should be increased by one size – to promote air separation.

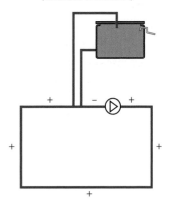

System under positive pressure (desirable connection)

▲ Close coupled pipework connections

A
B
C
D
E
F
G
H
I
J
K
L
M
N
O
P
Q
R
S
T
U
V
W
X
Y
Z

closed circuit

A pipework system where the same water is continually circulated without being drawn off, as in a *central-heating system*.

closed system

See *Sealed heating system*

closure plate

A metal plate sealed with heatproof tape to a *builder's opening* when fitting a gas fire. The closure plate maintains the correct *flue* draught and prevents flue products from entering the room. Before fitting a closure plate, make sure that the flue serves only one room and is clear. Any restrictions, such as *dampers*, should be removed and the void space should be checked to ensure that the size is adequate. All openings in the fireplace recess should be sealed.

▲ Closure plate

coach screws

These screws are supplied with a plastic plug and are fixed like a normal plug and screw but tightened using a ring spanner or adjustable grips, to provide a heavy-duty fixing.

coal tar coatings

A bituminous coating material which is a health hazard and is specifically forbidden in *wholesome water* supplies.

cock

A type of *valve* used to control the flow of fluids or liquids, and which may have a parallel or tapered plug. Special plug cocks are manufactured for use with gas and water supplies.

code of practice

See *British Standards Institution*

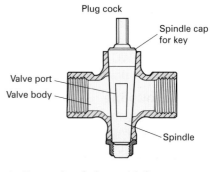

▲ Example of plug cock for use on water services

A
B
C
D
E
F
G
H
I
J
K
L
M
N
O
P
Q
R
S
T
U
V
W
X
Y
Z

coefficient of linear expansion

The proportion by which a particular material expands when heated by 1°C. The coefficient is used to calculate linear expansion using the formula:

Expansion (mm) = original length (mm) × temperature rise (°C) × coefficient of expansion.

The table shows the coefficient of linear expansion for materials often used in plumbing.

Material	Coefficient °C
Plastic	0.00018
Zinc	0.000029
Lead	0.000029
Aluminium	0.000026
Tin	0.000021
Copper	0.000016
Cast iron	0.000011
Mild steel	0.000011
Invar	0.0000009

◀ Coefficient of linear expansion values for different materials

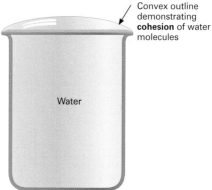

Convex outline demonstrating **cohesion** of water molecules

Water

▲ Surface tension and cohesion

cohesion

The tendency for water molecules to stick to each other, forming a skin on the surface of the liquid, called a *meniscus*. Cohesion and *adhesion* contribute to *capillary action*.

cold chisel

See *Chisel*

cold feed pipe

A pipe supplying water from a *cistern* to an *open-vented* hot-water or heating system.

cold flush

This is the first stage in a new *central-heating system* cleansing procedure designed to remove foreign matter such as *flux,* from the system. The cold flush is followed later by a *hot flush* and treatment with a *corrosion inhibitor*. It is part of the process of cleansing the system and treating the water in the *closed circuit* to prolong its life.

cold-water installation temperature

Under Water Regulation requirements domestic cold-water installations, including pipework and components such as *cisterns*, should be maintained below 25°C. The temperature of the *mains* water supply may vary from 4°C in

A
B
C
D
E
F
G
H
I
J
K
L
M
N
O
P
Q
R
S
T
U
V
W
X
Y
Z

winter to 25°C during summer. Mains water supplied from *surface* water has greater temperature variations. Pay particular attention to pipes passing through airing cupboards and heated rooms.

cold-water supply

Cold water is supplied from the mains via cold-water service pipework, through the *communication pipe* and the *supply pipe*. Underground pipework must be laid at a minimum depth of 750 mm and maximum depth of 1350 mm to protect against frost and mechanical damage. A *stop valve* is provided by the water supplier at the boundary to the property; with new properties a meter will be sited below ground with the supplier's stop valve. The pipe then runs below ground and into the customer's property through a *sleeve*, rising into the property; a minimum distance of 750 mm must be maintained from any exterior wall surface as a frost protection measure. If the pipe rises within 750 mm then it must be insulated in the sleeve. A *stop valve* is sited as close as possible to entry to the property, with a *drain valve* immediately above. The water is then supplied to the plumbing appliances and components in the property.

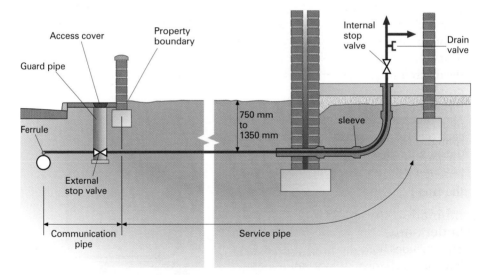

▲ Cold-water supply to a building

collar

A fitting used to join two pipe ends together. See *Socket*

collar boss (soil manifold)

A soil fitting with multiple-branch connections to allow waste discharge pipework to connect to a *discharge stack* at a number of points around its circumference. The collar boss overcomes problems associated with *cross-flow* due to the large pocket or space into which the pipework connects.

column radiator

See *Radiator*

combination boiler (combi boiler)

A type of boiler which heats up cold water instantaneously to supply hot water for domestic use. Hot-water demand usually takes priority over central-heating demand, when hot water is drawn off. One advantage with combi boilers is that no hot-water cylinder is required. There are a number of different designs of combination boiler. The diagram shows the most common design, which incorporates a *diverter valve* to direct water from the *heat exchanger* to provide heat either to the hot-water circuit or the *heating circuit*. In its normal position the diverter valve provides heat to the heating circuit; if a tap is opened the diverter valve closes the heating port and diverts circulation though a small heat exchanger to heat the *hot-water supply* to the taps.

combination storage cylinder (unit)

This includes both a hot-water cylinder and a cold-water storage *cistern* connected together in the one unit. These are used mainly in

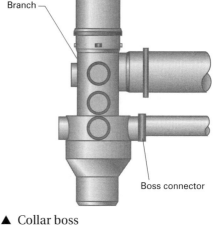

Branch

Boss connector

▲ Collar boss

Auto air vent

Pump

Diverter valve

Pressure gauge

DHW Expansion valve

Flow switch

Flow adjuster

Filter

Isolation valve

Calorifier

Pressure-relief valve

Boiler drain

Cold   Hot

▲ Combination boiler – domestic hot-water circuit

A B C D E F G H I J K L M N O P Q R S T U V W X Y Z

A
B
C
D
E
F
G
H
I
J
K
L
M
N
O
P
Q
R
S
T
U
V
W
X
Y
Z

flats as they take up less space. The base of the cistern must not be lower than the highest connected water outlet and should also be high enough to provide adequate water-flow rate to outlets.

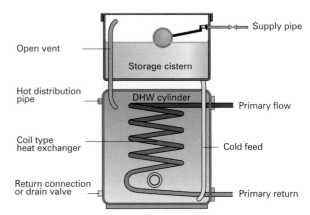

▲ Combination storage cylinder

combination tap

See *Mixer tap*

combination waste fitting

A type of *waste fitting* used to make a watertight connection between a sanitary appliance and its connecting *trap*. The combination waste fitting is used with appliances that include an overflow and ensures that a separate *overflow pipe* is not required for the appliance, that is, any overflowing water from the appliance runs into the waste discharge pipework.

▲ Combination waste fitting

combined drainage system

See *Types of drainage system*

combined heat and power (CHP)

This is a method of 'clean' energy production with reduced emission of *carbon dioxide*, which uses some of the heat produced when fossil fuel is burned, for example *natural gas*, and as a by-product generates small quantities of electricity that can be used to power a building or be input to the National Grid. CHP increases fuel efficiency in energy production.

combined pressure relief valve and pressure gauge

A *composite valve* used with a *sealed central-heating system*. It contains a *pressure-relief* and *pressure gauge* function in the one unit.

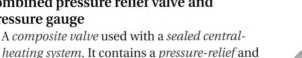

▲ Combined pressure relief valve and pressure gauge

combined temperature and pressure relief valve

A type of valve that may be fitted to an unvented hot-water system that contains a temperature relief and a pressure relief function sited in the one valve. See *Temperature-relief valve; Pressure-relief valve*

combustion

Combustion is the process of burning fuel. In plumbing it is used to generate heat for *central-heating* purposes or for heating *capillary joints* with a blowtorch. In order for combustion to take place correctly a correct mixture of air and fuel needs to be provided; this is known as the *stoichiometric mixture*. If *incomplete combustion* takes place then a dangerous gas called *carbon monoxide* can be released which is potentially life threatening.

combustion analysis

The process of taking a sample of *flue* gases for the purposes of determining the efficiency of a combustion appliance. See *Combustion efficiency test*

combustion chamber

The part of a boiler in which the fuel is ignited and burned.

combustion efficiency test

A test undertaken on oil-fired appliances and larger gas boilers to determine the combustion efficiency of the appliance. This is an essential test that is undertaken as part of the initial *commissioning* and future service and maintenance procedures. The test includes:

- taking readings when the appliance is at its full working temperature
- taking an *ambient air temperature* reading at the point that combustion air is being supplied into the appliance
- taking a flue gas temperature reading at the appliance sampling point using a *flue gas thermometer*
- taking a *carbon dioxide* reading of the flue gases at the sampling point using a *carbon dioxide indicator*.

The ambient air temperature is deducted from the flue gas temperature, with the resulting temperature being compared with the carbon dioxide sample in the flue gases using tables to determine the combustion efficiency of the appliance. An electronic *flue gas analyser* may be used to determine the flue temperature and carbon dioxide concentration as an alternative to the equipment detailed. See *Oil appliance commissioning procedures*

commissioning

The process of completing an installation by checking for faults, starting the system up and ensuring that all parts of the installation operate safely, efficiently and correctly. The commissioning part of the work may also include a basic instruction to the customer on the efficient operation of the system or appliance and the completion of any *commissioning report*.

A
B
C
D
E
F
G
H
I
J
K
L
M
N
O
P
Q
R
S
T
U
V
W
X
Y
Z

A
B
C
D
E
F
G
H
I
J
K
L
M
N
O
P
Q
R
S
T
U
V
W
X
Y
Z

commissioning report

A report filled out on completion of the *commissioning* of a system or appliance detailing any test results arising from the commissioning process and confirming that the system or appliance is operating safely and efficiently.

common discharge pipe

A common waste discharge pipe that serves a number of *sanitary appliances* such as a bath and a basin. Care needs to be taken when connecting a number of sanitary appliances into the one waste pipe in order to avoid *trap seal loss* that may occur.

common flue system

An *open-flued* system that serves two or more combustion appliances sited in the same room.

communication pipe

The section of cold-water *service pipe* from the mains to the boundary *stop valve*. See *Cold-water supply*

compartment

A non-habitable enclosed space adapted for the installation of a combustion appliance.

compartment ventilation

The requirement to provide air for the cooling of a combustion appliance when it is fitted in a small space such as a *compartment*.

compensator

See *Weather compensator*

complete combustion

The correct burning of a gas and air mixture in order to release heat which results in the discharge of the desired *products of combustion*, for example when *natural gas* is burned the combustion products should be *carbon dioxide* and water vapour. See *Incomplete combustion*

composite valve

A valve that provides two or more functions in the one unit. Most *unvented hot-water systems* now use composite control valves. In the diagram, the composite valve contains a *pressure-reducing valve*, a line *strainer*, an *expansion valve* and a *check valve*.

compression

See *Trap seal loss*

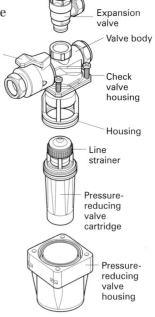

Expansion valve

Valve body

Isolating valve

Check valve housing

Housing

Line strainer

Pressure-reducing valve cartridge

Pressure-reducing valve housing

▲ Example of components in a composite valve

compression joint

A type of joint made by clamping a fitting to a pipe that is used for jointing a range of materials such as *copper*, *plastics*, *lead* and *low-carbon steel*. There are two types of fitting: the more popular *non-manipulative (Type A)*, which uses a compression ring to grab and seal the pipe, and the *manipulative (Type B) joint*, which is used in copper pipework. There are a variety of designs for a Type A fitting based on the material being jointed; for example plastics may require an insert sliding into the pipe at the point of fitting connection to support the pipe wall against the compression ring. Manipulative (Type B) compression fittings differ in that the pipe end has to be manipulated with a *drift* or *flaring tool* to form the joint seal. They tend to be less common and are only likely to be used in new installations for jointing below ground copper pipework where non-manipulative fittings are not approved for use.

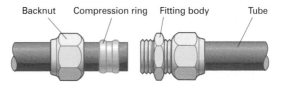

▲ Copper non-manipulative compression joint

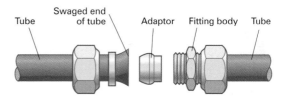

▲ Copper manipulative compression joint

compression ring (olive)

A ring used in a *compression joint* to form a pressure-tight seal.

concealed connection

A method of connecting pipework to an appliance in such a manner that pipework or fittings are not visible.

concentric flue

A flue in which one pipe passes inside another, for example a *room-sealed flue* system is a *concentric flue* where the flue system is essentially formed from a pipe sited within a pipe, in which the inner pipe conveys flue gas products safely to the outside air and the outer pipe conveys air for combustion to the appliance.

concentric reducer

See *Reducer*

condensate

The liquid that arises from the condensing (cooling) of water vapour or steam.

A
B
C
D
E
F
G
H
I
J
K
L
M
N
O
P
Q
R
S
T
U
V
W
X
Y
Z

condensate drain
A corrosion-resistant fixture in a *flue* or appliance supplied to drain off *condensate* formed as a product of *combustion*.

condensate pipe
A corrosion-resistant and leak-free pipe (usually plastic) along which *condensate* flows. Condensate from a combustion appliance is in the form of a weak acid and must be safely disposed of to waste, for example via the drainage system.

condensing appliance
An appliance which uses the *latent heat* from the water vapour in the *combustion* products by condensing the water vapour within the appliance to produce a higher combustion efficiency.

condensing boiler
An energy-efficient boiler which includes a fan and a large *heat exchanger*, enabling the boiler to extract more heat from the *combustion* process. As the flue gases cool, the water vapour turns to *condensate*, which is drained away. The higher efficiency comes from using a greater proportion of heat in the flue gases that would normally be discharged through the flue system to outside air.

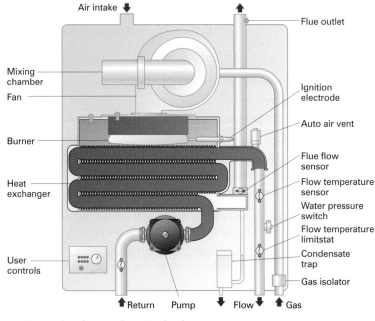

▲ Example of a condensing boiler

condensing gas fire
This uses a *fanned draught flue system* to draw air for combustion from the room, the air then passing through the *heat exchanger* and out of a small diameter plastic flue pipe. There must be a safety device fitted to close down the burner if

the fan fails, for example a pressure switch. The fire heat exchanger extracts more heat from the flue gas products than with a normal gas fire to the point at which *condensate* is produced. This condensate is discharged away to waste, with the overall efficiency of the fire increased over that of a traditional gas fire.

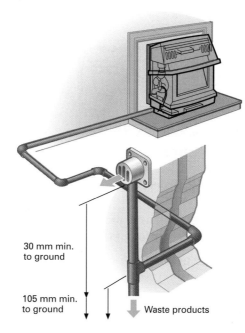

30 mm min. to ground

105 mm min. to ground

Waste products

▲ General layout of a condensing gas fire with a fanned flue

conduction

The transfer of heat energy through a solid material. For example, metals are very good conductors of heat, but wood does not conduct heat as readily. The heat transfers by the increased vibration of *molecules* when materials are heated. Copper has a higher conductivity than steel, iron or lead.

conductor

A material that allows the transfer of electricity by the ease of movement of the electrons. Good conductors include metals such as copper, aluminium and gold. The opposite of conductors are materials which do not allow electricity to pass through them; these are called *insulators* and include wood, plastic and rubber.

conduit

A preformed PVC steel channel used to cover and protect cables.

connecting flue pipe

A pipe component which connects the outlet of an appliance to the *flue* in the *chimney* or *flue system*.

constant oil level control

A control device fitted to an oil-fired appliance with a *vaporising burner*. The constant oil level control:

- shuts down the supply of oil to the appliance in a faulted condition
- provides an isolation point for the oil feed to the appliance
- maintains a constant level of oil for *combustion* purposes in the appliance regardless of the oil level in the storage tank
- controls the flow rate of oil to the *vaporising burner*. (See diagram overleaf.)

A
B
C
D
E
F
G
H
I
J
K
L
M
N
O
P
Q
R
S
T
U
V
W
X
Y
Z

A
B
C
D
E
F
G
H
I
J
K
L
M
N
O
P
Q
R
S
T
U
V
W
X
Y
Z

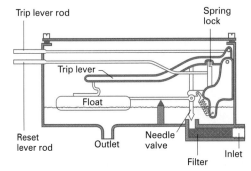

▲ Single float constant oil level control

The oil level control will need proper adjustment and setting on *commissioning* of the appliance in order for it to function correctly.

constant volume governor

See *Gas governor*

consumer unit

A unit sited usually at the point of entry of an electrical supply to a building and which contains the main electrical switch to isolate the property and the circuit isolation and protective devices, for example *miniature circuit breakers* that provide isolation to individual electrical circuits within the building.

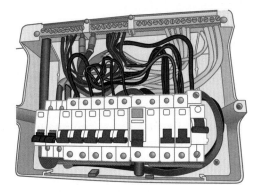

▲ Consumer unit

contamination

The introduction of potentially dangerous matter into the water supply.

This can occur, for example, if water fittings are laid or pass through foul soil, refuse or refuse chutes, ash pits, *sewer* drains, *cesspools*, *manholes* or *inspection chambers* where permeation or a rupture in the pipe could cause contamination; or, as in the illustration, if the end of the hosepipe lies in contaminated water and the water supply is contaminated by *backflow*. A *backflow prevention device*, in this case a *double-check valve*, should be fitted to prevent possible backflow into pipework in the property and the supplier's main, thus avoiding a possible contamination risk.

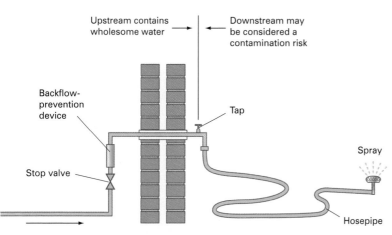

Upstream contains wholesome water → ← Downstream may be considered a contamination risk

Backflow-prevention device

Tap

Spray

Stop valve

Hosepipe

▲ Preventing contamination risk

continuity bonding
See *Bonding*

continuous step flashing
See *Lead flashing*

contraction
A reduction in the size or volume of a substance. See *Expansion*

Control of Substances Hazardous to Health (COSHH) Regulations
The legal framework for the control of hazardous substances which requires all employers to assess work that may expose employees to hazardous solids, liquids, dusts, fumes, vapours, gases or micro-organisms. Health risks must be evaluated, and actions to remove or reduce risks must be carried out.

control thermostat
See *Cylinder thermostat*

controls (central heating)
Central-heating controls include a *time switch*, full *programmer*, *room thermostat*, programmable room thermostat, *cylinder thermostat*, *frost thermostat*, *automatic bypass valves*, *motorised valves*, three-port *mid-position valves*, junction box or wiring centre and *boiler control interlocks*.

convection
The transfer of heat through the movement of locally heated air or water, for example a hot-water system heated by *gravity circulation*. When heated, the water in the primary flow pipe expands, increases in volume and becomes lighter per unit volume. The colder water in the primary return pipe pushes the

A
B
C
D
E
F
G
H
I
J
K
L
M
N
O
P
Q
R
S
T
U
V
W
X
Y
Z

A
B
C
D
E
F
G
H
I
J
K
L
M
N
O
P
Q
R
S
T
U
V
W
X
Y
Z

lighter water in the primary flow upwards towards the *cylinder* and a circulation effect is established between the *boiler*, cylinder and interconnecting pipework; this is a direct result of *convection*.

convector heater

A *heat emitter* that is designed to heat a room mainly by emitting air heated by convection, either by natural convection or by forced air circulation through the heater (fan-assisted). They usually include a low water content water-to-air *heat exchanger* which is surrounded by many fins to increase the heating surface area of the convector. The convector heater is normally fitted inside a decorative casing.

conventional flue

See *Open flue*

copper

A *non-ferrous* metal that that is used in many plumbing applications, such as copper tube for hot, cold and *central-heating* pipework, wire for the electrical connection of plumbing components, and copper sheet as a roof-covering material.

copper fittings

These are used for jointing copper tube and include: *capillary joints, compression joints, push-fit joints. Press-fit fittings* are now available. They achieve a sound joint through the exertion of pressure from a press-fit tool; a purpose-designed 'O' ring provides the mechanism by which a perfect seal is created between pipe and fitting.

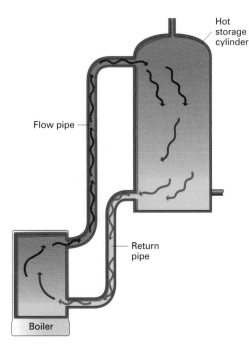

Hot storage cylinder

Flow pipe

Return pipe

Boiler

▲ Convection in a hot-water system

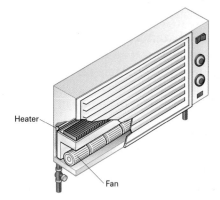

Heater

Fan

▲ Fan-assisted convector heater

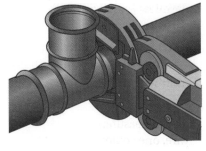

▲ Press-fit copper fitting

copper tube

This is a very *malleable* and *ductile* material used for pipework. The four main types are:

- R250 half hard – used above ground; for common plumbing applications
- R290 hard – this is unbendable because of its hardness and is not commonly used
- R220 microbore coils – used for micro-bore pipework in *central-heating systems*
- R220 soft coils – this is a type of copper tube with a thicker wall thickness and is also fully *annealed*. It can be used on below ground supply pipework and long radius bends can be formed without the use of bending equipment.

copper tube cutter

See *Pipe cutters*

cordless drills and screwdrivers

A battery-driven appliance, available in a range from 12V to 24V, and often capable of both drilling and screw driving functions. They are usually supplied with a spare battery and charger and are considered a safer alternative to using mains connected power tools owing to their lower voltage.

◀ Battery-operated hammer drill

CORGI (Council for Registered Gas Installers)

This organisation maintains a register of competent gas installation businesses, defined as a 'class of persons approved by the Health and Safety Executive to undertake gas work'. There are strict rules for registration which require competency and certification in gas installation.

corrosion

The degradation of materials, which may occur through a chemical reaction when a metal comes into contact with air, water, *acids*, *alkalis* or other chemicals; rusting is an example.

corrosion inhibitor

A chemical which is added to the water in a *central-heating system* to reduce the possible effects of corrosion. The corrosion inhibitor neutralises foreign material in the system, such as acidic *flux* residues, rendering them relatively harmless and thus increasing the lifespan of the system by reducing the extent of corrosion that may take place.

corrosive

This describes a substance, especially a strong *acid* or *alkali*, capable of destroying or eating away by chemical action.

coulomb

A unit measurement of electricity. If a current of one *ampere* is passing through a wire, one coulomb of electricity will pass though a point in one second.

A
B
C
D
E
F
G
H
I
J
K
L
M
N
O
P
Q
R
S
T
U
V
W
X
Y
Z

A
B
C
D
E
F
G
H
I
J
K
L
M
N
O
P
Q
R
S
T
U
V
W
X
Y
Z

countertop basin
See *Wash basin*

coupling
A fitting used on a pipeline to join two pieces of pipe together in a straight line.

cover flashing
See *Lead flashing*

crank passover bend
Forming of pipework to clear an obstacle, such as another pipe.

credit meter
An instrument installed to record the gas used by the customer. The record of gas consumed by the meter is the basis on which a periodic account is rendered to the customer.

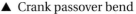
▲ Crank passover bend

creep
The tendency of metals to stretch slowly over time when subject to heating; on cooling the material will usually shrink back to its original size, but it is possible for the material to permanently stretch. The *thermal movement* or creep that takes place must be catered for in the design of a roof covering in order that it does not suffer breakdown.

cross-bonding (continuity bonding)
See *Bonding*

cross-connection to unwholesome water
This occurs when a pipe carrying *unwholesome water*, or contaminated fluid, is linked to a pipe carrying *wholesome water*, on which there is no *backflow prevention device* to prevent *contamination*. Water from a supply pipe from the mains is considered to be wholesome water whereas water in a *central-heating system* is an example of an unwholesome water supply, so the possibility of cross-connection with it should be avoided.

cross-flow (hot- and cold-water supply)
A fault in a hot- and cold-water system which includes *mixer taps* or *valves* that permit mixing of hot and cold water in the valve bodies. If the hot and cold pressures are unequal then the higher pressure water can drive water through the mixer tap to the lower pressure source by *back pressure*, resulting in a possible *contamination* risk, which may also cause a faulted condition with some plumbing equipment such as *unvented hot-water storage cylinders*.

cross-flow (sanitary pipework)
If two pipe branches are located directly opposite one another when connecting to a *discharge stack*, water may flow from one to the other affecting the pressure

in the *branch discharge pipework*, resulting in possible *trap seal loss*. Cross-flow can be prevented by ensuring branches are adequately spaced with a minimum gap of 200 mm, as shown in the diagram.

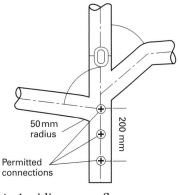

▲ Avoiding cross-flow

cross vent

A cross-connecting pipe in a *sanitary pipework* system used to connect the main *discharge stack* to the main *ventilating stack* and avoid any sizeable pressure build-up in the main discharge stack that may lead to *trap seal loss*. See *Types of sanitary pipework system*

crutch head

The name for a *stop tap* or *bib tap* handle.

cupro solvent

The ability of water to dissolve copper. The level of cupro solvency that takes place is usually dependent on the *pH value* of the water.

current

A flow of electrons around an electrical circuit. Current is measured in *amperes*.

curtilage

The enclosed land around a house or other building.

cutlery saver

An insert fitted into a *waste-disposal unit* to catch cutlery.

cutting torch

An oxyacetylene *welding blowpipe* used to cut *low-carbon steel* or *iron*. During the cutting process the metal is heated to a bright red colour by the blowpipe, a jet of high-pressure oxygen is then injected into the heated area by depressing a handle on the blowpipe causing a cutting effect on the metal surface.

CV

See *Calorific value*

cycling

A process that occurs in a *central-heating system* in which proper *boiler control interlock* has not been provided, so that when the *thermostats* reach their set *temperature* there is no mechanism for turning off the *boiler*, in which case it continues to turn on and off in response to small heat losses even though there is no demand for heat in the main circuits. Cycling in a system is wasteful of energy and must be avoided in order to comply with the requirements of the *Building Regulations*.

cylinder

A pipe-shaped component, mostly used as a device for the storage of hot water. See *Hot-water storage vessel*

cylinder air gap (bubble top)

A type of *unvented hot-water* storage *cylinder* which incorporates an air space within the cylinder for the purposes of accommodating expanded water as the system is heated up.

cylinder thermostat

A *thermostat* which controls the *temperature* of the water in the *hot-water storage vessel*. When the water reaches a preset temperature (usually 60–65°C), the thermostat turns off the hot-water circuit to the vessel through a connection to the *circulating pump* or *boiler*, or by operating a *motorised valve*.

cyltrol valve

A type of mechanical thermostatic control valve fitted to the *primary return* pipe of a *hot-water storage vessel*, operating by gravity circulation to control the rate of flow through the *cylinder* in relation to the water temperature.

▲ Cylinder air gap (bubble top)

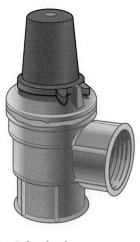

▲ Cyltrol valve

damp-proof course (DPC)

A layer of *impervious* material which is laid between building materials that are used to form walls in order to prevent the passage of moisture by *capillary action*. A layer of DPC material (predominantly plastics material in modern properties) is laid between brick or block courses a minimum of 150 mm above the outside ground level in order to prevent the transfer of moisture to building materials above the height of the DPC.

damp-proof membrane (DPM)

A moisture barrier used in floors between the *hardcore blinding* and the concrete slab, to prevent moisture from rising into the concrete floor. Sand blinding is laid above the hard blinding to provide a softer layer less likely to puncture the membrane. Plumbers need to take care when routing components such as pipework in order to avoid rupturing either DPCs or DPMs which could permit damp or moisture to enter the building.

damper

A device such as a hinged flap designed to adjust the amount of air flowing into an appliance such as a solid-fuel boiler. Simple solid-fuel boilers, such as open fires with *high-output back-boilers*,

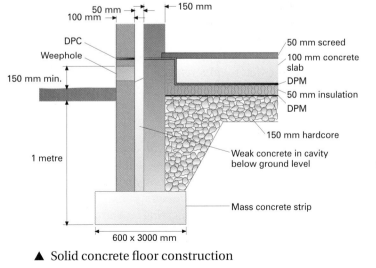

▲ Solid concrete floor construction

often have a low-level damper built into the firegrate in order to adjust the quantity of air supplied to the fuel for *combustion* purposes and hence control the rate of burning of the fuel.

data plate (data badge)

An information plate attached to an appliance giving all relevant details such as *heat output*, *heat input* and fuel type.

dead legs

Long lengths of pipe running from a *hot-water storage vessel* to hot-water appliances which waste the volume of water runoff before the water turns hot. The energy used to heat the volume of water left in the pipe, which then cools is therefore wasted. The hot-water storage vessel or heater should be located as close to the outlet taps as possible.

▶ Dead legs

Cold-water storage cistern

Warning pipe

Open vent

Bath

Basin

Hot distribution pipe

Primary flow

Primary return

Sink

Pipe runs away from hot-water cylinder known as dead-legs

de-aerator (Tigerloop™)

A device that can be used on a one-pipe oil line fed from a storage tank that is all or partly below the level of the burner on the boiler (sub-gravity system). The de-aerator removes any air from the pipeline dispersing it to atmosphere. See *Oil-supply system*

▲ Tigerloop de-aerator

decommissioning

Taking a system or appliance out of service, temporarily or permanently, by safely isolating it or completely removing it. It may take the form of:

- temporary decommissioning – the system or appliance is temporarily removed from service whilst work is carried out on it
- permanent decommissioning – a system or appliance is to be permanently taken out of action and removed.

For example, a *central-heating system* may be decommissioned if the old *gravity* solid-fuel system is being replaced with a new *fully-pumped condensing boiler* system. When decommissioning a system or appliance, ensure that: all relevant people are informed, all water supplies are isolated and capped (if required), electrical supplies are isolated, and 'do not use' notices may be required to be placed at the main isolation points.

decorative fuel-effect gas appliance (DFE)

An *open-flued* appliance providing radiant heat and designed to look like an attractive *solid-fuel* open fire. They are relatively inefficient and are usually fitted for decorative purposes rather than their ability to heat a room. The *flue* should usually have a cross-sectional dimension of not less than 175 mm. Some DFEs may be fitted under a canopy.

1 Builder's opening   2 Fireplace recess

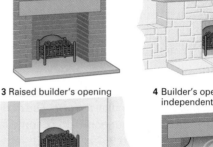

3 Raised builder's opening

4 Builder's opening with independent canopy

▲ Typical decorative fuel effect fire locations

deep seal trap

A *trap* which has a *trap seal depth* of at least 75 mm. A trap with this depth of seal is commonly used where waste-discharge pipework is connected to a *discharge stack* running to a *drainage system* in order to avoid *trap seal loss* caused by the pressures that may be created within the stack.

deep well

A source of water for domestic purposes, where the water is filtered as it passes through the rock and the only treatment that is usually needed is sterilisation, which keeps the water and the supply pipework free from bacteria.

deformation

A result of the application of force which prevents a material from returning to its original form.

A
B
C
D
E
F
G
H
I
J
K
L
M
N
O
P
Q
R
S
T
U
V
W
X
Y
Z

delayed-action ball valve

A type of inlet control device fitted to a cold-water *storage cistern* to regulate the flow of water into the cistern. The valve differs from a standard *float-operated valve* in that it does not open in response to a fall in water level until a pre-determined level in the cistern has been reached. It is used on systems supplied from a *booster pump* to prevent the pump from constantly turning on and off in response to small demands for water, thus minimising wear and tear to the *pump*.

▲ Delayed-action ball valve

density

The relative lightness or heaviness of materials.

density of solids

Density is the *mass* of a substance per unit *volume* of that substance and is represented using the formula:

$$\text{density} = \frac{\text{mass}}{\text{volume}}$$

density of water

The density of liquids, such as water, varies depending on the number of *molecules* in a particular *volume*. The density of water changes with *temperature*, as heat causes the molecules to become further apart. The mass of 1 m³ of water is 1000 kg at 4°C and 967 kg at 82°C.

depth of seal

See *Trap seal depth*

descaling

The process of removing *scale* (such as limescale) which has collected on the inner surfaces of hot-water components, the most susceptible in hot-water systems being *heat exchangers* such as *boilers* and *cylinders*. A descaling fluid can be used to remove scale from the inner surfaces of these components. Descaling can be a long job and therefore it is preferable to install a device such as a *water softener* to prevent the possible build-up of scale in the first place.

design heat requirement

This is the total heat required in a room to provide *space heating* under design conditions. It is the calculated *heat loss* through the building fabric and through air changes in the room due to *ventilation* plus any additional heating requirements for ensuring faster heat-up after a period where the system has not been operating. The design heat requirement of a domestic property is the sum of the heat requirements for each room or space.

deterioration of fittings

Some types of *plastic* can be damaged or permeated by fluids, such as petrol and gases (e.g. *natural gas*), so any water carried by pipes made from these plastics may be at risk of *contamination*. Always use water pipes and fittings that are protected from risk of *permeation*, or deterioration.

dew point

The dew point temperature is that to which the air must be cooled to reach saturation (assuming air pressure remains the same); the dew point is a direct measure of the amount of moisture (*humidity*) present in the air.

dezincification

A form of *electrolytic corrosion* in which the zinc in *brass* fittings is destroyed leaving the fitting in a brittle condition, as in the case of using brass fittings on underground pipework in the presence of damp soil. It is for this reason that brass fittings should not be used for underground pipework; *gunmetal* is used as an alternative.

diaphragm ball valve

A type of *float-operated valve*, made of *plastic* or *brass*, which uses a large diaphragm washer as part of its control mechanism. The valve can be manufactured from plastic or brass. Its features include:

- top outlet discharge – to minimise submersion in the water and hence a *contamination* risk
- easy adjustment of the *float* height by use of an adjusting screw.

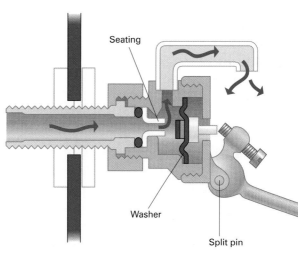

▲ Diaphragm float-operated valve

differential

The difference between two opposing forces.

diluted chlorine

Diluted chlorine, also known as sodium hypochlorite, is recommended for the *disinfection of drinking water*. Only substances listed by the Drinking Water Inspectorate may be used for such purposes.

diluting receiver

A device that is fitted under a laboratory sink to store the contents of the waste from the sink and hold it while it is further diluted with water until at a safe concentration to discharge down the waste pipework.

A
B
C
D
E
F
G
H
I
J
K
L
M
N
O
P
Q
R
S
T
U
V
W
X
Y
Z

A
B
C
D
E
F
G
H
I
J
K
L
M
N
O
P
Q
R
S
T
U
V
W
X
Y
Z

dilution

The process of adding air to a flue pipe in order to minimise the quantity of *condensate* in the *open-flue* system. The air in an open-flue system is usually admitted by the *draught diverter* for this purpose.

dip pipe

A return or cold-feed pipe entering the top of a *boiler* or hot-water *storage cylinder* that extends down to the bottom of the boiler or cylinder. Its purpose is to ensure that the return water is returned to the bottom of the boiler or cylinder for reheating rather than being mixed with hot water at the top of the boiler or cylinder.

direct cold-water system

A cold-water supply system where the pipes to the sink, bath, hand basin, WC or other appliances are taken off the rising mains *supply pipe* directly and operate under mains pressure. See *Indirect cold-water system*

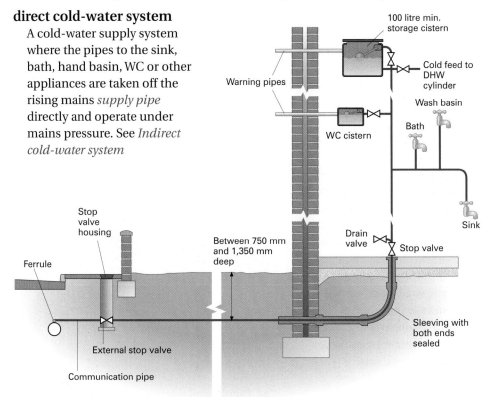

▲ Pipework layout for a direct cold-water system

direct current (DC)

One type of current that flows round an electric circuit, with the *electrons* always flowing in the same direction. For example, a direct current flows in a battery from the *anode* to the *cathode*, as in appliances such as torches and battery-operated power tools, and may be used in boiler-control circuits. Direct current can be produced from alternating current using a rectifier. See *Alternating current*

direct cylinder

A vessel for storing hot water that has been directly heated by a *boiler*, *circulator* or *immersion heater*. A direct hot-water cylinder must only be used in a system where the components are not subject to *corrosion* by fresh water, that is, system components made from *ferrous metals* are not suitable for use in this type of system. See *Direct hot-water system*

direct hot-water system

A centralised system of hot-water supply in which water is heated and stored in a *direct cylinder*, and in which heat may be provided by a separate *boiler* or an *immersion heater*. If a boiler is used then the water that is drawn off has also been circulated through the boiler. Care therefore needs to be taken with the materials that form the *primary circuit* to the cylinder which must be *non-ferrous* in order to avoid *corrosion* and *contamination* of the hot-water supply. The direct system is unlikely to be used in modern systems, other than when heating takes place by an electric *immersion heater*. See *Indirect hot-water system*

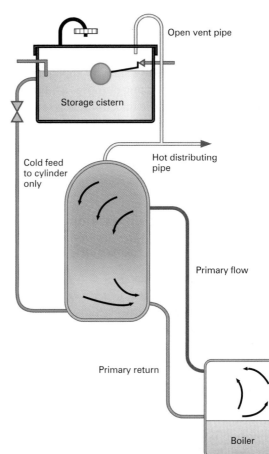

▲ Pipework layout for a direct hot-water system

disc valve

A type of valve which reduces the velocity (speed) of water entering an appliance, for example in feeding water into an *automatic flushing cistern* in order to control the rate of water entering the cistern and the flushing period of the cistern.

discharge pipework

Pipework conveying the discharge from sanitary appliances, that is, the wetted portion of the above ground system that includes the *discharge stack* and *branch discharge pipes*. See *Types of sanitary pipework system*

A
B
C
D
E
F
G
H
I
J
K
L
M
N
O
P
Q
R
S
T
U
V
W
X
Y
Z

discharge point

The point at which water is discharged either into or out of a system, for example water discharged from a tap, or water discharged from a *discharge stack* and into a *drainage system*.

discharge stack

Main pipe (usually vertical) that conveys the discharge from sanitary appliances to the *drainage system*.

discharge unit – sanitary pipework

A unit used in calculating the size of *discharge pipework* and representing the average discharge rate of a sanitary appliance expressed in litres per second (l/s). For example, for pipe-sizing purposes a 6-litre flush WC represents two *discharge* units, a basin 0.5 etc. The maximum flow rate can therefore be calculated from the total number of discharge units and, using tables, the pipe size can be determined.

disconnecting joint

A type of pipe fitting that can be easily disconnected from the pipe run. They include: *compression joints*, *push-fit fitting*, *union connectors* and *longscrew connectors*.

dishwashers – water conservation

Paragraph 29(1) of the *Water Regulations* states that dishwashers should be economical in the use of water and allows 4.5 litres of water per place setting.

disinfection fluid disposal

Fluids used for *disinfecting water systems* can usually be discharged into a *public sewer*, unless large quantities are discharged. In some circumstances disinfection fluid can interfere with sewage treatment, for example *cesspools* in rural areas. Consult the body responsible for the drainage system for information about the safe discharge of disinfection fluids.

disinfection of water systems

This is the process of cleansing a hot- and cold-water system following its installation or periodic maintenance to ensure that the water contained in the system is fit for domestic use, for example drinking, washing, food preparation, etc. Disinfection of a hot- and cold-water system is required under the *Water Regulations* in all property types other than single-family dwellings. The disinfection procedure is:

- Disinfection should take place from the entry to the system through to all outlets, that is, from *mains* through *supply pipes* to distribution pipes.
- The system should be thoroughly flushed prior to disinfection.
- The disinfection agent should be introduced and drawn through all parts of the system being disinfected so that it is fully saturated. If chlorine is used then the initial concentration should be 50 mg per litre or 50 parts per million (ppm).
- The part of the system being disinfected should be left for a contact period of one hour. If using chlorine, the free residual chlorine level at the end of the

contact period should be no less than 30 mg per litre; if less than this then the procedure should be repeated.

- Following successful disinfection, the system should be drained and thoroughly flushed until the chlorine level is the same as that supplied from the mains.

distribution main

The water supplier's mains pipework from the water-treatment works to domestic and non-domestic properties.

distribution pipe

Any pipe (other than a *warning*, *overflow* or flush pipe) conveying water from a *storage cistern*, or from a hot-water apparatus supplied from a cistern and under pressure from that cistern.

diverter valve

A two-position three-port diverter valve was used in one of the first types of fully-pumped central-heating systems installed in domestic properties, to provide independent temperature control of the heating and hot-water circuit. It is no longer widely used. See *Mid-position valve*

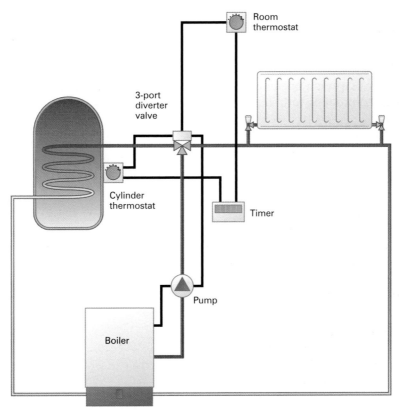

▲ Fully-pumped system with two-position diverter valve

domestic sanitary appliances

Fixed sanitary appliances supplied with water used for removal of body waste, cleaning or washing, for example baths, showers, basins, bidets, WCs, urinals, sinks, dishwashers, washing machines.

domestic waste water

Water contaminated through use, discharged from WCs, showers, basins, baths sinks and other similar appliances.

domestic water

Water supplied by a water supplier (*water undertaker*) for drinking, washing, cooking and sanitary purposes, including hot water supplied through any outlet. Domestic water is regarded as *wholesome* when provided through the supplier's main. Domestic water must be maintained in a wholesome condition when discharged through or stored in plumbing components inside a property.

domical cage

See *Balloon grating*

domical grating

A type of grating fitted over components such as the waste outlet from a *urinal* or the roof outlet to a *rainwater* pipework system, in order to prevent foreign matter from entering the system that may lead to blockage, for example by leaves.

dormer

A type of window opening that is formed in a pitched roof that may need weatherproofing with sheet metals.

double branch

A pipe fitting designed to connect two pipes into a branch from opposing sides. Care must be taken when fitting a double-branch pipe with sanitary pipework systems in order to minimise the risk of *cross-flow*.

▲ Double-branch fitting

double-check valve

See *Check valve*

double-feed indirect cylinder

A double-feed indirect cylinder requires separate water feeds to the *primary* and *secondary circuits*. The water in both circuits is kept totally separate by a coil inserted inside the cylinder which contains the primary water in order to avoid the waters mixing and *corrosion* taking place. The primary circuit is therefore a *closed circuit* and *ferrous metals* can be used in the primary system as the effects of corrosion are reduced. See *Indirect hot-water system*

down draught

A draught which blows down a flue pipe which may result in *vitiated air* being mixed with the fuel, resulting in *incomplete combustion* and a safety risk to the appliance user. See *Draught diverter*

downpipe

See *Rainwater pipe*

downstream

Further along the waterflow direction, for example a *supply pipe* is downstream of the *water meter*.

drain

A near horizontal pipe that may be suspended in a building or buried in the ground to which *discharge stacks*, ground floor *sanitary appliances* or *rainwater pipes* are connected. See *Types of drainage system*

drain cleaning

The process of clearing full or partial blockages from drainage systems, using a variety of equipment, such as plungers (force cups); augers (to cut through the blockage); scrapers and gully grabs; rods (so that tools such as augers, screws and plungers may be directed to the source of the blockage); and pressure jetting (to remove the source of the blockage using a high-pressure jet of water).

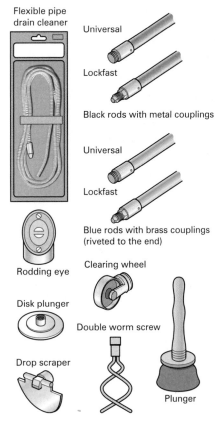

▲ Drain and pipe clearing equipment

A
B
C
D
E
F
G
H
I
J
K
L
M
N
O
P
Q
R
S
T
U
V
W
X
Y
Z

drain plug

An expandable device inserted into a discharge or drain pipe and tightened to form a seal in situ for the purposes of sealing the pipe for air testing or for maintenance purposes. See *Air test*

drain rods

A series of lockable rods that are used during *drain clearing*.

drain stop valve

A *composite valve* used to isolate the cold-water supply to all or part of a plumbing system. A *drain valve* is included for the purposes of draining the system down.

drain test

This is the process of testing drains for soundness. Types of test that may be undertaken include the *air test*, *smoke test* or *water test*. Drain testing may also include checking the system for alignment. See *Alignment test*

drain valves (drain tap)

Drain valves are covered by BS 2879 and installed on all the low points in a system in order that water may be drained from the system. For example, if a house is unoccupied over winter, the system should be drained to prevent frost damage. The location of the drain valves should allow easy access for maintenance and for connecting a hosepipe. In the diagram, the drain valves are located to avoid submergence in the case of floods and to prevent any contamination risk.

Drain valve

Stop valve

Timber floor surface

Insulation
to protect
against frost

Concrete

▲ Combined stop and drain valve

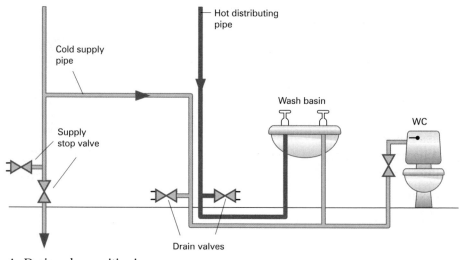

▲ Drain valve positioning

drainage system

A system that includes drainage equipment and other components that collect waste water and discharges by means of gravity. See *Types of drainage system*

draining down

Draining a system or part of a system of all the water, usually to complete a task, for example draining down a radiator to change a defective *radiator valve*.

draught break

Any opening in an *open-flue* system, such as a *draught diverter* or *draught stabiliser*.

draught diverter

Part of an *open-flue* system in a gas boiler, the draught diverter is fitted to divert any down draught from the flue system away from the boiler so that combustion of the fuel is not affected.

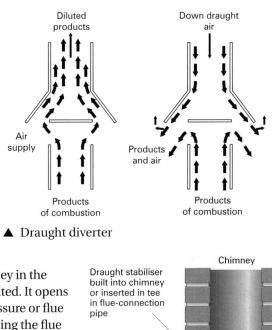

▲ Draught diverter

draught stabiliser

A device that includes a hinged flap, this is fitted to *open-flue* pipes or *chimneys* from combustion appliances with excessive flue draughts. The stabiliser must be fitted in a section of flue pipe or chimney in the room in which the appliance is sited. It opens in response to an increase in pressure or flue draught in the chimney, so reducing the flue draught through the combustion appliance, and it closes when the pressure recedes.

draw-off point

An outlet which is fitted with a control valve for the purposes of drawing off water, for example hot- and cold-water taps and shower mixers.

dress guard

An integral safety fitting to the front of, and forming part of, a gas fire.

dresser

See *Leadworking tools*

▲ Draught stabiliser

dressing

See *Lead bossing*

drift

Another name for a *swaging tool*, used to flare out the end of a tube. See *Compression fittings*

drinking bowls (animals)

There are drinking bowls designed for animals, which have a water feed into them. If it were possible for the inlet valve to become submerged, then the water must be supplied from a *storage cistern* via an independent dedicated *distribution pipe*. If the drinking bowl has a category 5 *backflow prevention device* fitted, the water may be fed from a *supply pipe*.

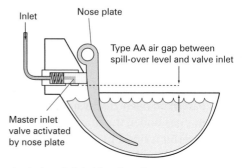

▲ Animal drinking bowl

drinking fountain

A small drinking-water supply device using a jet nozzle. There should be a 25 mm (minimum) gap between the jet nozzle and the *spill-over* level of the bowl. The nozzle should have a screen to protect it from *contamination*. The water supply into the fountain is controlled by means of a *non-concussive tap* which closes the supply automatically a few seconds after the valve has been opened, to prevent wastage of water.

drinking-water supplies and points

Drinking water can be supplied from a supply pipe, a pump delivery pipe drawing water from a *supply pipe*, or a *distribution pipe* drawing water from a *storage cistern* containing *wholesome water*; whatever the case, the water supplied for drinking water must be wholesome. In domestic properties at least one drinking-water tap is provided usually at the kitchen sink.

drip

A type of *expansion joint* that is used with metallic roof coverings which usually have a pitch of less than 15°, that is, nearly flat. The drip runs across the fall of the roof and caters for thermal expansion of the metallic sheets. The minimum drip height is usually 50 mm unless an *anti-capillarity groove* is incorporated into the drip design, in which case the minimum height is usually 40 mm.

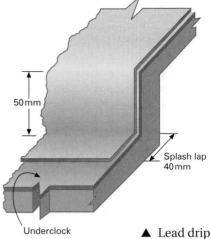

▲ Lead drip

drive-in bracket

A type of gutter bracket for fixing the gutter directly to masonry wall surfaces. The bracket is either driven into a brick seam or built into the seam with new buildings. The height of the bracket can normally be adjusted using an adjuster screw.

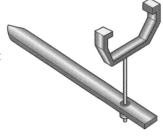

drop valve

A type of flushing valve used in a WC *flushing cistern* as its flushing mechanism. A push rod lifts a moving element in the valve during flushing, and the moving element seats against a rubber washer to form a watertight seal when the cistern is full.

▲ Drive-in bracket

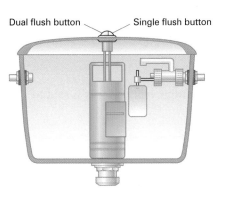

Dual flush button   Single flush button

▲ Dual-flush cistern with drop valve

dry-pipe sprinkler system

A type of *sprinkler system* in which the system is initially charged with compressed air which is holding back water contained behind a differential pressure valve. Should a sprinkler head open, the pressure in the pipeline reduces, allowing the differential pressure valve to open, thus discharging water into the system and through the sprinkler head that has opened. The system is usually installed in unheated buildings where the pipework system may be subject to freezing.

dry riser

A large diameter empty pipe that runs vertically inside a building (usually in the landing) which the fire authority uses to pump water to the various parts of the building during a fire.

A
B
C
D
E
F
G
H
I
J
K
L
M
N
O
P
Q
R
S
T
U
V
W
X
Y
Z

dual flush

This is a flushing system in which a *siphon* or *drop valve* fitted to a *flushing cistern* is designed to give two flushing options: a shorter flush and a longer flush. Under the Water Regulations the maximum flush volume for the short flush is 4 litres and the maximum for the long flush is 6 litres.

duct

A purpose-made enclosure designed to accommodate key services such as water/gas pipes and electric cables. If required it can be constructed so that access to the interior can be provided either throughout its length or at specific points by removal of covers.

ducted air heater

See *Warm air central-heating system*

ductile

The ability of a substance to be drawn out or stretched thin without breaking. *Copper* is said to be a ductile material as it can be readily drawn into wire for a variety of uses.

durability

A substance which is capable of withstanding wear, tear or decay is said to be durable.

A
B
C
D
E
F
G
H
I
J
K
L
M
N
O
P
Q
R
S
T
U
V
W
X
Y
Z

ear protection

Small earplugs and large industrial earmuffs are used to protect ears from being damaged at work by noise, because regular exposure to loud noise over time can cause partial deafness. To avoid this, ear protection is worn for a particular job; ear plugs are adequate for low noise levels, but for some jobs, for example using a large hammer drill, ear muffs are essential.

earth-bonding conductors

See *Bonding*

earth continuity

The requirement to ensure that electrical equipment and exposed metalwork in buildings, such as hot-water, cold-water and central-heating systems pipework and components, are effectively connected to a building's *earthing* system to ensure that any stray electric current that may occur in a faulted situation is safely discharged to earth (to ground).

earth equipotential bonding

See *Bonding*

earthenware

See *Ceramics*

earthing

An electric current that is run away to the ground, ensuring safety.

easy clean cover

The metallic decorative cover fitted to a range of taps to cover the headgear and *gland nut*.

eaves gutter

A type of guttering system that is fitted to pitch roofs. It is available in a variety of patterns, including square, half round and ogee, and can be manufactured from

A
B
C
D
E
F
G
H
I
J
K
L
M
N
O
P
Q
R
S
T
U
V
W
X
Y
Z

a variety of materials such as *cast iron*, aluminium, *copper* and *plastics*, the latter now being the most popular.

Standard half round | Square | Ogee

▲ Gutter profiles

Key features of a plastic gutter system are:
- Sufficient space should be allowed in gutter joints for *thermal movement* of the gutter system.
- Brackets should be fixed at a maximum 1 metre interval. *Fascia brackets* are used to fix gutters to timber surfaces, *rafter brackets* are used to make fixings to rafters, and *drive-in brackets* are used to make fixings directly to masonry wall surfaces.
- A gutter system is usually laid to a fall of 1 in 600.
- A rainwater outlet is sited at the low point of the gutter system connecting the gutter to the rainwater pipe.

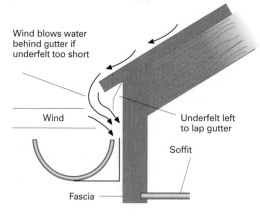

Wind blows water behind gutter if underfelt too short

Wind

Underfelt left to lap gutter

Soffit

Fascia

▲ Eaves gutter system

eccentric reducer
See *Reducer*

effective pipe length
This is the sum of the actual pipe length and the equivalent pipe length of all the valves and fittings in a hot- and cold-water system. These figures can then be used to size pipework and components in the system. Valves and fittings in hot- and

cold-water systems are allocated an equivalent pipe length to assist in calculating the resistance to the passage of water caused by each type of fitting. For example, installing a 20 mm stop valve is equivalent to adding another 7 m of pipe run.

Bore of pipe (mm)	Equivalent pipe length			
	Elbow (m)	Tee (m)	Stop valve (m)	Check valve (m)
12	0.5	0.6	4.0	2.5
20	0.8	1.0	7.0	4.3
25	1.0	1.5	10.0	5.6
32	1.4	2.0	12.0	6.0
40	1.7	2.5	16.0	7.9
50	2.3	3.5	22.0	11.5
65	3.0	4.5	–	–
73	3.4	5.8	34.0	–

▲ Equivalent pipe lengths for various types of fittings and pipe sizes in hot- and cold-water systems

elasticity
The property of materials to recover their original size and shape after removal of a force causing *deformation*.

elastomeric
The elastic, rubber-like properties of a material.

elbows
A pipe fitting which is used to give a tight 90° change of direction (bend) in a pipeline.
See *Bend*

electrical conductivity
A measure of how efficiently, or inefficiently, a material conducts electricity.

electric boiler
A type of boiler that supplies hot water to a wet *central-heating system*. There are two main methods of operation:
- A large volume of water is heated overnight using a low rate electricity tariff and is circulated to the heating system throughout the day without further heating required if at all possible.

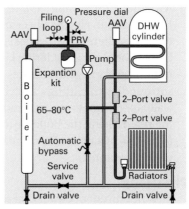

▲ Electric boiler supplying central-heating system with 2 × two-port valves

A
B
C
D
E
F
G
H
I
J
K
L
M
N
O
P
Q
R
S
T
U
V
W
X
Y
Z

- Water is heated in a boiler containing electric heating elements and supplied as per a normal wet central-heating boiler.

electric hot-water heating

There are two main methods of heating hot water by electricity:

- Storage system – here the water in the system is heated by one or more *immersion heaters*.

▲ Immersion heater

In a *direct system* electric hot water heating is usually carried out using low tariff electricity supplied during the night. A *direct cylinder* contains two immersion heaters in the side of the cylinder. The bottom immersion heater, capable of heating the entire contents of the cylinder, is connected to the low tariff electricity supply and heats the cylinder during the night. The top immersion heater is used by the customer to top up or boost the stored water temperature for short periods later in the day; the top-up immersion heater is run off the standard electricity tariff.

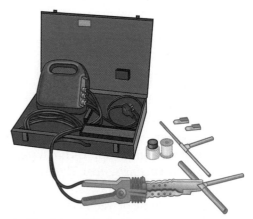

▲ Single-point vented electric water heater

- *Instantaneous water heaters* – these are connected directly to a supply or *distribution pipe* and heat the water instantaneously on demand and therefore store virtually no hot water. They are available as single point (feeding only one outlet) or multi-point (feeding more than one outlet) types.

electric soldering system

A method of soldering *capillary joints* using an electrically heated tool as an alternative to a naked flame. The electric soldering kit minimises damage to surfaces surrounding the fittings, such as wallpaper, carpets etc., and reduces the risk of fire in the building due to the use of a naked flame, such as with a *blowtorch*.

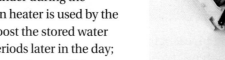

▲ Electric soldering system

electricity

Electric current or power that results from the movement of *electrons* in a *conductor* from a negatively charged point to a positively charged point.

electrochemical series (electromotive series)

A list of metals arranged in order of each metal's ability to resist *electrolytic (action) corrosion*. If two metals placed together in the presence of water are at further ends of the electrochemical series – one negatively charged (cathode) and one positively charged (*anode*) – *corrosion* will occur with the anode gradually being destroyed, a process known as *electrolytic action* (galvanic action). For example, in a *galvanised* steel cistern in which copper swarf is deposited, the zinc in the cistern will corrode at a rapid pace causing pin holing of the cistern.

Metal	Chemical symbol	Electrode potential (volts)
Silver	Ag	0.80 +
Copper	Cu	0.35 +
Lead	Pb	0.12 –
Tin	Sn	0.14 –
Nickel	Ni	0.23 –
Iron	Fe	0.44 –
Chromium	Cr	0.56 –
Zinc	Zn	0.76 –
Aluminium	Al	1.00 –
Magnesium	Mg	2.00 –
Sodium	Na	2.71 –

▲ The electrochemical series

electrode

Usually a metallic conductor which serves the purpose of conducting electric charge carriers (i.e. *electrons* or *ions*) into a liquid, a gas, a vacuum or on to the surface of a solid body. An electrode is used to generate a spark in combustion appliances to ignite the fuel.

electrofusion welding

A process used in the jointing of *polyethylene* pipe, by applying heat using special electrofusion welding equipment to a special fitting which, when sufficiently heated, melts the plastic, fusing it on to the pipe. This type of joint is commonly used on gas and water mains pipework.

electrolysis

The process in which a relatively small electric current is passed through an electrolytic solution, such as water, that is in contact with two dissimilar

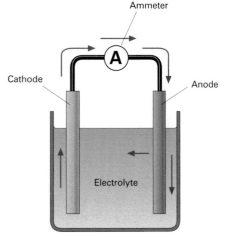

Ammeter

Cathode

Anode

Electrolyte

▲ The process of electrolysis

A
B
C
D
E
F
G
H
I
J
K
L
M
N
O
P
Q
R
S
T
U
V
W
X
Y
Z

metals – an *anode* and a *cathode* – causing a chemical reaction. The result is the destruction or disintegration of the anode which is deposited on the cathode.

electrolyte
A liquid that is used in the process of *electrolysis* which will conduct electricity.

electrolytic action (corrosion)
The flow of electrically charged *ions* from an *anode* to a *cathode* through an *electrolyte* (usually water), during which the anode is gradually destroyed.

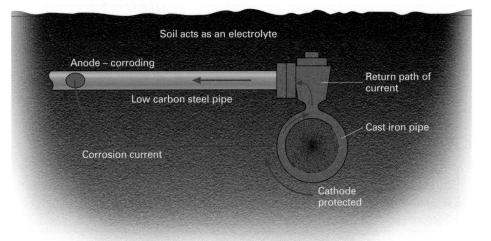

▲ Example of possible electrolytic corrosion in pipework systems

electromagnetism
This is magnetism produced by an electric current. For example, a *copper* wire carrying an electric current can magnetise pieces of iron or steel near it.

electromotive force (EMF)
The electrical force that exists across the terminals of an electrical generator, or battery. When connected to a load in a closed circuit, this force produces a *voltage* across the load and causes *current* to flow in that circuit. EMF is measured in volts and designated with the letter E (supply voltage) or V (load voltage).

electromotive series
See *Electrochemical series*

electron
A negatively charged particle which orbits the *nucleus* of an *atom*. Electricity is created when electrons break out of orbit and flow to a neighbouring atom.

electronic ignition
A method of automatically igniting the fuel in gas and oil-fired appliances using a spark that jumps across two *electrodes* or an electrode and the head of a burner.

electronic manometer (digital differential manometer)

An electronic type of *manometer* that can be used for gas *tightness testing* and determining *standing* and *working pressures* of gas systems and appliances.

electronic portable gas analyser

An electronic device that can be used to measure the levels of the different combustion products from a combustion appliance, for example *carbon dioxide*, and that can therefore be used in the correct *commissioning* of gas and oil-fired appliances. Electronic portable gas analysers can also be purchased to measure the concentration of *carbon monoxide* in a location; they can therefore be used to identify if a combustion appliance is burning correctly and for incident investigation should suspected carbon monoxide poisoning arise.

▲ Electronic manometer

emergency control valve

A valve installed for shutting off the mains supply of gas in an emergency.

emergency shut-off valve

A valve which must be fitted on the outside of buildings with *LPG* bulk tank and multicylinder installations, at the point where the gas supply enters the building. The valve must be clearly labelled with the opening and closing directions.

end-feed capillary joint

See *Capillary joint*

energy

This is the ability of a substance to do work and is usually measured in joules (J). It comes in different forms – heat (thermal), light (radiant), mechanical, electrical and chemical – and there are two types: stored (potential) energy and working (kinetic) energy. For example, much of the energy we use comes from non-renewable sources, such as fossil fuels (coal, oil and gas), and renewable energy sources, such as solar power, wind power and hydroelectric power.

energy conservation

This covers strategies for reducing *carbon dioxide* emissions produced when burning fossil fuel; carbon dioxide released into the atmosphere contributes to *global warming*. For example, the government has introduced legislation to ensure that buildings are better insulated and heating appliances more efficient.

A
B
C
D
E
F
G
H
I
J
K
L
M
N
O
P
Q
R
S
T
U
V
W
X
Y
Z

environmental hazards

Any situation or activity which could be harmful to the environment. One of the most dangerous hazards in the plumbing industry is working with *asbestos*. There are special arrangements for the disposal of waste asbestos. Burning waste material is another environmental hazard, forbidden on most sites. Burning *plastics* and paint cans produces dangerous fumes. Make sure that waste is disposed of safely and never overfill or put flammable material into skips.

equilibrium ball valve

A sophisticated design of *float-operated valve* in which pressure is exerted by the water supply on both sides of the valve washer. This ensures that the valve in its normal operation only has to lift the weight of the arm as opposed to the valve having to lift the weight of the arm and deal with the pressure exerted in the valve by the incoming water pressure in a conventional valve. The equilibrium valve is best suited to high-pressure water areas and in overcoming *water hammer* that may be created by float valves in *cisterns*.

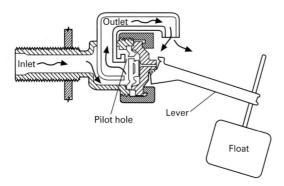

▲ Equilibrium ball valve with diaphragm washer for use in WCs

equipment – tool safety

The safe use of hand and power tools includes:
- Never use a hammer on a tool with a wooden handle (e.g. wood chisel).
- Keep cutting tools, saws and drills sharp and in good condition.
- Ensure that blades on hacksaws and woodsaws are fitted properly and are sharp; guards should be re-fitted after use.
- Make sure that handles are properly fitted to hammers and files, and that the handles have no splinters.
- Check that hammerheads are secured using metal or wooden wedges.
- Check for fraying cables on hand-held electrically operated power tools and check that plugs are in good condition.
- Check all electrical equipment and test labels to ensure they are in safe working order.

equipotential bonding

See *Bonding*

equivalent height

The effective height of a flue allowing for the restrictions caused by the flue pipe fittings, for example *bends*.

erosion

The wearing away of a substance or piece of equipment through contact. Erosion is different to *corrosion*, in which a chemical reaction takes place.

Essex flange

A type of boss that can be used to make an additional pipe connection to a hot-water storage cylinder. The flange has a unique design whereby access is only required from one side of the cylinder to fix it in position.

ethene (ethylene)

This is produced from crude oil and is the basic building block of plastics. Single ethene *molecules* (monomers) contain carbon, hydrogen and oxygen *atoms* and can link together into long chains to make polythene (polymer). If one hydrogen atom in the ethene monomer is replaced a different monomer is created producing a different type of plastic. This is called *polymerisation*. The two main categories of plastics used in the plumbing industry are *thermo-setting plastics* and *thermoplastics*.

European Standards (EN)

If a product is certified to an EN standard it means the manufacturer has tested the product thoroughly under EC Quality Control Schemes.

evaporation

The conversion (*change of state*) of a liquid (e.g. water) into a vapour (a gaseous state), usually through the application of heat energy but below the liquid's *boiling point*.

excavations

These are trenches or holes below ground in which work, such as laying or mending pipes, needs to be carried out. For such work the specific Health and Safety guidelines need to be applied; these are designed to prevent people falling into the excavation and the collapse of the excavation walls on to people within them; trench supports may be required if the excavation is sufficiently deep.

excess air

Additional air provided to a combustion appliance in order to ensure complete *combustion* of the fuel. More air is normally provided over that which is required to ensure a safe margin for complete combustion.

A
B
C
D
E
F
G
H
I
J
K
L
M
N
O
P
Q
R
S
T
U
V
W
X
Y
Z

expanding tool

See *Socket expander*

expansion

This occurs when a substance or material is heated and its *molecules* begin to move apart, resulting in the object becoming larger or increasing in volume. This increase in size is known as expansion. As the object cools the molecules move closer together and it reduces in size or volume, that is, there is *contraction*, the reverse of expansion.

expansion joint

A joint installed in a pipework system to permit *thermal movement* (*expansion* and *contraction*) when the pipe is subject to heating or cooling. Expansion and contraction needs

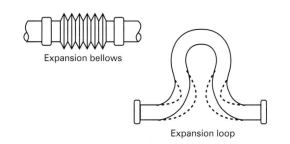

Expansion bellows

Expansion loop

▲ Expansion bellows and expansion loop

to be catered for in pipework systems in order that damage does not occur to the pipe materials and fittings, and in order to avoid noise from the system which may be annoying to the building users. *Plastics* materials have the highest rate of expansion and contraction. There are a variety of different expansion joints available for pipework systems, including:

- leaving a gap in a *push-fit joint* for the pipe to expand and contract
- in a long pipeline, fitting an expansion loop which moves as the pipe is heated up or cooled
- fitting expansion bellows in the pipeline which permit an increase or reduction in the pipe length as it is heated or cooled.

Expansion joints also need to be included in metallic roof covering materials to permit expansion and contraction; they come in the form of *laps*, *drips* and *rolls*.

expansion noise

This occurs in hot-water and central-heating pipework causing creaks and cracking sounds. The noise can be reduced using pipe clips, brackets or pads between pipes, fittings and pipework surfaces, and ensuring that there is sufficient room for thermal expansion of the pipework in the system. In larger systems with long straight pipe runs it may be necessary to fit *expansion joints* to cater for the *expansion* and *contraction* that occurs in the pipeline.

expansion pipe

See *Vent pipe*

expansion valve

A type of *pressure-relief valve* fitted to relieve excess pressure build-up in an *unvented hot-water system,* usually caused by component failure. The manufacturer of the cylinder specifies the pressure at which the valve begins to operate; this is usually between 6 and 8 bar. The expansion valve protects the system if the *pressure reducing valve* fails to maintain the inlet cold-water pressure at the designed system operating pressure or if the expansion device fails (e.g the expansion vessel ruptures). There should be no other valve fitted in between the expansion valve and the *storage cylinder.* Expansion valves are either 'lever-top' pattern (operates by lifting a lever) or 'twist-top' as shown in the photo.

▲ Expansion valve and tundish

expansion vessel

A gas- or air-charged device fitted to a *closed system,* (pressurised) hot-water or central-heating, to take up the expanded water when the system is heated. The vessel is gas or air charged on one side of a flexible rubber membrane or diaphragm. As the system heats, the increased volume of water is taken up by the compressed gas or air in the vessel. The vessel is normally fitted on the cold or return side of a system in order to prolong the life of the diaphragm. The vessel should be correctly sized in order to accept the extent of the expanded water in the system when heated; this is usually about 4 per cent of the system contents when cold; specific tables are available for the purposes of sizing an expansion vessel. See *Cylinder air gap*

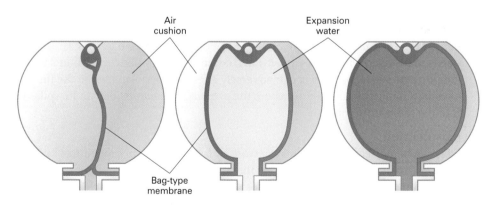

▲ Operation of an expansion vessel

A
B
C
D
E
F
G
H
I
J
K
L
M
N
O
P
Q
R
S
T
U
V
W
X
Y
Z

A
B
C
D
E
F
G
H
I
J
K
L
M
N
O
P
Q
R
S
T
U
V
W
X
Y
Z

▶ External stop valve and
water meter installation

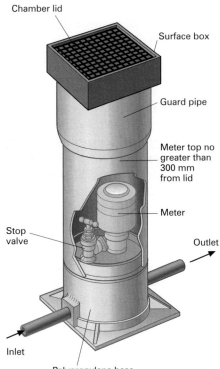

Chamber lid

Surface box

Guard pipe

Meter top no
greater than
300 mm
from lid

Meter

Stop
valve

Outlet

Inlet

Polypropylene base

external corner
See *Lead corners*

external stop valve
This is used to isolate the *service pipe*
to a building from the mains using an
external stop valve sited at the boundary
to the property. The stop valve should
be located in a special stop-valve
chamber to ensure easy access. The
chamber should have a firm base and
be constructed using 150 mm *polyvinyl
chloride (PVC)*, or earthenware pipe. The
stop-valve cover should be made from
steel plate, or a combination of steel
plate and plastic. In new properties the
stop valve chamber is likely to include a
water meter used for billing purposes to
measure the quantity of water used in
the property.

extractor fans
These are used to remove stale air from a room or a building, and therefore assist
in ensuring a continual flow of fresh air into the building. They are also used
in parts of the building where the moisture content of the air is high, such as
kitchens and bathrooms, in order to minimise the opportunity for water vapour
in the saturated air to condense on building components such as tiles. Great care
needs to be taken when siting *open-flued* combustion appliances in rooms which
contain extractor fans as they can adversely affect the performance of the flue,
causing a dangerous condition where the *products of combustion* can be spilled
into the room from the flue.

eye protection
Eyes can be protected from injury at work by following safety procedures and
injuries can be prevented by wearing the recommended eye protection, such as
safety glasses, safety goggles or goggles with coloured lenses for welding.

factory-made insulated chimney

A complete assembly of all factory-made insulated sections, fittings and accessories necessary to convey the *products of combustion* to outside air, supplied by the manufacturer in one complete unit.

fahrenheit

The old imperial method of measuring temperature; for example the freezing point of water is 32°F while the boiling point is 212°F.

fall pipe

See *Rainwater pipe*

fanned draught flue system (fan-assisted flue)

A *flue system* in which the draught is created by a fan incorporated in the appliance. The fan allows the use of a flue system with a smaller cross-sectional area than would normally be used with a *natural draught flued* appliance. A safety device, such as a *pressure switch*, needs to be included in the design of the appliance so that, in the event of the fan failing, the boiler will not light.

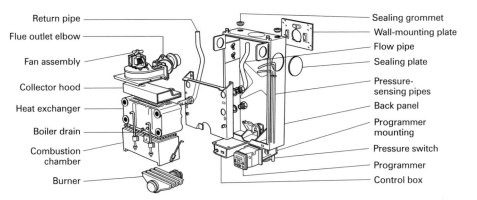

Return pipe
Flue outlet elbow
Fan assembly
Collector hood
Heat exchanger
Boiler drain
Combustion chamber
Burner

Sealing grommet
Wall-mounting plate
Flow pipe
Sealing plate
Pressure-sensing pipes
Back panel
Programmer mounting
Pressure switch
Programmer
Control box

▲ Section through a wall-mounted fanned draught flue boiler

A
B
C
D
E
F
G
H
I
J
K
L
M
N
O
P
Q
R
S
T
U
V
W
X
Y
Z

fascia bracket

A type of bracket used to fix an *eaves gutter* system to a *fascia board*.

fascia, fascia boards

A length of wood or plastic fixed to the rafters. The fascia board is used to fix the *eaves gutter* system to it.

fatigue (sheet lead)

The reduction in the strength of lead sheet caused by *thermal movement*. Excessive fatigue causes cracking,

▲ Fascia bracket

so there is a standard requirement for the lead sheet grain structure, to maintain *malleability* and provide resistance to thermal fatigue. Joints such as *lap joints drips* and *rolls* are included in sheet lead roofing designs to allow for thermal movement so as to avoid fatigue to the sheet lead which may result in cracking or splitting.

feed and expansion (F&E) cistern

A cistern used in an *open-vented system* or an *indirect hot-water system*, allowing the system to be filled up and providing space for the water in the system to expand. It should be sized to accept approximately 4 per cent of the system volume measured at cold start-up. When setting the *float-operated valve*, the water level in the cistern when heated should not be higher than 25 mm below the invert level of the *warning pipe*. The F&E cistern should be installed at the highest point in the system. As a rule of thumb, in a fully pumped system the level of water in the F&E cistern should usually be at least one metre above the highest point in the system

Vent pipe to terminate not less than twice the diameter of the vent pipe above the top of the float-operated valve A or the top of the overflow pipe B, whichever is greater

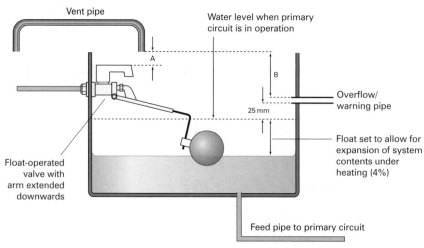

▲ Feed and expansion cistern

feed cistern

A cistern that feeds the *hot-water storage vessel* only and no other outlets.

female thread

An internal thread cut inside a fitting or component and into which a *male threaded* fitting can be fitted.

ferrous metal

A metal that is made of, or contains *iron*, for example *low-carbon steel*. See *non-ferrous metals*

ferrule

A type of isolation valve used to make the *mains connection* between a high-pressure water main and the cold-water *service pipework* to a building. A ferrule can be inserted into the water mains under pressure without isolating or draining down the mains by using a mains tapping machine.

filament igniters

A small coil of thin wire used to light the *pilot light* on a gas appliance. The filament heats to red-hot heat when fed with electricity from a battery or transformer.

Sealing plug — Valve head

Rubber seals

Water outlet holes

Plug valve

Outlet can be rotated on ferrule body

▲ Ferrule

file

A hand tool used to provide a finish to a piece of metalwork. They come in a variety of shapes to suit particular jobs, including flat, triangular, square, round and half round. The file should always

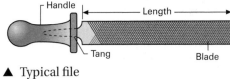

Handle — Length

Tang — Blade

▲ Typical file

be used with a proper handle to ensure that the 'tang' or end of the file which is pointed does not puncture the skin whilst in use. See *Rasp*

filler rod

The metal rod used as the filler material when making a welded joint.

fillet welding

Welding of two pieces of material at different angles. See *Angle welded joint*

A
B
C
D
E
F
G
H
I
J
K
L
M
N
O
P
Q
R
S
T
U
V
W
X
Y
Z

A
B
C
D
E
F
G
H
I
J
K
L
M
N
O
P
Q
R
S
T
U
V
W
X
Y
Z

filling loop

A method of filling a sealed *central-heating system* with water, using a temporary connection to the system comprising a flexible hose, *stop valve* and double *check valve*.

filter

See *Strainer*

firebed

Part of a combustion appliance on which the fuel is burned.

fire box

The part of a combustion appliance in which fuel is burned and combustion takes place.

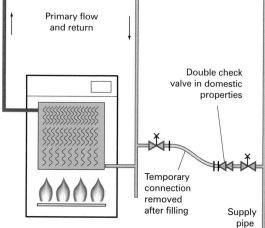
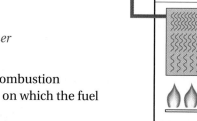

Primary flow and return

Double check valve in domestic properties

Temporary connection removed after filling

Supply pipe

▲ Filling loop

fire brick

A type of brick that is able to store heat. They are also used as *insulators* to prevent heat being wasted through the outer surface of a *fire box* and to protect the materials from which the fire box is manufactured.

fire cement

A heat-resistant pre-mixed cement used in the sealing of flue component joints, for example sealing a boiler *flue spigot* to its adjoining *flue pipe*.

fire compartment

A room in a building that is specifically sited and constructed so as to minimise the spread of fire. Plumbers need to be particularly careful when routing pipework through fire compartments in order to ensure that they do not compromise the building's safety, for example by leaving gaps round pipework etc.

fireclay

See *Ceramics*

fireplace opening

An aperture formed in the face of a *builder's opening, fireplace recess, flue box* or *fire surround*.

fireplace recess

A recess formed by the inclusion of fireplace components in the *builder's opening*.

fire-protection systems

These are fitted to buildings to minimise the spread of fire should it occur. See *Dry-pipe sprinkler system*; *Wet-pipe sprinkler system*

fire stop

A method of sleeving and sealing a pipe as it passes through parts of the building structure, such as walls and floors, in order to prevent the spread of hot air, smoke and fire from room to room. Pipework and *flues* should be properly fire-stopped where they cut through such building components under the requirements of the *Building Regulations*.

Sealed with fire resistant mastic

Block wall or fire partition

Collars fixed to both sides of wall to stop fire spread from both directions

▲ Fire stop to pipework using an intumescent collar

fire surround

A purpose-designed setting for a gas fire, fitted against a wall at the base of a *flue* and usually including a *hearth*.

fire valve

A type of valve fitted to an oil supply line to isolate the oil flow to a combustion appliance in the event of fire. There are three main types:

- Fusible link type fire valve in which a tensioned wire with a low melting point fusible link is strung across the face of a boiler and which, under normal operating conditions, is tensioned to keep the *isolation valve* open. If the fusible link melts, the tension is removed and the valve closes, isolating the supply to the appliance.
- Drop head type fire valve – here a low melting point solder is included in the head of the valve which, when subjected to heat, melts and the valve isolates itself.
- Remote sensing phial type fire valve – here a sensing phial is connected by a small capillary tube to the fire valve, which can be sited remotely. On sensing a fire the valve closes.

The remote sensing phial type tends to be the preferred option as it is safer because the valve can be sited external to the building (it cannot with the other types), and the sensing phial can be located in the boiler case above the burner. (See diagram overleaf.)

A
B
C
D
E
F
G
H
I
J
K
L
M
N
O
P
Q
R
S
T
U
V
W
X
Y
Z

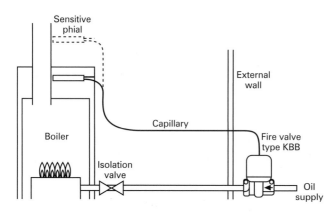

▲ Remote sensing phial type fire valve

first-aid kit

There should be at least one first-aid kit at a workplace and it should be easily accessible to all employees. For work at a customer's home, the first-aid kit should be carried in the vehicle. A basic first-aid kit should contain:

- 20 adhesive dressings (assorted sizes)
- two sterile eye pads
- six triangular bandages
- six unmedicated wound dressings, sizes 10 cm and 8 cm
- two unmedicated wound dressings, sizes 13 cm and 9 cm
- six safety pins
- three sterile unmedicated wound dressings, sizes 28 cm and 17.5 cm.

first fix

The first fixing of pipework in a building takes place before surface finishes, such as floor boarding and plasterboard surfaces, have been applied, that is, whilst access is still available. See *Second fix*

fixed jumper

The *jumper plate* which is fixed in position in a *screwdown stop valve* or a *bib tap* to which the washer is fixed.

fixing devices

Various types of fixing devices are used to secure pipework, sanitary ware and appliances, such as: screws, e.g. brass wood screws, self-tapping screws, turn-threaded wood screws, steel countersunk screws, chipboard screws, mirror screws and plastic plugs, plasterboard fixings, cavity fixings and nails. Fixings should provide enough support to make a neat and tidy component installation and to prevent accidental damage from occurring through insecure fixings.

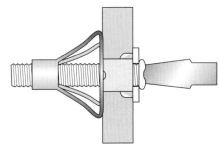

▲ Cavity wall fixing

flame arrestor

A device, usually a gauze screen through which gas can pass, fitted to a gas line to prevent the flame at the end of the line from passing back down into the pipeline.

flame conduction and rectification

This is a type of *flame supervision device* designed to prevent gas from continuing to be provided into an appliance should the flame be extinguished. The chemical reaction of combustion produces ions, that is, electrically charged particles. In the presence of an electrode these *ions rectify alternating current* and produce a small *direct current*.

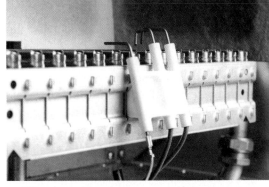

▲ Flame rectification

This operates a relay which activates the gas valve. Electronic flame-protection methods are used in domestic gas appliances such as boilers.

flame failure device

See *Flame protection*

flame lift

The opposite of *lighting back*, this happens when the speed of the gas mixture is too great, resulting in the flame being pushed away from the burner ports.

flame protection devices

These devices can detect the presence of a flame and will prevent unlit gas from entering the *combustion*

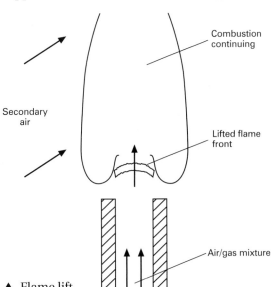

Secondary air

Combustion continuing

Lifted flame front

Air/gas mixture

▲ Flame lift

A
B
C
D
E
F
G
H
I
J
K
L
M
N
O
P
Q
R
S
T
U
V
W
X
Y
Z

A
B
C
D
E
F
G
H
I
J
K
L
M
N
O
P
Q
R
S
T
U
V
W
X
Y
Z

chamber of an appliance if there is no flame. They include: *bi-metal strip, flame conduction and rectification, thermoelectric devices* and *vapour pressure flame failure devices*. These devices are also known by the older term flame failure devices (FFD) and by the more modern term *flame supervision devices* (FSD).

flame retention

A method of ensuring that *flame lift* does not occur. Some burners contain flame retention ports, which are small holes sited below the main burner ports to keep the flame stable and avoid lift off. The flame retention ports must be cleaned as part of the appliance service procedure.

flame speed

The pressure of the gas supplied to an appliance and the size of the injector must be correct to ensure that a fixed and acceptable flame speed is maintained. If the gas mixture is too fast, *flame lift* may result. If the gas mixture is too slow, *lighting back* into the burner tube may occur.

flame supervision device

A device fitted to gas appliances which senses the presence of a flame. If a flame ceases in the appliance, the flame supervision device ensures that the gas supply is cut, preventing the *combustion chamber* continuing to fill with gas. See *Flame protection devices*

flammability levels, flammability limits

Gas will only burn when mixed with air in the correct quantities. The lower flammability level (LFL) is the lowest percentage of air required for a particular gas and the upper flammability level (UFL) is the higher figure given for each gas. For example, the flammability level for *natural gas* is 5–15 per cent. If there is between 5–15 per cent of natural gas mixed with air then the mixture can be ignited and will burn. *Propane* has a flammability level of 2–10 per cent and *butane* 2–9 per cent.

flammables

These are liquids and gases that ignite and burn readily, for example methanol, ethanol, ether, LPG and petrol. When working with flammables, use the smallest quantities possible, store and dispose of flammables safely, and make absolutely sure that there is no risk of flames or sparks. In an emergency, evacuate and ventilate the area thoroughly and call the emergency services.

flanged joint

A round disc incorporating bolt holes that may be welded or screwed on to a pipe in order to join on to another pipe or a vessel such as a boiler. The two sections of the flange are bolted together with a *gasket* in

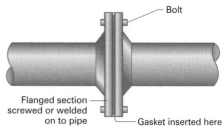

Bolt

Flanged section screwed or welded on to pipe

Gasket inserted here

▲ Flanged joint

the middle forming the seal. This type of joint is commonly used with *low-carbon steel* pipework.

flap valve

A type of *non-return valve* that includes a hinged flap to ensure that water flows only in one direction. It may also be used as a flushing mechanism in a WC *flushing cistern*.

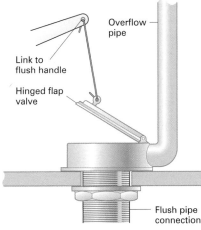

▲ Flap valve in flushing cistern

flaring tool

See *Compression joint swaging tool*

flashback

The ignition of gases in the welding nozzle of a *blowpipe* when using oxyacetylene *welding equipment*. Flashback is noticeable through a series of bangs in quick succession from the blowpipe. The problem can usually be overcome by turning off the gas and re-lighting; in more serious cases the nozzle should be plunged into a bucket of cold water with the oxygen valve left open; this will cool down the blowpipe and nozzle.

flashback arrestors

Devices that are fitted to oxyacetylene hoses and cylinders to prevent flame from a *flashback* getting into the hoses and cylinder during the welding process and causing fire and explosion.

flashings

See *Lead flashing*

flat-butted seams

A seam used for jointing two pieces of sheet lead in which the pieces of lead are butted together and a weld formed to joint them.

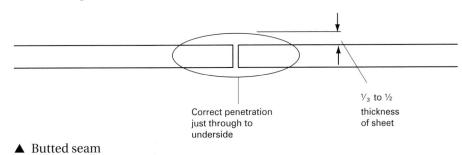

▲ Butted seam

flat dresser

See *Leadworking tools*

flat-lapped seam

A *lead welding* alternative to a *flat-butted* seam in which one piece of lead is lapped over the other. A lapped seam is commonly used where lead welding takes place against a flammable sub-structure.

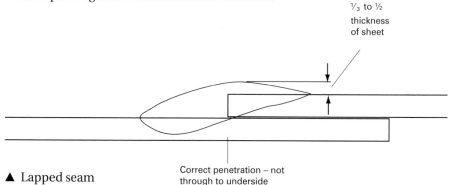

⅓ to ½ thickness of sheet

▲ Lapped seam

Correct penetration – not through to underside

flat roofs

Some properties have a flat roof instead of the usual pitched roof, and will therefore need a different weatherproof covering to traditional tiles for which sheet lead may be used.

flexible appliance connector

A connector with a self-sealing plug-in device used for slide-in appliances such as gas cookers. Those approved for use with *LPG* have a higher specification than *natural gas* types. A stability device must be used for free-standing appliances, for example cookers with flexible connectors, in order to prevent tipping of the appliance.

▲ Cooker bayonet/flex connection

flexible push-fit plumbing systems

A system of plastic pipes and fittings using *push-fit joints*.

flexible stainless-steel flue liner

A liner used for chimneys without clay lining or for chimneys and flues which perform unsatisfactorily. The top and base of the chimney or flue must be sealed and the liner should be one continuous length without joints or tight bends. A

▶ Flexible stainless-steel flue liner to a chimney

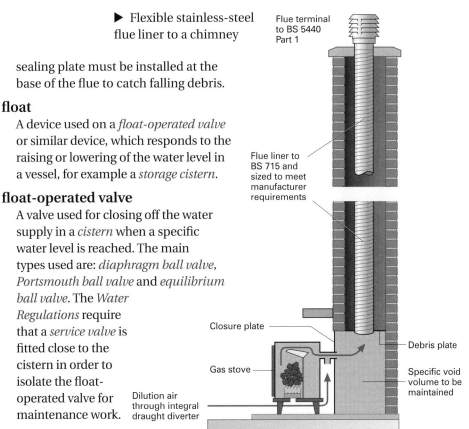

Flue terminal to BS 5440 Part 1

Flue liner to BS 715 and sized to meet manufacturer requirements

Closure plate

Debris plate

Gas stove

Specific void volume to be maintained

Dilution air through integral draught diverter

sealing plate must be installed at the base of the flue to catch falling debris.

float

A device used on a *float-operated valve* or similar device, which responds to the raising or lowering of the water level in a vessel, for example a *storage cistern*.

float-operated valve

A valve used for closing off the water supply in a *cistern* when a specific water level is reached. The main types used are: *diaphragm ball valve*, *Portsmouth ball valve* and *equilibrium ball valve*. The *Water Regulations* require that a *service valve* is fitted close to the cistern in order to isolate the float-operated valve for maintenance work.

float switch

A device which includes a float and an electrical switch. It can be used as an alternative inlet-control device in a *storage cistern*, whereby the float responds to the rising or falling water levels in the cistern by turning a switch on and off, which in turn controls a *booster pump* supplying the cistern.

flood level

The maximum level to which *waste water* can rise in a *drainage system*.

floor gully

A discharge fitting intended to receive water from floors either through a grating or from pipes connected to the body of the gully. A gully may include a *trap*. See *Gully*

flow noise

The noise of water flow in pipework can be annoying to building users, therefore the velocity (speed) of the water in the pipework needs to be controlled in order for this noise not to occur. In hot- and cold-water systems it can be reduced by keeping the velocity of the water below 3 metres per second. This may be accomplished by increasing the diameter of the pipe or by installing a *pressure-reducing valve*.

A
B
C
D
E
F
G
H
I
J
K
L
M
N
O
P
Q
R
S
T
U
V
W
X
Y
Z

A
B
C
D
E
F
G
H
I
J
K
L
M
N
O
P
Q
R
S
T
U
V
W
X
Y
Z

flow pipe

A pipe in a primary heating or hot-water circuit that moves heated water away from a boiler or *circulator* to equipment such as radiators.

flow rate

This is the amount of water passing through a pipe over a specific time period. Flow rate is usually measured in litres/second and is the basis on which pipe sizing is carried out. See *Loading unit*

flow switch

An electrical switch fitted in a hot or cold pipeline which contains a moving element that activates a pump or similar device when an outlet is opened. The flow switch is then kept open by the operation of the pump. When the outlet is closed the element moves back to its starting position, the switch closes and the pump turns off. A flow switch is commonly fitted to control the operation of a *shower booster pump*.

flue

The passage or space for conveying the *products of combustion* to the outside air.

flue blocks

See *Pre-cast concrete flue blocks*

flue box

A non-combustible enclosure that provides a substitute *builder's opening* or *fireplace recess*.

flue break

An opening in a *secondary flue*. See *Draught diverter*

flue-flow testing

A test used to ensure that a flue operates efficiently. The procedure is as follows: check the air supply, close doors and windows, check that there is some draught pulling up the flue, using a match or taper, light a smoke pellet placed at the base of the flue, check that there is no leakage of smoke into any part of the property adjacent to the flue and check that the smoke exits from only one terminal. Rectify any faults and re-test the flue.

▲ Flue-flow testing – no pull

▲ Flue-flow testing – pulling

flue gas analyser

See *Electronic portable gas analyser*

flue gas thermometer

A device that can be used during a *combustion efficiency* test to take readings of the flue gas temperature from a combustion appliance.

flue liner

See *Flexible stainless-steel flue liner*

▲ Flue gas thermometer

flueless appliance

An appliance which is designed to be used without a flue, for example a cooker, and in which the *products of combustion* mix with the surrounding air. Flueless appliances must have a constant supply of fresh air. *Incomplete combustion* in flueless appliances, such as cookers and some water heaters in small rooms, may produce *carbon monoxide* due to oxygen depletion.

flue-operating principles

The two main flue systems for boilers are *open flues* and *room-sealed flues*. Open flues draw air for combustion from the room in which the appliance is installed, through *air vents* in the outside wall. Heated air and combustion products are drawn through the flue by *convection*. The higher the flue is, the greater the flue draught created. Room-sealed flues are safer, drawing air for combustion directly from outside the room. Cool air is drawn in through the outside terminal of the flue and is supplied up through the burner and the *products of combustion* are collected in the flue hood and discharged to the outside through the *flue terminal*. See *Open flue; Room-sealed flue*

flue pipe

A pipe enclosing a flue; for a *twin wall flue pipe* it is the inner pipe.

flue spigot

The connection point between a combustion appliance and the flue system.

flue spigot restrictor

A plate designed to be fitted to the flue spigot on a gas fire to reduce the effect of flue pull on the appliance. A flue spigot restrictor may be supplied by a gas fire manufacturer to restrict the flue pull where the vertical height between the appliance flue outlet (spigot) and the flue termination is above a specific measurement.

flue system

A continuous flue, or assembly of flue components, from an appliance itself, a *builder's opening, fireplace recess, flue box* or independent canopy to a *chimney pot, terminal* or flue outlet.

A
B
C
D
E
F
G
H
I
J
K
L
M
N
O
P
Q
R
S
T
U
V
W
X
Y
Z

A
B
C
D
E
F
G
H
I
J
K
L
M
N
O
P
Q
R
S
T
U
V
W
X
Y
Z

flue terminal
See *Terminal*

flue terminal guard
See *Terminal guard*

flue termination
This is the point at which the flue system from a combustion appliance ends or is terminated. There is strict guidance laid down in the *Building Regulations* as to where flues may terminate in relation to: contact with persons (burning); discharge of the *products of combustion* into properties; *down draught* occurring owing to poor terminal siting; and proper combustion taking place in the appliance which may be affected by the improper positioning of the flue system and terminal.

fluid
Any substance which can flow and has no defined shape, for example a gas or a liquid.

fluid risk categories
The *Water Regulations* apply five fluid risk categories to define the drinkability, presence of impurities and the level of danger to health of different water sources. The categories are based on those developed by the Union of Water Supply Associations of Europe, and are also used in North America and Australia.

Fluid category	Description	Application
1	Wholesome water supplied by a water undertaker complying with the Requirements of the Regulations made under Schedule 67 of the Water Industry Act 1991	
2	Water that would be classed as fluid category 1 except for odour, appearance or temperature. These changes in water quality are aesthetic changes only and the water is not considered a hazard to human health	(a) water heated in a hot-water secondary system (b) mixtures of fluids from categories 1 and 2 discharged from combination taps or showers (c) water that has been softened by a domestic common salt regeneration process

continued on the next page

Fluid category	Description	Application

3	These fluids represent a slight health hazard and aren't suitable for drinking or other domestic purposes	(a) in houses or other single-occupancy dwellings
		  (i) water in primary circuits and heating systems, whether additives to the system have been used or not
		  (ii) water in wash basins, baths or shower trays
		  (iii) washing machines and dishwashers
		  (iv) home dialysing machines
		  (v) hand-held garden hoses with flow-control spray or shut-off control
		  (vi) hand-held garden fertiliser sprays
		(b) in premises other than a single-occupancy dwelling
		(c) where domestic fittings such as wash basins, baths or showers are installed in premises other than a single-occupancy dwelling (that is, commercial, industrial or other premises) these appliances may still be regarded as a fluid category 3, unless there's a potentially higher risk. Typical premises that justify a higher fluid risk category include hospitals and other medical establishments
		(d) house, garden or commercial irrigation systems without insecticide or fertiliser additives, with fixed sprinkler heads not less than 150 mm above ground level
		(e) fluids that represent a slight health hazard because of the concentrations of substances of low toxicity include any fluid that contains:
		  – ethylene glycol, copper sulphate solution or similar chemical additives or
		  – sodium hypochlorite (chloro's and common disinfectants)

continued on the next page

A
B
C
D
E
F
G
H
I
J
K
L
M
N
O
P
Q
R
S
T
U
V
W
X
Y
Z

A
B
C
D
E
F
G
H
I
J
K
L
M
N
O
P
Q
R
S
T
U
V
W
X
Y
Z

Fluid category	Description	Application
4	These fluids represent a significant health hazard and aren't suitable for drinking or other domestic purposes. They contain concentrations of toxic substances.	(a) water containing chemical carcinogenic substances or pesticides (b) water containing environmental organisms of potential health significance (micro-organisms, bacteria, viruses and parasites of significance for human health which can occur and survive in the general environment) (c) water in primary circuits and heating systems other than in a house, irrespective of whether additives have been used or not (d) water treatment or softeners using other than salt (e) water used in washing machines and dishwashing machines for other than domestic use (f) water used in mini-irrigation systems in a house garden without fertiliser or insecticide applications such as pop-up sprinklers, permeable hoses or fixed or rotating sprinkler heads fixed less than 150 mm above ground level
5	Fluids representing a serious health risk because of the concentration of **pathogenic organisms**, radioactive or very toxic substances, including any fluid which contains: (a) faecal material or other human waste, or (b) butchery or other animal waste, or (c) pathogens from any other source	(a) sinks, urinals, WC pans and bidets in any location (b) permeable pipes or hoses in other than domestic gardens, laid below ground or at ground level with or without chemical additives (c) grey-water recycling systems (d) washing machines and dishwashers in high-risk premises (e) appliances and supplies in medical establishments

▲ The fluid risk categories which describe water, based on how drinkable it is and how dangerous to health it may be, depending on impurities

flush grated waste fitting

A type of *waste fitting* with a flush grating to prevent foreign matter entering the waste system and which does not have space for a waste plug. A flush grated waste fitting is commonly fitted to a shower tray.

flushing cistern

A device designed to flush a WC. There are two main types: siphon and drop valve. The flushing cistern is designed to prevent water wastage by ensuring that only a given flush of water is provided to the *WC pan* at any one time. The *Water Regulations* lay down the maximum flush volume for flushing cisterns; in terms of WCs this is currently 6 litre maximum flush and 4 litre short flush when fitted to a *dual flush* cistern. Flushing cisterns may also be used as a means of flushing and cleansing *urinals*, either manually, as with the WC cistern, or automatically, as in the *automatic flushing cistern*.

flushing valve (pressure flushing valve)

A type of flushing device connected to a *WC pan* or *urinal* for the purpose of flushing the pan or urinal, the flushing valve is an alternative method of flushing to the traditional *flushing cistern*. The flushing valve can be connected to a *supply pipe* or a *distribution pipe* and therefore needs no dedicated water storage near the pan for the purpose of flushing. The flushing valve can only be fitted in non-domestic properties and requires a minimum water-flow rate of 1.2 litres/second. A *backflow prevention device* in the form of a type DC *pipe interrupter* must be fitted between the flushing valve and the WC pan to protect against *backflow*.

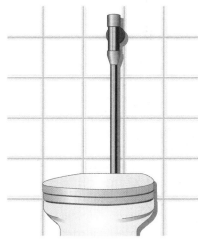

▲ Example of a pressure flushing valve

flushpipe

A section of pipe used to carry water from a *flushing cistern* to a *WC pan* or a *urinal*.

flushpipe connector

A fitting used to make a connection between a *flushpipe* and a *WC pan*, it is primarily used with low- and high-level patterns of WC. The various designs include: specific manufacturer devices, internal cone and external cone.

▲ Internal cone flushpipe connector

A
B
C
D
E
F
G
H
I
J
K
L
M
N
O
P
Q
R
S
T
U
V
W
X
Y
Z

A
B
C
D
E
F
G
H
I
J
K
L
M
N
O
P
Q
R
S
T
U
V
W
X
Y
Z

flux

A substance that is applied to metallic material to be jointed before *soft soldering* or *hard soldering*. Fluxes are classified as either non-active (e.g. tallow) or active (e.g. zinc ammonium chloride). Active fluxes may also have self-cleaning properties, so pipe or fitting surfaces may not need cleaning prior to the application of the flux. A flux is usually applied after cleaning a pipe or fitting to prevent oxidation of the surface, that is, the pipe or fitting surface must be properly cleaned in order that the solder adheres and flows across the surfaces. The flux also helps the solder flow across the pipe and fitting surface during its application. Flux should be applied sparingly during the jointing process; any flux residue should be wiped from the pipe surface on completion of the joint, and the pipe should be thoroughly flushed through on *commissioning* (water-based systems) in order to remove any flux residues that may lead to *corrosion* of the system.

food waste-disposal unit

An electrically operated grinding device installed in a kitchen sink unit. A large diameter waste hole will normally be required in the sink in order to site the waste disposal unit. The unit is flushed with water while grinding organic food waste into paste and discharging it into the drainage system. A *bottle trap* must not be used on the waste discharge system and the waste disposal unit must not discharge into a *grease gulley*, in either case, in order to avoid blockages. The unit can discharge into a *gully* or directly into the *soil stack*.

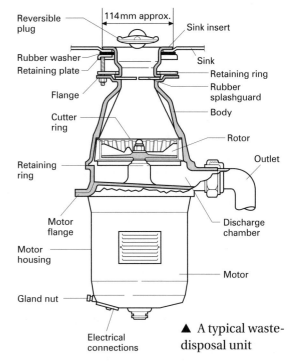

114mm approx.

Reversible plug
Sink insert
Rubber washer
Retaining plate
Sink
Retaining ring
Rubber splashguard
Flange
Body
Cutter ring
Rotor
Outlet
Retaining ring
Motor flange
Discharge chamber
Motor housing
Motor
Gland nut
Electrical connections

▲ A typical waste-disposal unit

foot protection

The wearing of recommended work footwear to protect toes, ankles and feet from injury, and the whole body from electric shock. Safety shoes should normally be used for most plumbing work, incorporating metal toe protection and with strong rubber soles.

foot valve

A type of *non-return valve* which is fitted to the bottom of a suction pipe feeding a pump, such as that fitted in a well or borehole. The foot valve prevents the suction line emptying during the pumping cycle.

'footing' a ladder

Steadying a ladder by holding the stiles, and placing one foot on the bottom rung assists in preventing the bottom of the ladder from slipping outwards from the wall. If you are responsible for footing a ladder while someone is working, you must not move or disturb the ladder, or let it go.

force cup – plunger

A device used in clearing sanitary appliances that have become blocked by waste. To unblock the waste, the overflow inlet has to be temporarily blocked, the force cup placed over the waste outlet, and then you pump up and down to remove the blockage from the waste. The device works on the principle that the pressure created by it should be sufficient to dislodge the blockage. See *Drain cleaning*

forced draught burner

A type of gas or oil burner in which the fuel/combustion air is forced into the *combustion chamber* by means of a pump/fan. See *Pressure jet burner*

former

See *Bending machine*

foul water

See *Black water*

free area

The total area of the individual unobstructed openings of an *air vent*. This is calculated by working out the area of the actual openings in the vent and not the actual dimensions of the vent itself.

free-standing boiler

A type of boiler that stands on the floor.

freezing equipment

See *Pipe-freezing equipment*

freezing point

The point at which a liquid *changes state* to a solid. Solid ice, for example, is formed from liquid water at a temperature of 0°C.

friction

This is the force that resists the motion of an object. It results from the close interaction between two surfaces that are sliding across each other. For example, when you slam on your brakes and your car skids to a stop with locked wheels, it is the force of friction that brings it to a stop, that is, friction resists the car's motion.

frictional resistance

This is the *pressure loss* caused by *friction* in water and gas pipes and fittings as the *fluid* passes along them. Accounting for the frictional resistance of pipes and fittings is a fundamental part of sizing pipework in systems.

A
B
C
D
E
F
G
H
I
J
K
L
M
N
O
P
Q
R
S
T
U
V
W
X
Y
Z

front apron

See *Apron flashing*

frost precautions

Water-borne pipes and fittings must be protected from frost to prevent the water in them from freezing. For example, *thermal insulation* is helpful and, in the case of a new installation, pipes and fittings should not, if possible, be installed in cold areas such as those near draughts, roof spaces, areas beneath suspended ventilated floors, external above ground positions, cellars, outbuildings or external walls.

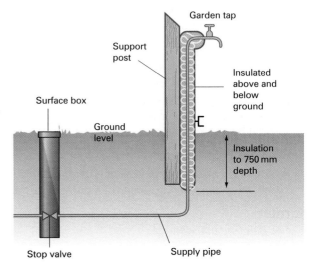

▲ Frost precaution measures for external pipework installations

frost thermostat

A thermostat which automatically protects boilers and heating pipework that are unavoidably located in frost risk areas, for example external boilers. The frost thermostat is tamper-proof, located next to the appliance and usually set to about 4°C. When the frost thermostat is activated, the pump and boiler are started up by a feed to the *motorised valve*. The frost thermostat must be used in conjunction with a *pipe thermostat*, to reduce any energy wastage. The pipe thermostat is usually set to around 40–50°C

'Full Plans' application

A means of obtaining *Building Regulations* approval from the local authority, of a detailed scheme before starting the work. The 'Full Plans' application is submitted to the local authority and may take up to five weeks to be processed as they may need to consult with statutory bodies. When approved, a Full Plans application will receive a formal certificate for starting the work. The progress of the work will be inspected and a Completion Certificate will be issued when the work is satisfactorily finished.

fullway gate valve

See *Gate valve*

fully-pumped system

This is used with *small* and *microbore heating systems*, where the hot water and the heating circuits are operated by the pump with no *gravity circulation*, that is, all circuits in the system are pumped. The boiler may be installed higher than the *cylinder*, giving more design options. See *Types of fully-pumped central-heating system*

fuse

A small device used in electrical circuits, containing a strip of wire which melts and breaks the circuit when the current exceeds a specific level. Fuses are available in a variety of ratings and should be properly selected to cover the correct appliance or circuit rating. A fuse is a type of *overcurrent protection device*.

fusion welding

See *Electrofusion welding*

A
B
C
D
E
F
G
H
I
J
K
L
M
N
O
P
Q
R
S
T
U
V
W
X
Y
Z

gable end

The triangular edge of a building where the *pitched roof* angles up to the *ridge*. Details of the way a roof is finished at one gable end are shown in the diagram.

galvanic action

Another term for *electrolytic action*.

galvanic protection

See *Cathodic protection*

galvanised

This is the process of coating *ferrous metals* with zinc to provide protection from corrosion; examples are galvanised *low-carbon steel* tubes and galvanised cold-water *storage cisterns*.

garage gully

A gully, which contains a large galvanised bucket, that is used in areas where there are likely to be relatively large deposits of silt or grit; it collects the silt or grit to prevent it being discharged into the *drainage system* and, potentially, causing blockage of the system.

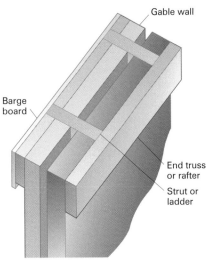

Gable wall

Barge board

End truss or rafter

Strut or ladder

▲ Gable end construction

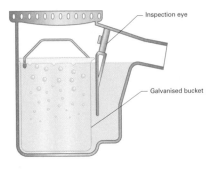

Inspection eye

Galvanised bucket

▲ Garage gulley

garden taps and hosepipes (domestic properties)

Garden taps used for hose connections must be located for maximum frost prevention and be fitted with a *backflow prevention device* in the form of a *double-check valve*, which guards against a *fluid risk category* 3. Hand-held hosepipes must have a self-closing mechanism at the hose outlet to minimise the wastage of water. New outside taps in domestic properties must be fitted with a double-check valve sited inside the property. With existing outside taps the double-check valve should preferably be sited inside the property to guard against frost; alternatively (with existing taps only) it may include a double-check valve within the tap body or be fitted with a backflow preventer. Hose union taps in non-domestic properties tend to present a higher fluid risk category and a different backflow prevention device will be required.

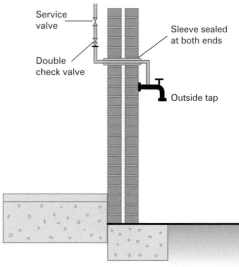

▲ Installation requirements for an outside tap in a domestic property

Service valve

Sleeve sealed at both ends

Double check valve

Outside tap

▲ Hose union backflow preventer

gas boilers

The three main types of gas boiler are: traditional (see diagram overleaf), *combination* and *condensing*. Gas boilers are available as floor-standing, wall-mounted or fireback models, with *room-sealed* or *open-flued* flueing options. All new oil and gas boilers must meet the minimum efficiency standards classified under the Seasonal Efficiency of Domestic Boilers in the UK (SEDBUK). The detailed energy efficiency requirements of new and replacement boilers are detailed under Approved Documents at the Department of Communities and Local Government (DCLG) website – www.communities.gov.uk. In the majority of cases new or replacement boilers must be of the high-efficiency (condensing) type.

A B C D E F G H I J K L M N O P Q R S T U V W X Y Z

A
B
C
D
E
F
G
H
I
J
K
L
M
N
O
P
Q
R
S
T
U
V
W
X
Y
Z

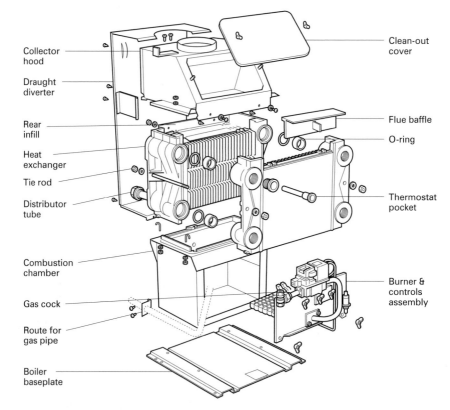

Collector hood

Draught diverter

Rear infill

Heat exchanger

Tie rod

Distributor tube

Combustion chamber

Gas cock

Route for gas pipe

Boiler baseplate

Clean-out cover

Flue baffle

O-ring

Thermostat pocket

Burner & controls assembly

▲ Traditional open-flued floor standing gas boiler

gas burner

The component in a gas appliance where gas is mixed with air and ignited. There are two main types of burner: those which aerate the flame after the gas is discharged (the *post-aerated flame*) and those where the gas is mixed with air prior to ignition (the *pre-aerated flame*). Post-aerated burners were commonly used with old town gas appliances, pre-aerated burners are commonly used on modern natural gas appliances. The burner design is influenced by the *flame speed* or velocity of the gas air mixture at the burner. Burners are designed to ensure that the gas flame is stabilised on the surface of the burner and to ensure that *flame lift* or *lighting back* do not occur by:

- carefully controlling the flame speed at the burner head; properly sized *injectors* are used to ensure that the rate of gas supplied and air mixture are correct
- *flame retention* ports are often incorporated in the burner design to prevent flame lift from occurring.

Key
A – Injector
B – Primary air port
C – Aeration control shutter
D – Throat restrictor
F – Venturi throat
G – Burner port
H – Retention port

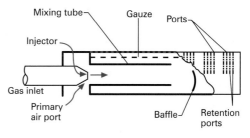

▲ Cooker ring type burner

▲ Typical bar burner as used in a gas boiler

gas circulator

A small type of gas boiler used to heat hot water only. The circulator can be mounted near to the hot-water cylinder, sited behind a gas fire (fire-back circulator) or be fitted inside a warm-air central-heating unit. Other than in warm-air units, circulators are not now widely used.

gas cock

A type of *isolation valve* that can be used in a gas supply system. See *Cock*

gas families

The classification of gases related to the amount of heat released when the fuel is burned, often expressed as the *wobbe number*. The classifications are:
Gas family 1 (manufactured gases, e.g. town gas), Gas family 2 (natural gas), Gas family 3 (*liquefied petroleum gases*, e.g. *propane* and *butane*).

gas fire

A *flued* appliance for heating one room and including a radiating surface, either in the form of a radiant or imitation fuel. See *Radiant convector gas fire; Radiant gas fire; Inset live fuel effect gas fire; Decorative fuel effect gas appliance*

gas-fired instantaneous water heater

These heaters provide instant hot water when the hot top is opened. The *heat exchanger* heats water to the required temperature as it passes through, and the rate of water flow controls the temperature. In larger models the temperature of the water may be controlled by a *thermostat*. Single-point hot-water heaters supply one outlet and usually have no flue. Multi-point hot-water heaters supply

A
B
C
D
E
F
G
H
I
J
K
L
M
N
O
P
Q
R
S
T
U
V
W
X
Y
Z

A
B
C
D
E
F
G
H
I
J
K
L
M
N
O
P
Q
R
S
T
U
V
W
X
Y
Z

many outlets and must have a flue, usually a *room-sealed flue*. The *automatic valve* in the heater turns the gas on when the tap is opened and off when the tap is closed.

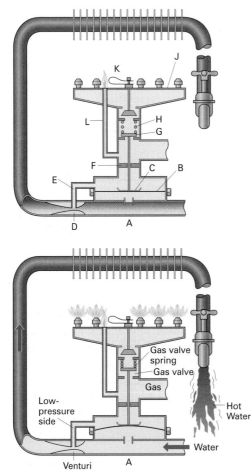

Key
A – automatic valve/diaphragm
B – rubber diaphragm
C – plate
D – venturi
E – low-pressure side
F – gland for push rod
G – gas-valve
H – gas-valve spring
J – burner
K – flame supervision strip
　　(bi-metal type)
L – pilot feed

◀▲ Instantaneous hot-water heater in closed and open positions

gas governor

This is a device for regulating the pressure and hence the gas flow in a pipeline. Gas is supplied at higher pressure through the mains and therefore needs to be regulated as it enters the property; this is achieved by the installation of a governor or regulator sited at the inlet to a *gas meter*; only authorised gas supplier personnel may make adjustment to this device. Governors are also fitted to individual gas appliances to prevent pressure fluctuations occurring in the gas pipeline when multiple appliances are used together. Governors that are fitted to appliances fall into two categories:

- Adjustable governor – the outlet pressure from the governor to the burner can be adjusted to suit the requirements of a *range rated* appliance; adjustable governors are available as single or double diaphragm spring-loaded devices.

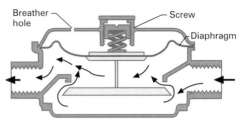

▲ Typical adjustable single diaphragm spring loaded governor

- Constant pressure governor – this type of governor is fitted to gas appliances where the outlet pressure does not need to be adjusted, for example some types of gas fire include a constant pressure governor.

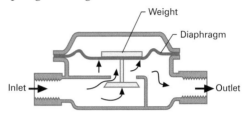

▲ Typical constant pressure governor

The gas governor is often included in a *multi-functional control valve* which is designed to provide several gas controls in a single unit.

gas meter

A device designed to record and possibly control the gas supply into a property. There are two types: *credit meter* and *pre-payment meter*. The gas meter must be fitted in an acceptable location in a property, usually in a dry location and where it will not pose a fire risk; the *Gas Safety (Installation and Use) Regulations* lay down permissible locations for gas meters. In new-build properties the meter is normally located in a meter box external to the property for ease of meter reading. In larger properties there may be a *primary meter*, which is the responsibility of the gas supplier, and secondary meters, which are located so that the user has access to them. The meter will usually be fitted with a *gas governor* at its inlet to regulate the incoming *gas pressure*, and an *emergency control valve* will also be sited before its inlet; this is the main isolation point for the supply into the property. There are many types of meter design available; the most common meters used in domestic properties are:

- U6/G4 – credit meters – these tend to be the most common types of meter (U6 measures gas on an imperial scale, G4 measures gas on a metric scale).
- E6 – a type of electronic credit meter measuring gas on a metric scale. The meter can include a device that permits the remote reading of the amount of gas consumed.
- Electronic token meter – a pre-payment type meter.

See diagrams overleaf.

See *Gas governor*

A
B
C
D
E
F
G
H
I
J
K
L
M
N
O
P
Q
R
S
T
U
V
W
X
Y
Z

A
B
C
D
E
F
G
H
I
J
K
L
M
N
O
P
Q
R
S
T
U
V
W
X
Y
Z

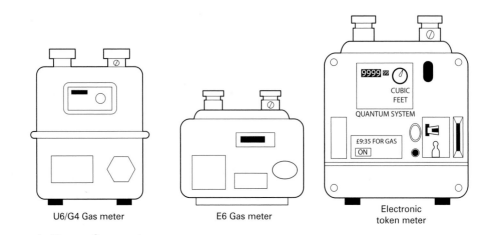

U6/G4 Gas meter   E6 Gas meter   Electronic token meter

▲ Types of gas meter

gas pressure

It is important to ensure that the gas pressures are correct in a gas supply system in order that appliances operate correctly and safely. Gas pressure readings are measured as either:

- Standing pressure – this is the gas pressure reading taken with no appliances working. In a domestic system the standing pressure at the meter test point should typically be between 21 and 26 mbar.
- Working pressure – this is the gas pressure with the appliances in operation. The working pressure at the domestic gas meter with appliances operating should be 21 mbar +/− 1 mbar. The pressure loss at the inlet of the appliance should be no less than 1 mbar below the working pressure at the meter. If this is incorrect then the pipeline may be blocked or incorrectly sized; in either case attention is required as the appliance will be regarded as unsafe to operate.

gas properties

Each gas has a different *specific gravity, calorific value, stoichiometric mixture, flammability limit* and *flame speed.*

- The *specific gravity* is the mass of a specific volume of the gas at a given pressure. If this is lower than air, then the gas will rise, if it is higher than air, the gas will fall.
- The *calorific value* is the amount of heat energy released when a specific quantity of fuel is burned, expressed as megajoules per cubic metre: MJ/m^3.
- The *stoichiometric mixture* is the number of cubic metres of air required for the complete combustion of one cubic metre of the particular gas.
- The *flammability limit* is the percentage of gas required in the gas/air mixture in order for it to burn.
- The *flame speed* is a result of the pressure of the gas supplied and the injector size. If the speed is too high, *flame lift* occurs and if the speed is too low, *light back* into the burner may result.

The table identifies the key properties of the various gas fuels that are commonly used.

Characteristic	Natural gas*	Propane	Butane	Notes
Specific gravity (SG of air = 1.0)	0.6	1.5	2.0	Methane will rise but propane and butane will fall to low level
Calorific value	39 MJ/m³	93 MJ/m³	122 MJ/m³	Appliances are designed to burn a particular gas
Stoichiometric air requirements	10:1	24:1	30:1	Methane requires 10 volumes of air to 1 volume of gas; LPG requires more
Supply pressure	21 mbar	37 mbar	28 mbar	Appliances must be matched to the gas used
Flammability limits	5 to 15% in air	2 to 10% in air	2 to 9% in air	Ranges within which gas/air mixtures will burn
Flame speed	0.36 m/sec	0.46 m/sec	0.45 m/sec	This is the speed at which a flame will burn along a gas mixture
Ignition temperature	704°C	530°C	408°C	Approximate temperatures
Flame temperatures	1930°C	1980°C	1996°C	Approximate temperatures

▲ Key properties of gases

* methane

gas rate

This is the rate of consumption of a gas appliance. It needs to be carefully checked on *commissioning* an appliance to ensure that the gas consumption rate is correct and an unsafe condition known as *incomplete combustion* is not occurring. Checking the gas rate is dependent on the type of meter found; the following are examples:

In the case of the Imperial U6 meter, the *calorific value* (CV) of the gas is usually the following:

- *Natural gas* average CV is 38.76 MJ/m³ Gross or 1040 btu/ft³
- *Propane* average CV is 93.1 MJ/m³ Gross or 2496 btu/ft³
- *Butane* average CV is 121.8 MJ/m³ Gross or 3265 btu/ft³

A
B
C
D
E
F
G
H
I
J
K
L
M
N
O
P
Q
R
S
T
U
V
W
X
Y
Z

A

B

C

D

E

F

G

H

I

J

K

L

M

N

O

P

Q

R

S

T

U

V

W

X

Y

Z

The formula for checking gas rate using natural gas, for example, is:

$$\frac{\text{Seconds in one hour (3600)} \times \text{the CV of the gas (1040 btu/ft}^3)}{\text{Number of seconds for one revolution of the dial}}$$

For example, the time taken for one revolution of the test dial is 84 seconds:

$$\frac{3600 \times 1040}{84 \text{ seconds}} = 44,571 \text{ btu/hr}$$

Convert btus to kW by dividing by a constant of 3412:

$$\frac{44,571}{3412} = 13.06 \text{ kW (the approx dataplate reading)}$$

In the case of the metric G4/E6 meter there is no test dial with this meter, so the gas rate is determined by identifying the amount of gas burned across a fixed period:

$$\frac{3600 \times m^3 \times \text{CV of gas in MJ/m}^3}{\text{time in seconds}}$$

CV of gas is usually given in kilowatt-hours (kWh) where 1 MJ = 3.6 kWh. Therefore, for natural gas, CV = 38.76/3.6 = 10.7 kWh

For example, over a 90-second period if:

The first meter reading was 41276.040 m^3
The second meter reading was 41276.075 m^3

The amount of gas used was 0.035 m^3

Gas rate is:

$$\frac{3600 \times 0.035 \times 10.76}{90} = 15.06 \text{ kW}$$

Again this can be checked against the data plate on the appliance.

As an additional point, this calculation produces the gross rating of the appliance. Some appliances quote net figures. So, with the calculation shown before, the gross figure is divided by one of the constants shown below (dependent on the fuel type):

Natural gas – 1.1
Propane – 1.09
Butane – 1.08

Therefore, in the previous calculation the net value is 15.06/1.1 = 13.69kW
See *Calorific value*

Gas Safety (Installation and Use) Regulations

The legal requirements that must be followed when undertaking work on gas systems and appliances. Work that is found to be defective under the Gas Safety Regulations may be subject to prosecution.

gasket

A material used to make a water-, air- or gas-tight seal between two surfaces. Gaskets can be made from a variety of different materials; neoprene rubber and fibre are two examples.

gate valve

A valve with an opening gate which gives full-bore flow; they are often called full-way gate valves. This valve has a wheel head attached to the spindle, so that when the head is turned anti-clockwise, the spindle screws into the gate, raising it towards the head. Gate valves are used as *service valves* in low-pressure pipelines, such as the cold feed from a cold-water *storage cistern* to a hot-water *storage cylinder*, or on the supply to a shower *valve*.

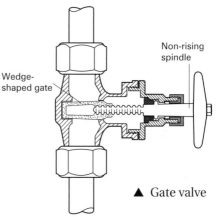

Wedge-shaped gate

Non-rising spindle

▲ Gate valve

gathers

A smooth transitional reduction from above the *builder's opening* or *fireplace recess* into the *flue*.

gauge

A type of instrument used for measurement, e.g. temperature or pressure; or the exposed part of a slate or tile on a roof. See *Soakers*

gauge pressure

The pressure in a system in excess of *atmospheric pressure*, that is, the pressure in a system created by the *head* of water, usually measured on a *gauge*.

gland

A method of making a seal between moving parts of a plumbing component, typically a watertight seal where a rising spindle exits a valve body (e.g. *screwdown stop valve*).

gland nut

The nut which retains the packing into the gland of a valve. The spindle moves up and down through the gland nut of the valve and the packing under the gland nut ensures a watertight seal. See *Screwdown stop valve*

gland-nut pliers

A type of pliers used to effect repairs to gland nuts. See *Pliers*

A
B
C
D
E
F
G
H
I
J
K
L
M
N
O
P
Q
R
S
T
U
V
W
X
Y
Z

global warming

Warming of the Earth's temperature due to increased gases (e.g. carbon dioxide) in the atmosphere. Energy efficiency measures aim to reduce this effect. For new properties these measures include higher levels of insulation, certification of heating and hot-water systems, better standards of design and workmanship. *Standard Assessment Procedure* (SAP) outlines minimum levels of boiler efficiency and requirements for central-heating control systems.

globe tap

A tap that may be found on an older-type bath installation. This type of tap discharges below the *spill-over* level of the bath and poses a *backflow* water-supply contamination risk and will therefore require a *backflow prevention device* against a *fluid risk category* 3 to be fitted, typically a double-*check valve*. The outlet from the water supply has a *male thread* and is connected through prefabricated holes in the bath. The tap has a *female thread* and is screwed on to the fitting.

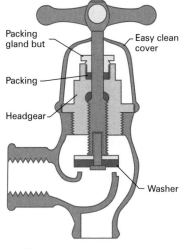

Packing gland but

Easy clean cover

Packing

Headgear

Washer

▲ Globe tap

goose neck

A form of pipe bends inserted into the *communication pipe* near the *ferrule* of a cold-water service to allow for ground movement. A goose neck is not now commonly used with plastic service pipework.

governor

A device fitted into a pipeline to control the pressure and hence the flow rate of water or gas entering the appliance or system. See *Gas governor; Pressure-reducing valve*

gradient

The rate of fall or rise of a pipeline or component. The gradient can be expressed in degrees or as a gradient of, say, 1 in 600. As an example, if 6 m of gutter is required to be laid to a fall of 1 in 600 what is the vertical drop at the far end? $6 \times 1000/600 = 10$ mm across the 6 m length.

grated waste

See *flush grated waste fitting*

gravity

A force of attraction resulting from the relative mass of bodies. Hence, the large Earth mass pulls all objects to its surface.

gravity circulation

The process of natural circulation of hot water by *convection*.

gravity primaries

The pipes which carry hot water from the boiler to the *cylinder* in a *solid fuel* system using the force of *gravity*. These pipes are usually 28 mm and must rise continuously from the boiler to the cylinder. The pressures involved in *gravity circulation* are very low, and it is important to make sure that the pipework has the correct falls so that air is correctly vented during initial fill-up. The *circulating head* should be a minimum of one metre. Avoid long horizontal runs and changes of direction as they create resistance to the flow of water and reduce the circulation.

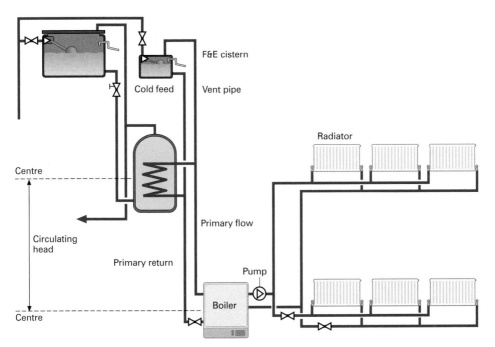

▲ Two-pipe central-heating system with gravity primaries

grease gully

A type of *trap* fitted to the *drainage system* to receive water from commercial catering establishments. The gully (trap) is purpose-designed so that lighter grease deposits collect as a cake on the water surface in the gully and heavier deposits sink to the bottom and collect on a galvanised tray. The gully should be cleaned from time to time by removing the tray, which lifts out the deposits from the gully.

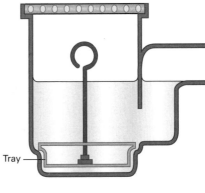

▲ Grease gully

A
B
C
D
E
F
G
H
I
J
K
L
M
N
O
P
Q
R
S
T
U
V
W
X
Y
Z

greenhouse effect

This is the warming of the air, which increases partly because of the gases, such as *carbon dioxide*, which are emitted into the atmosphere through burning fossil fuels, such as coal. It is a cause of *global warming*. New measures aim to reduce carbon dioxide emissions from buildings and vehicles.

grey water

This is waste water not containing faecal matter or urine, for example water from baths and sinks.

grey water recycling system

This type of system is a water conservation measure designed to collect the waste water from appliances such as baths, showers and basins. It is then filtered, cleaned and stored for future use in the property, such as WC flushing, watering gardens and washing cars.

grill

See *Air vent*

grommet

A small ring of a sealant material used to make a watertight connection between plumbing components.

guide

See *Bending machine*

gully

A drainage fitting designed to receive the discharge from *rainwater* pipes or *black water* from waste pipes. Some gullies (surface water gullies connected to surface water drains) are usually trapless, while others (black water systems) contain a trap. In new properties the waste pipe must discharge below the grating of the *trap*, there are numerous designs available. See *Back inlet gully; Garage gully; Grease gully*

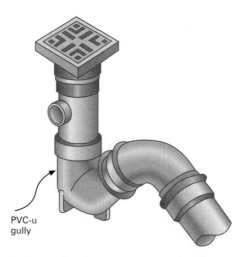

PVC-u
gully

▲ Example of a PVC-u trapped gully

gully grab

A gully cleaning device which is made up of a long handle with a hinged bowl connected to the bottom of it. The grab is lowered with the bowl vertical into the gully, the bowl is moved to the horizontal position with a handle and, in so doing, the deposits in the gully are scooped into the bowl and can be removed from the gully.

▲ Gully grab

gunmetal

An *alloy* of *copper* and *tin*. It is particularly resistant to *corrosion* and is used extensively in circumstances where *dezincification* could lead to problems with the use of standard *brass* fittings.

gusset

A piece of sheet lead inserted into a sheet lead component that is to be lead welded. See *Back gutter*

gutter

A channel fitted at the lowest point of a roof, designed to receive the *rainwater* run-off from the roof. There are various types of gutter system that may be used. See *Eaves gutter; Parapet gutter; Valley gutter*

gutter flow capacity

The volume of water that a gutter can manage effectively. The gutter flow capacity is influenced by: the type of system, size of the gutter, the position of the outlet, the fall of the gutter, and the rate of water discharging into it, determined by the area and slope of the roof.

H cowl

An H-shaped *flue terminal* designed to overcome problems with *down draught* in chimneys.

hacksaw

A hand tool used to cut metal or plastics. When using a hacksaw, make sure you use the correct blade for the job (32 teeth per inch for light-gauge tube and 24 teeth per inch for heavier-gauge tube), and check that the blade is tightened. Make sure that the teeth are in good condition and that the blade is fitted so that the teeth are pointing forward. Pressure should therefore only be applied during the forward stroke as this is the point at which the material is being cut. See *Equipment – tool safety*

▲ Hacksaw

hairfelt

A type of insulation that was commonly fitted to pipework. Older types of hairfelt lagging were not fire resistant and could pose a significant fire risk if exposed to an ignition source. Hairfelt insulation does not meet current insulation standards for pipework.

hammers

These include the lump hammer, ball pein hammer, cross pein hammer and claw hammer. When using hammers, make sure that the head is secured safely and correctly to the shaft, and never use a hammer with a splintered or defective shaft. See *Equipment – tool safety*

▲ A selection of hammers

hand bender

See *Bending machine*

hand protection

Hands and fingers may need to be protected when working, to prevent injuries such as cutting, crushing or puncturing the hands or fingers, and injury caused by dermatitis (e.g. sores and blisters). Dermatitis causes inflammation and irritation of the skin and can be severe, causing sores, blisters, redness or dry, cracked areas that are at risk of infection. If you have to use irritants, such as chemicals and cleaning substances, clean your hands regularly, use barrier creams and wear a strong pair of gloves when required. Gloves come in the form of general-purpose gloves, as used for lifting activities to prevent cuts and abrasions, rubber gloves to protect against contaminants such as faecal matter, and specialist gloves as in the case of welding gloves designed to protect against contact with heated metals.

hand-rinse basins

A very small basin used in cloakrooms with WCs. Hand-rinse basins are available in a corner or traditional design and may be countertop, pedestal or bracket-mounted.

hand tools

The basic tools needed to work on systems, for example: cold chisels, plugging chisels and club hammers for brick, block and concrete work; claw hammers, wood chisels for notching joists; and copper tube cutters.

hard soldering

A type of *capillary joint* in which a high-temperature melting-point solder is used, typically between 600–850°C, the joint therefore being much stronger by design and capable of withstanding higher pipework operating pressures. There are a variety of different hard solders available, including silver and silver alloys. See *Brazed joint; Silver soldered joint*

hard water

A type of water that during rainfall has filtered through salts, such as limestone or chalk, and taken them it into suspension. It can be *temporarily hard* or *permanently hard*. Temporarily hard supplies can cause problems with *scale* build-up in systems. One of the effects of hard water is that soap is unable to lather when used with it.

A
B
C
D
E
F
G
H
I
J
K
L
M
N
O
P
Q
R
S
T
U
V
W
X
Y
Z

hardcore blinding

A rubble underlay used in the construction of a solid concrete floor. After excavating the foundation perimeter, the ground is compacted then the hardcore blinding is placed and compacted before laying the concrete.

hardening

The process of hardening metals which increases their durability. Excessively hardened materials, however, may become brittle.

hazardous operations checklist

This is a list of possible hazardous operations that may be faced when starting a new task or working on a new site. Hazards are associated with these operations, equipment and sites:

- electrical powered plant, such as: power transformers, extension cables, plugs and sockets, portable tools, electric arc welders, threading machines, large hammer drills, specialist equipment, fixed equipment
- tools and equipment, such as: hand tools, specialist tools, pneumatic tools, hydraulic tools
- heavy equipment or supplies which require manual handling
- hazardous substances
- excavations, where hazards include physical conditions, interruption of gas, water or electrical services
- industrial vehicles, such as forklift trucks, dump trucks, JCBs/tractors, tail-lift vehicles, road vehicles,
- flammable liquids, such as liquefied petroleum gas
- lead, including manual handling, lead hygiene
- heights, including ladders or scaffolds and using ropes or harnesses
- demolition areas
- electrical installations
- fumes, noise, dust, asbestos
- confined spaces.

Check that you know the correct Health and Safety procedures for all of these situations.

head

The height of water, measured in metres, above a fixed point in a system.

head protection

The risk of head injury while working can be reduced by using the appropriate head protection equipment, such as wearing a hard hat on a site where there is a risk of head injury from falling objects and objects positioned at head height. Head protection measures are usually mandatory on all construction sites. When using a safety helmet: remove any other hat or head covering, make sure the helmet is the right way round and not tilted, and adjust the straps so that they are close-fitting. Take care of your helmet, handle it carefully without throwing or dropping it, inspect it for cracks, dents or signs of wear, also check the specified 'use-by' date. Never paint a safety helmet; this may soften the shell or reduce electrical protection. Damaged safety helmets should be immediately replaced.

header pipe

A large pipe used in a high-rise building, sized to store a reserve of drinking water in the supply pipe in order to prevent nuisance short-term operation of the pump. See *Boosted cold-water system*

Health and Safety at Work Act 1974

An Act of Parliament which lays down key requirements for employers and employees to ensure the safety of all those who may be affected by work activities, from the workers themselves and to members of the public. Key duties are therefore laid down in the Act for employers and employees; failure to meet the requirements of the Act can lead to prosecution, ranging from fines to imprisonment. The Act enables more detailed Health and Safety regulations to be made under it.

hearth

A floor-level slab of fire-resistant material to prevent overheating of the surface beneath a *combustion* appliance. Hearths used with combustion appliances under the *Building Regulations* must be supplied with a hearth *data plate* confirming that the hearth conforms to requirements.

heat and temperature

Heat is the amount of heat energy contained within the substance measured in joules (J). The temperature of a substance is the degree of hotness, measured on the Celsius (C) scale. A length of wire with a temperature of 350°C may contain fewer joules of heat energy than a quantity of water at a temperature of 70°C.

heat emitter

This is a generic term used for *radiators, convector heaters, skirting heaters* and *radiant heaters.*

heat emitters – sizing

The heat emitter selected for a particular area must have the capacity to provide heat output which maintains a comfortable room temperature. The sizing of heat emitters required for an area involves calculating the heat loss through the fabric of the building (e.g. floor and walls), and the heat loss through ventilation in the building, dependent on the rate of *air change*. To work out the size of heat emitter required for a room, you may use a central-heating calculator, such as a Mears wheel, a manufacturer's heat emitter computer program, such as the Stars Myson heat loss calculator, or your own mathematical calculation. The usage of the rooms in a building also has an impact on the size of heat emitter; if the room is intermittently heated, for example turned off at night, then a larger sized heat emitter will be required as opposed to a room that is constantly heated 24 hours a day. See *Heat loss calculation*

A
B
C
D
E
F
G
H
I
J
K
L
M
N
O
P
Q
R
S
T
U
V
W
X
Y
Z

heat exchanger

Any device which will transfer heat from one source to another. As an example, in a cast-iron heat exchanger boiler, water is heated by hot gases passing though the heat exchanger. Another example of a heat exchanger is the coil fitted inside a *double-feed indirect cylinder*, where heat transfer occurs from water to water.

heat input

The amount of energy supplied to a combustion appliance during the combustion process. See *Heat output*

heat-leak (heat-sink) radiator

Most *solid-fuel* appliances feeding *central-heating systems* require a heat-leak or heat-sink radiator in order to accommodate the heat produced when the boiler is in an idling condition (up to temperature; the fuel supply cannot be fully turned off as the appliance will need re-lighting). This radiator takes heat away from the boiler when the cylinder reaches its operating temperature and prevents the boiler from overheating. The heat-leak radiator is connected to the gravity primaries to the cylinder and ensures a minimum amount of heat circulation though the gravity primaries.

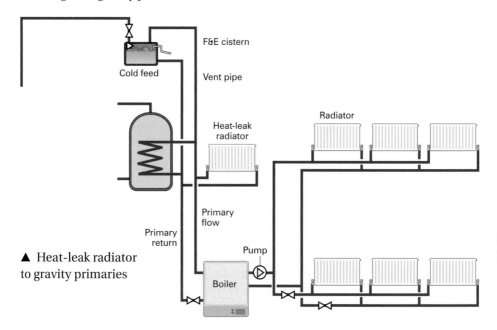

▲ Heat-leak radiator to gravity primaries

heat loss calculation

To work out the amount of heat loss from a room, you need to calculate the rate of heat loss through individual components in the room, such as external walls, floors and ceilings. The rate of heat loss is dependent on the temperature difference across the component, that is, inside the room and outside the room, and the thermal transmittance rate (U value) of the building material; the

U value varies dependent on the insulation properties of the individual building material itself.

The formula for calculating heat loss through the building fabric is:

Heat loss (W) = Surface area (m²) × temperature difference (°C) × U value (W/m² degC)

heat loss due to ventilation

This is the rate of heat loss from a room, brought about by either mechanical or natural ventilation. To calculate the rate of heat loss due to ventilation (W), multiply the room volume (m³) × temperature difference (°C) × the number of air changes per hour × a constant of 0.33. *British Standards Institution* requirements detail typical air change rates for different rooms in properties.

heat output

The heat available from a combustion appliance that may be used to heat a room or *central-heating system*. Heat is supplied and consumed by an appliance at a specific rate – the *heat input*. During the combustion process some of the heat is lost through the flue system in removing the combustion products. The remaining heat is therefore the heat output of the appliance, which will always be less than the heat input. See *Heat input*

heat pump

This is an electric or gas-driven device which moves heat energy from one place to another and from a lower to a higher temperature. A domestic refrigerator, for example, is a heat pump. In heating applications, heat is removed from the *ambient air*, water, soil or bedrock and delivered to where it is needed. In cooling applications, the reverse happens and heat is removed, to be discharged to the ambient air, water, soil or rock. The working *fluid* changes from liquid to gas (evaporates) as heat is absorbed from the heat source. Later in the cycle, the working fluid condenses to liquid as heat is released to where it is needed.

A heat pump can be used for cooling with the addition of a reversing valve that reverses the direction of the working fluid and so the direction of the heat transfer. The central component of the heat pump is the compressor. This is usually driven by an electric motor, although gas engine-driven compressors are also available.

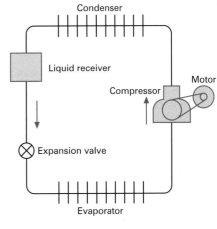

▲ Heat pump circuit

A
B
C
D
E
F
G
H
I
J
K
L
M
N
O
P
Q
R
S
T
U
V
W
X
Y
Z

heat transfer

The three methods of heat transfer are: *conduction* (heat transfer through a solid), *convection* (heat transfer through rising air or water currents) and *radiation* (heat transfer via infra-red rays from a heated surface to its receiver).

heating circuit

The circuit in a central-heating system supplying water to the *heat emitters*.

heating stoves (gas)

A type of gas-fired room heater designed to heat a single room. The two main types of room heating stoves are: free-standing stoves with a top flue outlet and fitted stoves with a rear *flue spigot* connected to a *closure plate*.

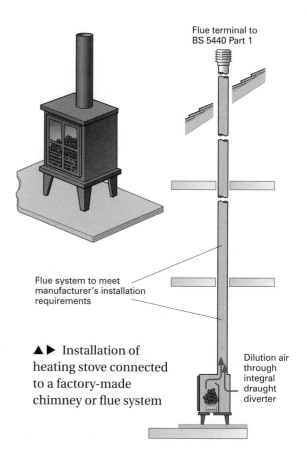

Flue terminal to BS 5440 Part 1

Flue system to meet manufacturer's installation requirements

Dilution air through integral draught diverter

▲▶ Installation of heating stove connected to a factory-made chimney or flue system

heating zone size

Part L1 of the Building Regulations specifies that larger houses with a floor area in excess of 150 m² should have two or more separate space heating zones. A two-port *motorised valve* is used to control each zone, with a separate *room thermostat* and timing control device.

hemp

A type of sealing material that can be used in the making of screwed pipework joints, primarily in *central-heating systems* which include *low-carbon steel* pipework. Hemp is applied together with a *jointing compound* to form the pipe joint. Hemp should not be used to make joints in hot- and cold-water pipework as it may lead to water contamination.

HepvO™ valve

See *Self-sealing valve*

hertz

A measure of the frequency of electricity, that is, the number of cycles of AC produced per second. Single-phase 230 V electricity in the UK is supplied at a frequency of 50 Hz.

high-flow-rate boilers

These are a type of boiler with a high efficiency *heat exchanger* in them. Boilers, such as *combination boilers*, with low-water-content heat exchangers tend to require a higher flow rate through them than that which may ordinarily be required by the heating or hot-water circuit. The manufacturer will specify the minimum water-flow rate requirement through the heat exchanger. If the boiler requires say a minimum flow rate of 0.4 kg/s and the system only requires 0.2 kg/s, a system bypass is required. 0.2 kg/s circulates around the bypass circuit which is controlled by an *automatic bypass valve* to ensure the minimum flow through the boiler.

high-level flushing cistern

A type of *flushing cistern* used for flushing a water closet or urinal that is sited at high level. See *Urinal; Water closet*

high-limit thermostat

Also called an overheat thermostat or energy cut-out device, this is an electrical control component that is an essential back-up thermostat used to ensure that the system shuts down if the normal thermostat fails and a specific high temperature is reached. It is installed on components such as boilers and

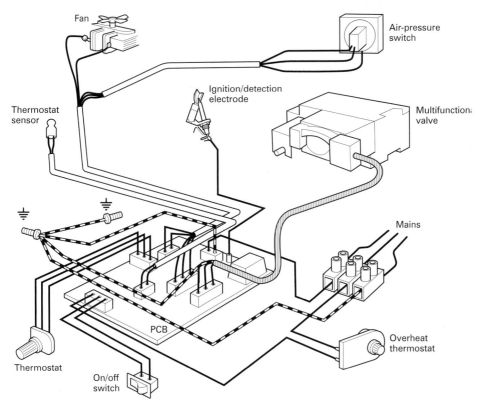

▲ Boiler controls circuit showing overheat thermostat

A
B
C
D
E
F
G
H
I
J
K
L
M
N
O
P
Q
R
S
T
U
V
W
X
Y
Z

unvented hot-water cylinders. There are two types of thermostat: the first automatically resets if the temperature setting is exceeded; the second requires manual resetting if the temperature is exceeded, via a push-button. An unvented system must include a high-limit thermostat of the non-self-resetting (manual) type. The high-limit thermostat is usually activated between about 80°C and 85°C.

high-output back-boiler

A type of *solid-fuel* open fire with a *back-boiler* that has a larger than normal surface area which can be used not only to heat hot water but also for central-heating purposes.

hip

The point of connection of two sloping roofs.

hole saws

A tool designed to cut a circular hole in a flat surface and used, for example, to drill through kitchen units to make way for waste pipes to pass through the side or back of cabinets and to drill holes in plastic cold-water *storage cisterns.*

hollow partitions

A type of internal partition wall constructed using *stud partitioning,* that is, vertical softwood studs braced with horizontal cross-pieces. Plasterboard is fixed to the studs and finished with a plaster skim or is taped.

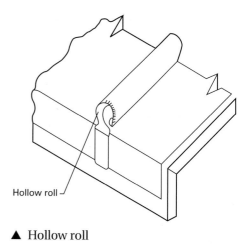

hollow roll

A type of *expansion joint* used on sheet-lead roofs which have a steep vertical pitch. The hollow roll should not be used on flat roofs as it can be easily damaged due to pedestrian traffic. *Solid rolls* should be used to make joints with the run of the roof on flat-roof surfaces.

Hollow roll

▲ Hollow roll

honeycomb walls

A method of wall construction where gaps are provided for timber floor joists. Hard core is compacted over the ground and covered with 100 mm of oversite concrete to provide a sound and level surface for the construction of the honeycomb walls which provide interim support for long spans of timber floor joists. Moisture penetration is prevented by the *damp-proof course* between the honeycomb brickwork and the timber wall plate.

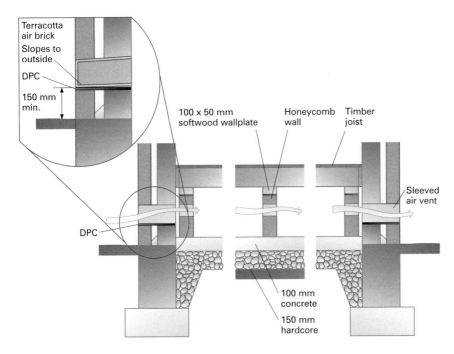

Terracotta
air brick

Slopes to
outside

DPC

150 mm
min.

DPC

100 x 50 mm
softwood wallplate

Honeycomb
wall

Timber
joist

Sleeved
air vent

100 mm
concrete

150 mm
hardcore

▲ Suspended timber ground floor showing honeycomb walls

hopper-fed boiler

A type of independent *solid-fuel* boiler which includes a large fuel store. The fuel is supplied to the *firebed* in the boiler either from higher level by gravity or using a worm-feed screw (a device that is driven by a motor which draws coal from the hopper to the boiler).

hopper head

A rainwater fitting that has a large box section and an outlet connection to a *rainwater pipe*. The box section is designed to receive discharge from a gutter or another rainwater pipe.

horizontal cylinder

A type of *hot-water storage vessel* (cylinder) that is mounted horizontally rather than vertically. An indirect horizontal cylinder requires an annulus-type *heat exchanger* (mini-cylinder within the main cylinder), rather than a coil, in order that air is not trapped in the cylinder primaries on filling. The horizontal cylinder is normally used in locations where there is limited headroom. See *Indirect cylinder*

▲ Hopper head

A
B
C
D
E
F
G
H
I
J
K
L
M
N
O
P
Q
R
S
T
U
V
W
X
Y
Z

A
B
C
D
E
F
G
H
I
J
K
L
M
N
O
P
Q
R
S
T
U
V
W
X
Y
Z

hose reel system

A type of fire-fighting system used in multi-storey buildings. Hose reels are located at strategic positions throughout the building, including emergency exits, for use when a fire has been identified. A hose reel system is usually fed from a *boosted cold-water system* fed from a *break cistern*.

hose union bib tap

A type of *bib tap* that includes a male connection for the purposes of attaching a union hose coupling feeding a hosepipe. Protection against *backflow* needs to be taken when installing a hose union bib tap. See *Garden taps and hosepipes*

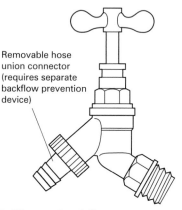

Removable hose union connector (requires separate backflow prevention device)

hot flush

A part of the process of *commissioning* a *central-heating system* in which the electrical supply to the system is turned off, the *drain valves* opened full bore and the system contents completely emptied; make sure that air *valves* and *motorised valves* are also

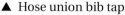
▲ Hose union bib tap

opened. When contents have drained, the valves are closed and the correct quantity of *corrosion inhibitor* is added to the system. The system is refilled and the air vented. The electrical supply is turned on and the system run up to temperature. Air is vented throughout this process. Whilst the system is still hot, thermostatic radiator valve heads are fitted and temperature controls set to the correct levels. See *Cold flush*

hot-water heating system

A heating system that uses a boiler to heat water which is circulated to *heat emitters* which are sized to correctly heat the rooms in the building.

hot-water storage vessel

A vessel for storing hot water. See *Direct cylinder; Indirect cylinder*

hot-water supply

The method of heating hot water to use for washing, cooking purposes, etc. These fall into two categories: *localised hot-water system* (a single-point instantaneous heater designed to supply only one outlet, e.g. a kitchen sink) and *centralised hot-water system* (water is stored for distribution to multiple outlets in the building, e.g. gas-fired *multipoint water heater, direct cylinder, indirect cylinder*).

humidity

This is the quantity of water vapour in the air. Relative humidity is the ratio between the actual quantity of water vapour and the amount of water vapour that the air can hold at a given temperature.

hydrant

A valve which discharges large quantities of high-pressure water for the purposes of fighting fires. Hydrants are installed at strategic points in the cold-water mains for the use of the fire authority in fighting fires. Hydrant valves are also used in wet- and dry-riser systems as the point of connection with the fire authority hose. See *Dry riser; Wet riser*

hydraulic gradient

A change in hydraulic *head* per unit of horizontal distance in a given direction. This is particularly important when making higher level connections into pipework in low-pressure storage systems. As can be seen in the diagram, water is available at Tap B when the other taps are not in use, but if other taps are opened the water flow ceases at tap B. This is because the point of connection is above the hydraulic gradient line. Hydraulic gradient therefore needs to be carefully considered when designing hot- and cold-water systems.

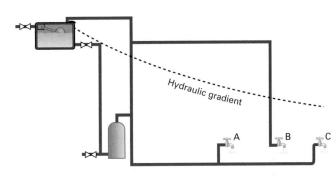

▲ Hydraulic gradient

hydraulic pipe bender

A hydraulic machine for bending *low-carbon steel* (LCS) tube and larger diameter *copper tubes*, it can be used to form 90° bends and offsets.

◀ Hydraulic pipe-bending machine for LCS tube

A
B
C
D
E
F
G
H
I
J
K
L
M
N
O
P
Q
R
S
T
U
V
W
X
Y
Z

hydraulic test equipment

This is used for *pressure-testing water-based systems*. The open ends of the system are sealed temporarily and a test point provided to connect the hydraulic kit. For the test, the pressure in the system is increased by 50 per cent above the maximum system operating pressure and left to stand for the required test period. Large systems are tested in sections, for example one zone at a time. See *Soundness test*

▲ Hydraulic test equipment

hydraulically operated valve

A control valve fitted to a water supply line, for example the supply to a urinal *automatic flushing cistern*. The valve is used to control the flow of water into the *cistern* based on the usage of other sanitary appliances in a public convenience that are *upstream* of the valve itself. The valve is a water conservation device which only permits flushing of the urinal *cistern* when the convenience is in use, that is, flushing does not take place when the building is unoccupied.

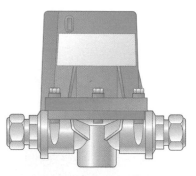

▲ Hydraulically operated valve

hydropneumatic accumulator

See *Shock arrestor*

hydrostatic pressure

This is the pressure established by the weight of water in a plumbing system.

ice

This is water in its solid state, which occurs when the water is cooled to 0°C. See *Change of state*

ignition device

A device sited in close proximity to a boiler main burner or pilot light in order to ignite the fuel/air mixture for combustion purposes. See *Electrode*; *Filament igniter*; *Piezo igniter*

ignition temperature

The temperature that a combustion material, such as *natural gas*, has to reach before it will ignite and burn. For example, natural gas needs to be heated to approximately 700°C before it will ignite.

immersion heater

An electric heating element controlled by a switch and *thermostat*, and fitted inside a *hot-water storage vessel*. An immersion heater is wired from the *consumer unit* and has an *overcurrent protection device* rating of 16 amps. The wiring is fed to a double-pole switch within one metre of the connection. A double-pole switch provides extra safety as both the live and neutral wires are isolated when it is switched off. See *Electric hot-water heating*

immersion heater boss

The connection point for an *immersion heater* in a *hot-water storage vessel*. Standard immersion heater bosses in vented hot-water storage cylinders are sized at 2¼" whereas immersion heater bosses in unvented cylinders tend to vary in size.

immersion heater spanner

A special type of spanner designed to install and remove immersion heaters from cylinder bosses.

▲ Immersion heater spanner

impervious

This describes any material which will not allow water to pass through it.

implosion

A collapse in the walls of a hot-water *storage cylinder*. It occurs when the pressure inside the cylinder is reduced to below *atmospheric pressure*, in which case, if the walls of the cylinder are not sufficiently strong, they can collapse. Implosion can occur in the following circumstances:

- It can occur when there is a blockage in both the *open vent* and *cold feed pipework* in the system caused by frost. If the cylinder is heated and begins to cool whilst the pipes are blocked, it will contract and draw the cylinder sides in. Alternatively, if water is drawn off from lower level taps when the two pipes are blocked, that too creates suction pressure with the possibility of the side walls being drawn in.
- It can occur in early unvented cylinders that were manufactured from thinner gauge copper. If the cold-water supply was isolated and a hot tap at a lower level than the cylinder was opened, there is a possibility that the cylinder walls could collapse owing to the negative pressure created inside the cylinder.

Implosion is not a common problem and is therefore largely ignored. It may be overcome by the use of an *anti-vacuum valve*.

impounding reservoir

A man-made reservoir, falling into the category of *upland surface water*. Impounding reservoirs are made by damming streams and flooding a prepared area. The water quality is quite good and *soft* as it runs directly off the ground surface. The water can become acidic if it comes into contact with peat.

inactive flux

See *Flux*

incandescent

The production of bright light from a heated or glowing part.

inclined lead weld

There are two methods of inclined lead welding: using a butt or lapped joint, where the lead weld beads are deposited up a straight incline with each bead overlapping the previous one; and jointing two pieces of lead with an angled lap joint, the bead held in position by the projection of the cooled beads lower down the welded joint.
See *Welding*

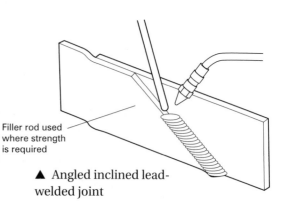

Filler rod used where strength is required

▲ Angled inclined lead-welded joint

inclined manometer

A device used for measuring flue draught, this is used when commissioning oil and solid-fuel appliances. The flue-draught requirements are specified by the manufacturer. For an oil appliance a flue draught reading is taken at the appliance test point whilst it is in its fully heated condition. With a solid-fuel appliance, connect the *manometer* via tubing according to the manufacturer's instructions, usually just over the firebed. Take the reading when there is no heat demand. If there is insufficient draught or air supply, the appliance will go out.

If there is too much draught or air the appliance may overheat. Take readings again with the appliance operating under full load and adjust the air supply. If a *draught stabiliser* is fitted, this is also adjusted, based on the manometer readings.

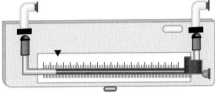

▲ Inclined manometer

incomplete combustion

A condition in which the fuel that is being burned in the combustion appliance does not produce the required *products of combustion*. This can occur through *chilling* of the flame or through a *vitiated air* supply to the appliance. The result of incomplete combustion is an inefficient appliance and possibly the production of *carbon monoxide*, which can be potentially lethal.

independent scaffold

A type of fixed scaffold system that is erected independent to the building. Bracing of the scaffold may occur at openings in the building for stability purposes.

index circuit

The circuit in a *central-heating system* which has the largest heating load and/or resistance. When designing a system, the pump selected must provide adequate water flow rate from the boiler to the *cylinder* and *radiators*. The pressure that must be overcome relates to the *frictional resistance* of the index circuit, which is invariably a circuit to one radiator that has the highest flow rate and resistance. If the pump meets the resistance of the index circuit it will deliver the flow rate required to any other radiator or cylinder circuit, as these have less resistance. The rest of the radiators are balanced (flow restricted through them) to ensure that they do not 'rob' the flow through the index circuit. See *Balancing*

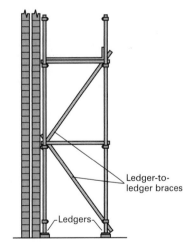

Ledger-to-ledger braces

Ledgers

▲ Independent scaffold

indirect cold-water system

A cold-water system that is primarily used in low-pressure water areas where the mains supply pipework cannot supply the full system requirement. The majority of cold-water *draw-off points* are fed indirectly from the cold-water *storage cistern* which has a stored water reserve. There is a reduced risk of system noise and wear and tear on taps and valves due to the lower pressure. However, this system is more open to frost damage and requires more space for the storage cistern which will be larger in capacity than a direct cold-water system. See *Direct cold-water system*

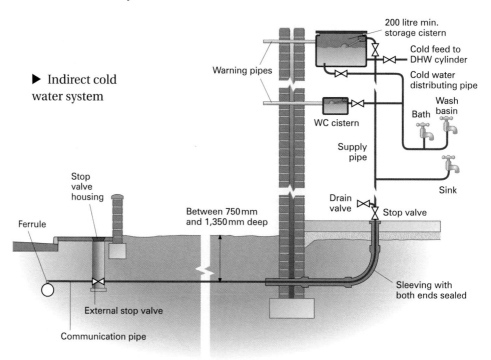

▶ Indirect cold water system

indirect cylinder

A hot-water storage vessel in which the stored water in a *secondary circuit* is heated by hot water in a *primary circuit* via a *heat exchanger*. The mixing of primary and secondary water should not therefore take place. There are two types of indirect cylinder: *single-feed indirect cylinder* and *double-feed indirect cylinder*. See *Indirect hot-water system*

indirect hot-water system

A system of *centralised hot-water* supply where the water that is drawn off has been heated via a *heat exchanger* in an *indirect cylinder*. Essentially there are two separate circuits, the *primary circuit* feeding the cylinder coil and the *secondary circuit* feeding water from the cylinder to the taps. An indirect system permits the use of *ferrous metals* in the primary circuit that would otherwise cause corrosion and *contamination* of the water in a *direct hot-water system*.

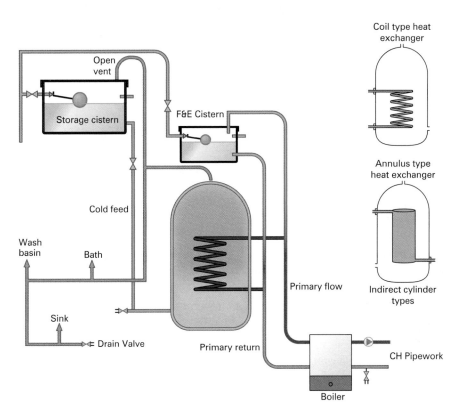

▲ Double-feed indirect hot-water system

individual flue system

A type of flue system that serves a single appliance only.

induced siphonage

See *Trap seal loss*

infiltration

The entry of air into the rooms in a building through gaps and cracks around components such as doors and windows.

A
B
C
D
E
F
G
H
I
J
K
L
M
N
O
P
Q
R
S
T
U
V
W
X
Y
Z

inflatable stopper

An expandable device, which can be inflated with a hand pump, that is inserted into *sanitary pipework* or drainage pipework for the purposes of sealing the pipe for air testing. See *Air testing*

infrared sensor

A device that detects motion which can be used in public conveniences to operate a pressure-*flushing valve*. It can be incorporated into tap assemblies so that they automatically turn on and off when the hands are placed under the tap, or to control the water flow to an *automatic flushing cistern* by opening and closing a *solenoid valve*.

inhibitor

See *Corrosion inhibitor*

injector

A device for controlling and directing fluid flow into a plumbing component (e.g. to ensure the correct gas rate is supplied to a gas burner).

injector tee

Designed to assist the flow of water connected to its branch connection. It may be used to improve *gravity circulation* from a hot-water storage cylinder by using the pumped return connection from the heating circuit. It is mostly used with solid-fuel heating systems.

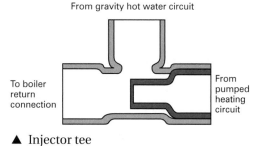

From gravity hot water circuit

To boiler return connection

From pumped heating circuit

▲ Injector tee

insert

A short piece of copper tube that is inserted inside a plastic pipe at the point where a joint is made with a *compression joint*. It strengthens the plastic pipe and permits the *compression ring* to be properly clamped (tightened) on to the pipe.

inset live fuel effect gas fire (ILFE)

An appliance designed to simulate a *solid-fuel* appliance and intended to be installed so that the passage of the *products of combustion* from the *firebed* to the *chimney* or *flue* is restricted, and so that the air enters the fireplace only through specific openings.

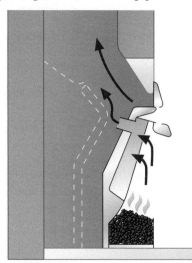

▶ Typical ILFE gas fire

inspection chamber

A type of chamber that is placed at key points along a *drain* or *sewer* to provide access for inspection and clearance of pipework. The inspection chamber can be built with brickwork when using *clay pipes* or a pre-fabricated chamber can be purchased with plastic or *cast-iron* drain pipes.

inspection cover

The cover to an *inspection chamber*. A standard cover for outdoor purposes usually sits in a simple frame and is held down by its own weight or by screws. A heavier one is needed where the cover will be exposed to sizeable weights, such as motor vehicles, and ones with an airtight seal are sited inside buildings to prevent noxious smells entering the building.

▲ Plastic inspection chamber

inspection eye

Access in a sanitary pipework system for the purposes of clearing blockages. See *Access point*

installation pipework (gas)

The pipework that runs from the fitting on the primary meter to the appliances in the building.

instantaneous electric showers

An electric water heater used for shower installations which may be mains fed or fed indirectly from storage. An electric shower is a type of *localised hot-water* heater. The shower should have an isolation switch and be fed directly from the *consumer unit*, pressure variations in the cold-water supply are controlled by a flow governor. Most instantaneous electric showers have a flexible hose outlet and must have a check valve fitted to prevent contamination through the hose being dropped into contaminated water in the bath or shower.

instantaneous water heaters

See *Gas-fired instantaneous water heater*

▲ Instantaneous electric shower

A
B
C
D
E
F
G
H
I
J
K
L
M
N
O
P
Q
R
S
T
U
V
W
X
Y
Z

A
B
C
D
E
F
G
H
I
J
K
L
M
N
O
P
Q
R
S
T
U
V
W
X
Y
Z

Institute of Plumbing and Heating Engineering (IPHE)

The UK's professional and technical body for plumbing professionals. The institute is a registered educational charity with the objective of improving the science, practice and principles of plumbing and heating engineering.

insulation

A layer of material that can be used to prevent the loss of heat from plumbing pipework and components. Insulation is also used to eliminate contact with metallic electrical cables and to minimise sound from plumbing components.

insulation material thickness (pipework)

Insulation material is used to protect pipework from freezing or to prevent heat loss. The thickness of material required depends on the insulation properties. The table below shows the recommended minimum thickness of insulation for 15 mm, 22 mm and 28 mm water pipes to protect against freezing in normal conditions. These recommendations comply with the requirements of the *Water Regulations*.

External diameter of pipe	Thermal conductivity of materials 0°C in W/mK				
	0.02	0.025	0.03	0.35	0.04
15	20	30	25	25	32
22	15	15	19	19	25
28	15	15	13	19	22

▲ Minimum recommended insulation thickness in normal conditions

insulation resistance

Conductors, electrical appliances and components are tested for insulation resistance to ensure that they are not short-circuited and that the level of insulation is high enough. All tests should show an insulation resistance of at least 0.5 Mohms.

insulator

A device or material used to prevent the transfer of electricity in electrical systems and for reducing the heat loss in heating and hot-water systems. Insulators are made from materials in which the *electrons* do not move very freely, such as wood, plastic and rubber.

integral overflow

An overflow which is integral to the appliance itself. See *Combination waste fitting*

intensity of pressure

See *Water pressure*

interlock

See *Boiler control interlock*

intermittent pilot

A pilot light in a gas appliance that does not burn constantly and therefore reduces fuel consumption. When the boiler *thermostat* calls for heat, the control board activates a mains-fed spark ignition at the *electrode* adjacent to the pilot assembly and the *solenoid valve* lets gas through to the pilot. The pilot ignites. The ignition detection electrode stops the spark, the main solenoid opens and gas flows to the main burner. The intermittent pilot, now alight, will ignite the gas at the main burner. The ignition system also includes a *flame protection device* via the electrode, working on the principle of *flame conduction and rectification*.

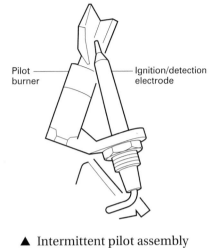

Pilot burner — Ignition/detection electrode

▲ Intermittent pilot assembly

internal corner

See *Lead corners*

international standards

The international standards for the manufacture and installation of materials or components are set by the International Organisation for Standardisation (ISO). These standards are used by countries throughout the world to ensure that materials or components manufactured and installed in one country have the same features and properties as those manufactured and installed in another country. Whatever is made to these standards bears the prefix ISO followed by a number which signifies what the standard applies to, for example ISO 9000 is the standard for quality control.

interposed cistern

A type of *backflow prevention device* in which a water container, such as a WC pan, is separated from the *supply pipe* feeding it via a *storage cistern* which includes appropriate *air gap* arrangements. A correctly configured water closet fed by a *flushing cistern* is an example of an interposed cistern.

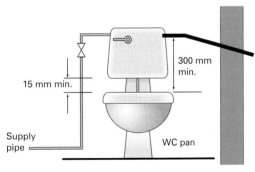

15 mm min.

300 mm min.

Supply pipe

WC pan

▲ WC cistern as an interposed cistern

intrinsically safe

A device or component that is so designed that its use will not create a danger or safety risk to anyone or other processes that are being carried out.

intumescent collar

A type of pipe *collar* used in the fire stopping of pipework and flue components through building structures. See *Fire stop*

invar

A metallic alloy of iron and nickel, often used in temperature or heat measuring devices (e.g. thermostats) owing to its low rate of expansion when heated.

invert level

The bottom of a pipe or channel when fitted horizontally.

ions

Positively or negatively charged particles that flow through gases and liquids. A battery works on the principle of ion exchange (*electrolysis*) and breaking down the metals during *electrolytic action*.

iron

This is produced from haematite, which is heated by hot air in a blast furnace with coke and limestone. Molten iron is tapped from the base of the furnace into billets known as 'pigs'; the solidified impure iron is known as pig iron or *cast iron*.

irrigation systems

Irrigation and porous-hose systems are laid above or below ground to water plants and crops. These systems have a *fluid risk category* 4 or 5 of backflow, depending on the application. Irrigation systems with fixed sprinkler heads at least 150 mm above ground level, are considered fluid risk category 3, as long as insecticides, fertilisers or additives are not used.

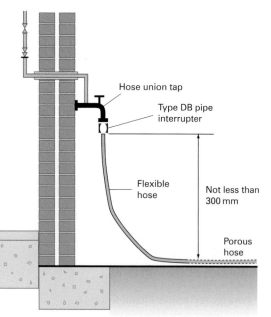

Hose union tap

Type DB pipe interrupter

Flexible hose

Not less than 300 mm

Porous hose

▲ Installation details for a porous hose with a fluid category 4 risk

isolation valve

A general term for a valve, such as a *screwdown stop valve*, *gate valve*, etc., which is fitted to isolate or stop the flow of fluid to a system or component. An isolation valve essentially serves the same purpose as a *service valve*.

jacuzzi

See *Jet-system bath*

jamb

The side of a door or window frame. Wall ties should be included at the jambs of window and door openings for additional strength and the openings must be sealed at the jambs, using an insulated *damp-proof course* material.

jet-system bath

The jet-system or 'spa' bath is a luxury item which usually has a number of jets in the side and/or floor of the bath, fed from a pump which mixes water and air, distributing it at a high flow rate to produce a body and foot massaging effect.

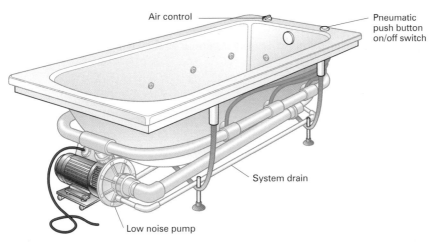

Air control

Pneumatic push button on/off switch

System drain

Low noise pump

▲ Typical jet-system bath

JIB for PMES

The Joint Industry Board for Plumbing and Mechanical Engineering Services (JIB for PMES) is the organisation responsible for determining industrial relations issues, such as pay and conditions for plumbers, and includes representation from plumbing employer and employee organisations.

job order sheet

A written confirmation of the job to be done.

job specifications

Documentation for large projects, including details about the components, materials, fittings and fixings to be installed, the system testing specifications and any specific installation requirements. The specifications usually have site and services drawings and details with them. Specifications can only be altered by the client or project manager.

Joint Industry Board for PMES

See *JIB for PMES*

jointing compound

This is a substance used in the jointing of pipe fittings. There are different types of jointing compound manufactured for use in *wholesome water* systems, heating systems, gas and oil pipelines. The manufacturer's instructions must be consulted to establish that the jointing compound is suitable for use with a particular fluid type. Care must be taken when selecting a jointing compound for use with wholesome water supplies in order to avoid contaminating the water.

jointing types

These are materials used for joining components together, such as *solder*. They must comply with the relevant British or European Standard specification, listed in the *Water Regulations* or the *Water Fittings and Materials Directory*. For example, solders containing lead must never be used on domestic water pipework, except in central-heating installations where water cannot be drawn off. (See table opposite.)

Type	Used for	Standard
Soft solder	Capillary jointing of copper or copper alloy water fittings may consist of: • Type 23 or 24 tin/copper alloy • Type 28 or 29 tin/silver alloy	BS EN 29453
Silver solder or silver brazing metal	Capillary jointing of copper or copper alloy may consist of: • Type AG14 • Type AG20	BS 1845, Table 2
Copper phosphorus brazing filler metals	• Type CP1 to CP6 (all brazing alloys should be free from cadmium)	BS 1845, Table 3
Jointing compounds	Sealing screwed water fittings (other proprietary compounds and hemp aren't acceptable as they may promote microbiological growth)	BS 6956, Part 5
PTFE tape (un-sintered polytetrafluoroethylene tape)	Thread-sealing applications	BS 6974 and BS 6920, Part I

▲ The uses of different jointing types and the standards that apply

joule (J)
A unit of energy, equivalent to the work done in lifting a weight of one newton a distance of one metre.

JTL
The plumbing and electrical apprenticeship managing agent, jointly owned by the Electrical Contractors' Association (ECA) and AMICUS (a trade union). JTL is the leading training provider for apprenticeships in the plumbing and electrical industries.

jumper plate
The *brass* or plastic component that is used to secure the washer in taps and valves. See *Screwdown stop valve*

junior hacksaw
A small type of hacksaw used, for example, when cutting small-diameter *copper tube* (e.g. 15 mm and 22 mm).

A
B
C
D
E
F
G
H
I
J
K
L
M
N
O
P
Q
R
S
T
U
V
W
X
Y
Z

kerosene

The most common type of heating oil used with oil-fired appliances in domestic properties. It is a relatively clear oil and is often described as 28-second heating oil. See *Viscocity*

kettling

This occurs in low-water-content boilers when the water circulation slows down too much, so that the water overheats and boils, producing noises like a boiling kettle, hence the term kettling. A boiler may have small or low-water-content

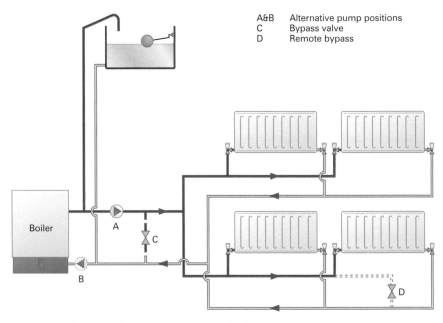

A&B	Alternative pump positions
C	Bypass valve
D	Remote bypass

▲ Installation with bypass fitted to minimise the possibility of kettling

heat exchangers that may contain as little as one litre of water, but the problem of noise can be avoided by fitting a 22 mm pipe with an *automatic bypass valve* to the boiler or the system to ensure that a minimum water flow rate is achieved. The bypass can be installed between the main flow and return pipe either internal or external to the boiler. See *Boiler noise*

kilogram (kg)

The unit of mass in the metric system.

kilonewton (kN)

The kilonewton (kN) is an SI unit of force, equal to 1000 newtons (N).

kilowatt (kW)

The unit of power which equals 1000 watts or 1.341 horsepower. Since one watt equals one joule per second, a kilowatt equals 1000 joules per second. The kilowatt-hour (kWh) is the basic unit of electric energy. It equals one kilowatt of power applied for one hour. Heating appliances are rated in kilowatts, identifying their power or energy consumption.

kinetic

The energy that produces movement.

kitchen sink

This is a cleaning and waste disposal facility located in a kitchen. It is fitted to a wall or to the floor and comprises taps, a bowl with a drain, and a drain pipe. They are available in stainless steel, plastic-coated pressed steel, fireclay and acetyl plastic, and come in the form of a single sink with drainer or double drainer, a single sink with a basket (suitable for connection to a small food *waste-disposal unit*) and a double sink with a single drainer. Kitchen sinks usually take a 1½ inch slotted waste for use with a sink overflow or *combination waste fitting*. Taps are usually monobloc or pillar. *Bib taps* may be used over *London sinks* or *Belfast sinks*.

kitemark

See *British Standards Institution*

knuckle elbow

A type of *elbow* with a very short or tight radius. A knuckle elbow therefore has a greater frictional resistance to the passage of fluids than a *long radius bend*.

A B C D E F G H I J K L M N O P Q R S T U V W X Y Z

ladders – safety

Ladders are used to access an area, such as a platform, from where work can be carried out safely. Work from the ladder should be of short duration – usually no longer than 30 minutes. A ladder should be placed on firm, level ground, positioned at an angle of 75° from the building surface, and secured at the top and at the bottom. In using it, use both hands to grip the rungs. Never use aluminium ladders for electrical work. Inspect a ladder before using it, checking that the stiles and rungs are in good condition and clean of any splits or dirt, that the tie-rods are in good condition, and check, if it is a wooden ladder, that there is no rot and no temporary repairs. Ladders should never be painted, as this may conceal defects. Take care when carrying ladders, and get assistance if required.

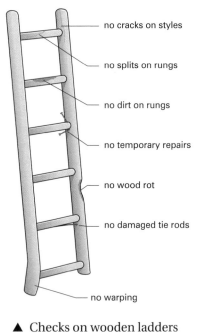

no cracks on styles
no splits on rungs
no dirt on rungs
no temporary repairs
no wood rot
no damaged tie rods
no warping

▲ Checks on wooden ladders

lagging

See *Insulation; Insulation material thickness*

land drain

A system of perforated pipework laid in the ground to drain away excess *surface water*. Land drains are used where land is subject to waterlogging, such as land adjacent to properties, in gardens, and they are used extensively in agriculture to drain fields.

lap joint

A simple type of joint used in sheet lead weathering on vertical surfaces or steeply pitched roofs. The lead *overcloak* simply lays over the top of the *undercloak* by a distance of 75 mm in order to avoid *capillary action*. The overcloak is clipped at its lower surface in order to avoid wind lift.

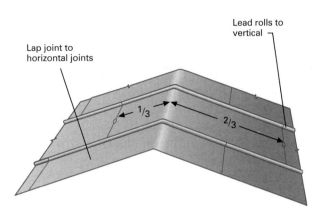

Lap joint to horizontal joints

Lead rolls to vertical

$\frac{1}{3}$ $\frac{2}{3}$

▲ Pitched roof including lap joints

lap-welded joint (overlap joint)

A method of making a lead-welded joint in which one piece of lead overlaps the other and is then welded together. An example is the fabrication of an *internal corner*. In the diagram, the corner is marked and cut as shown in (a), folded as in (b), then the diagonal overlap is welded (c).

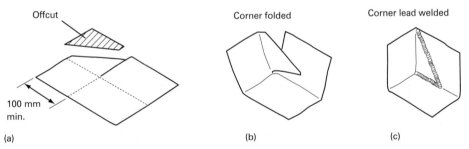

Offcut

100 mm min.

Corner folded

Corner lead welded

(a)   (b)   (c)

▲ Fabricating an internal corner using a lap-welded joint

latent heat

The heat absorbed or given off when a material melts or freezes, or boils or condenses. For example, when ice is heated and the temperature reaches 0°C, its temperature will not increase further until all the ice is melted. The ice has to absorb heat in order to melt. However, even though it's absorbing heat, its temperature stays the same until all the ice has melted. The heat required to melt the ice is called the latent heat. The water will give off the same amount of latent heat when you freeze it again. See *Change of state; Sensible heat*

lead

Lead is a very *ductile*, *malleable* and *corrosion*-resistant metal which requires specialist handling as ingested lead is poisonous and lead fumes are toxic. Lead in sheet form is used for weatherings (*flashings*) on buildings. You may also find old installations of lead pipe in mains, sanitary and rainwater systems. Plumbers have

A
B
C
D
E
F
G
H
I
J
K
L
M
N
O
P
Q
R
S
T
U
V
W
X
Y
Z

always been considered to be lead-work specialists; the word 'plumber' comes from the Latin name for lead. There are two methods of sheet lead production:

- The standard rolled (milled) sheet lead that is used by plumbers is manufactured to BS EN 12588 by passing lead slabs back and forth through a rolling mill containing two closing rollers that continually reduce the thickness of the sheet lead as it passes back and forth. The finished sheet is then cut to standard sizes and formed into sheet lead coils of varying widths and lengths ready for distribution.
- Cast sheet lead is the traditional method of sheet lead manufacture: molten lead is poured across a bed of sand; it is allowed to cool, and then cut into the required sizes. This type of sheet lead is used on historic buildings such as cathedrals.

lead bossing

This is the process of moving (working) lead from one place to another using *leadworking tools* to make it fit the intricate shapes required to weatherproof the surfaces of buildings. During lead bossing, lead is either lost, for example in the production of an *internal corner*, or gained, as in the production of an *external corner*. Lead bossing is a highly skilled art that involves working the lead successfully without unduly thickening the material at various points or thinning it to the point where it may crack. The following photographic sequences show the production of an internal and external corner using lead-bossing techniques where the lead is either lost or gained to form the finished component. The alternative to lead bossing is to form the component by lead welding. See *Lead welding*

 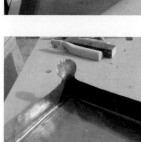 

▲ Forming an internal corner by lead bossing

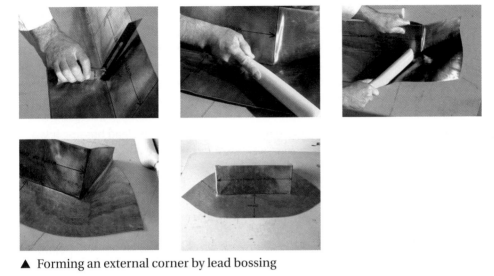

▲ Forming an external corner by lead bossing

lead burning

The old term for *lead welding*.

lead codes

Sheet lead is supplied in a number of thicknesses (codes) to suit particular sheet lead components being fabricated. For example:

- Code 3 is commonly used for *soakers*.
- Code 4 is for lead-welded components.
- Code 5 is for standard lead-bossed components, for example front *aprons* and *back gutters*.

BS 12588 Code No	Thickness mm	Weight kg/m²	Colour code
3	1.32	14.97	Green
4	1.80	20.41	Blue
5	2.24	25.45	Red
6	2.65	30.05	Black
7	3.15	35.72	White
8	3.55	40.26	Orange

▲ Codes and sizes of sheet lead

A
B
C
D
E
F
G
H
I
J
K
L
M
N
O
P
Q
R
S
T
U
V
W
X
Y
Z

lead corners

It is necessary to shape sheet-lead components to meet the requirements of various building details. During that shaping process it may be necessary to form lead components to go around corners. Lead corners are produced as either:

- internal corners – lead is lost in forming the corner; by *lead bossing* it is moved away from the corner, or by *lead welding* a piece of lead is cut from the sheet, or as
- external corners – lead is gained in forming the corner; by lead bossing it is moved into the corner, or by lead welding a *gusset* piece is added to the sheet.

For examples, see the photographs in the *lead bossing* entry.

lead flashing

The weatherproofing of buildings at abutments or junctions between building surfaces. In the case of simple *abutment flashings*, the flashings may comprise of a simple *cover flashing* produced to cover the gap between two types of building material. In the case of flashings between an abutment and a pitched-roof covering, there are a number of options based on the type of roofing material:

- An abutment with *soakers* and *step flashings* – this is applied to roofs covered with slates or plain tiles. Two separate flashing pieces are used: the soaker and the cover flashing. The cover flashing may be produced in single steps or continuous steps.
- An abutment with a step and cover flashing – this is used for deeply profiled and interlocking types of tiles where a soaker is not used, merely a cover flashing projecting over both the wall and roof surfaces; the flashing is produced in continuous steps.
- An abutment with single-step flashings – this is commonly used to weather abutments to stone wall surfaces that have deeply profiled or interlocking tiles; it ensures a more watertight joint at the vulnerable position where the raking cut meets the turn-in on a *continuous step flashing*. See *Chimney weathering set*

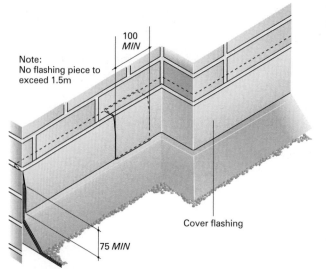

◄ Weathering to a simple abutment

100 MIN

Note:
No flashing piece to exceed 1.5m

Cover flashing

75 MIN

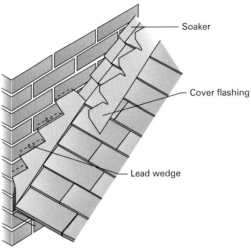

▲ Abutment with soakers and step flashings

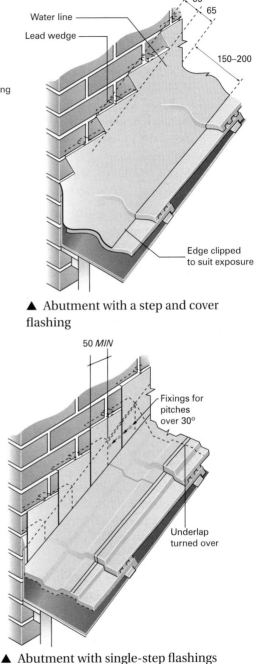

▲ Abutment with a step and cover flashing

▲ Abutment with single-step flashings

lead-free solder
See *solder*

lead knife
See *Leadworking tools*

lead pipe connections
This involves making a connection to an existing lead pipe, by using *WRAS*-approved products such as 'Leadloc joints', manufactured specifically for connecting to lead. Lead pipe, however, can no longer be used in new installations, or for replacing old lead pipe in an existing installation. It is advisable to remove as much of an existing defective lead pipe as possible, and preferably the whole lead pipe installation. Joint wiping lead to copper is no longer permitted under the *Water Regulations*. Make sure that the connection prevents any *electrolytic action* taking place through the use of dissimilar metals. See *Jointing types*

A
B
C
D
E
F
G
H
I
J
K
L
M
N
O
P
Q
R
S
T
U
V
W
X
Y
Z

A
B
C
D
E
F
G
H
I
J
K
L
M
N
O
P
Q
R
S
T
U
V
W
X
Y
Z

lead safety

The safe use of lead is covered by the Control of Lead at Work Regulations. It covers these tasks:

- Lead handling tasks – protective measures should be taken to prevent lead entering the body through the skin: use PPE such as barrier cream, gloves, eye protection and overalls.
- Lead heating tasks, such as *lead welding* – extensive precautions must be taken to prevent breathing in toxic lead fumes, for example the use of respiratory protective equipment (RPE) and local extraction ventilation systems (LEV).
- Manual handling heavy lead; coils may need to be lifted by mechanical lifting devices or by two people, owing to their weight.

Always wash your hands, arms and face after working with lead, and eat or drink well away from the worksite after washing the hands.

lead slate

A type of flashing used where a pipe, such as a plastic soil and vent pipe, penetrates a roof covering. A lead slate is usually formed by lead welding. A typical slate for a 100 mm pipe should be 400 mm wide; the base should extend 150 mm from the front and at least 100 mm under the slate, and the upstand should be at least 150 mm high.

▲ Lead slate in-situ

lead tack

A type of fixing used on sheet lead work.

lead wedges

A type of sheet lead fixing used for securing sheet lead *cover flashings* to the cement mortar joints in masonry wall surfaces. The lead wedge is formed from a 25 mm-wide off-cut of lead that is rolled into shape and flattened to a slight taper. The wedge is then inserted in the gap in the masonry wall and lightly driven in between the brick and lead to secure the cover flashing in position.

lead welding

This is the jointing of two pieces of lead by melting the edges of the lead together whilst also strengthening the joint by adding lead from a lead filler rod. There are two types of joint: the *butt joint* and the *lap joint*. Key points in the lead welding process are:

- The two surfaces being welded should be cleaned to a distance of approximately 10 mm; the filler rod should also be shaved clean.
- The correct lead welding nozzle is selected, usually number 2 and 3 for common applications; the oxygen and acetylene pressures on the gauges are set at 0.14 bar and a *neutral flame* established.

- When making the weld the lead should be correctly penetrated to ensure strength in the joint; *undercutting* the material during the welding process should be avoided as it causes joint weakness.

The diagrams show the key points in lead welding.

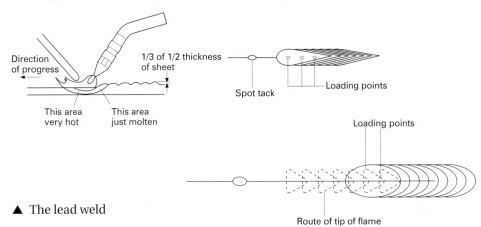

▲ The lead weld

leadworking tools

These are the key *hand tools* that are used in the fabrication and installation of sheet lead. The following are some of the key tools used:

- Dresser (1) – used to make the metal lie flat on a surface (remove any humps).
- Bossing stick (2) – used with a mallet to boss the lead into shape.
- Bending stick (3) – used with a mallet to boss the lead into shape. (Continued overleaf.)

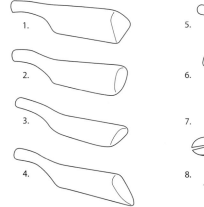
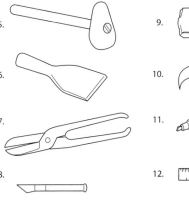

Key

Lead bossing tools: 1 Flat dresser; 2 Bossing stick; 3 Bending stick; 4 Setting-in stick; 5 Bossing mallet; 6 Chase wedge; 7 Snips; 8 Plugging chisel – used to chisel out mortar from brickwork to let in the lead work; 9 Club hammer – for use with the plugging chisel; 10 Lead knife; 11 Spirit-based marker pen and straight edge – used for marking and cutting lines without damaging the surface of the lead; 12 Ruler

▲ Leadworking tools

- Setting-in stick (4) – used to reinforce or sharpen folds or angles.
- Mallet (5) – used to boss the lead in conjunction with the other bossing tools.
- Chase wedge (6) – used for setting-in the corner or a fold or crease.

leak detection fluid

A liquid used to check connections or trace gas leaks. Leak detection fluid is used to test small sections of a pipework system at key potential weep points until the source of a leak is identified.

legionella bacteria

The bacteria which causes the potentially fatal illness Legionnaires disease when breathed into the lungs. Legionella may be found in water – the bacteria can survive under a wide variety of environmental conditions and have been found in water temperatures in the range of 20°C to 45°C. The organisms tend not to multiply below 20°C and will not survive above 60°C. They may, however, remain dormant in cool water and multiply only when water temperatures reach a suitable level. Larger hot- and cold-water systems are *disinfected* to guard against the growth of the legionella bacteria.

'let by' test

One step in the key stages of *tightness testing* a low- or medium-pressure *natural-gas* system. The 'let by' test ensures that the main *emergency control valve* is not passing gas that could give a false reading during the tightness test. To conduct a 'let by' test on an installation with the gas connected, use the control valve to very slowly raise the pressure to 10 mbar and isolate the supply. If the pressure rises at all over a one-minute period, then the control valve is 'letting gas by' when closed. Apply *leak-detection fluid* on the open end of the installation to confirm the test. If confirmed, then you must call in the gas emergency service provider immediately to make the installation safe.

lever-operated spherical plug valve

A type of *service valve* approved for use on above ground components in hot- and cold-water systems.

lifting – safety

The safe lifting and manual handling of loads at work to avoid injury. Lifting or manual handling includes pushing, pulling, lifting and lowering. Always plan carefully when moving loads. The maximum load for a fit person to lift by themselves is 20 kg, although maximum lifting loads do vary from person to person. Key points in a safe manual lifting procedure are:

- Make sure that the path is clear, doors are open and the set down location is in a clear area.

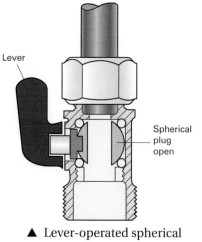

Lever

Spherical plug open

▲ Lever-operated spherical plug valve

- Keep your back straight, bend your knees, grip the load firmly, using gloves if appropriate.
- Balance the load, and use the leg and thigh muscles to straighten the body.
- Keep your arms close to the body, avoid twisting, move steadily without rushing.
- Reverse the lifting process for placing the load down safely.

lifting off
See *Flame lift*

lighting back
The flame at a burner port will burn back down the burner tube to the *injector* when the speed of the gas/air mixture is too low. Lighting back is caused by low pressure in the air/gas mixture. This is also called light back or striking back.

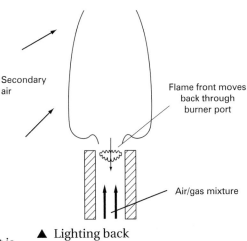

Secondary air

Flame front moves back through burner port

Air/gas mixture

▲ Lighting back

lighting circuit
A radial electrical circuit feeding the overhead lights and wall lights. It is usually fed by a 1.5 mm twin and earth PVC-insulated cable and protected by a 6 amp MCB or a 5 amp fuse at the consumer unit in domestic properties. Domestic properties often have two separate lighting circuits, one for the ground floor, and one for the rest of the building.

limited-capacity relief valve
A valve used inside another valve to allow a discharge of excess pressure to atmosphere. For example, a limited-capacity relief valve is used to trigger an 'under pressure shut-off/over pressure shut-off' (OPSO/UPSO) valve to a closed position. The OPSO/UPSO valve is a requirement of the *Gas Safety (Installation and Use) Regulations* where gas is supplied from an LPG bulk vessel of four or more cylinders. The OPSO/UPSO valve prevents extreme pressures. The limited-capacity relief valve allows excess pressure to discharge to atmosphere and triggers the valve to a closed position.

limits of flammability
See *Flammability levels*

line strainer
See *Strainer*

linear expansion
See *Coefficient of linear expansion*

A
B
C
D
E
F
G
H
I
J
K
L
M
N
O
P
Q
R
S
T
U
V
W
X
Y
Z

linear (spider) manifold

Microbore heating systems use small pipe diameters (8 mm and 10 mm) to feed the radiator circuits. The supply from the heating mains to the radiators can be provided through a manifold, which feeds the radiators through individual 8 mm or 10 mm flow and return pipes. The diagram shows a layout for a microbore system which incorporates a linear- or spider-type manifold, made up to suit the number of connections required.

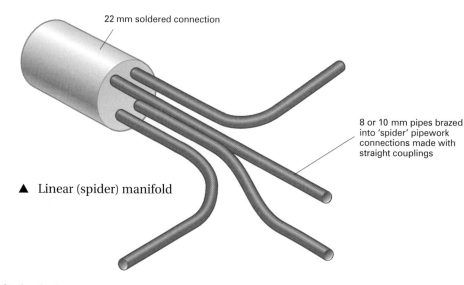

22 mm soldered connection

8 or 10 mm pipes brazed into 'spider' pipework connections made with straight couplings

▲ Linear (spider) manifold

linked cistern

In certain circumstances it may be necessary to install two or more cold-water *storage cisterns* as an alternative to a single cistern. This is particularly the case when large quantities of water are required. However there may be restrictions on the dimensions of openings in the building through which a cistern can be passed, in which case more than one cistern is used and they are linked together.

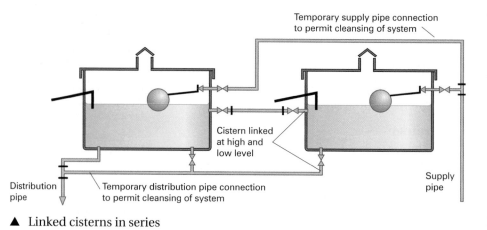

Temporary supply pipe connection to permit cleansing of system

Cistern linked at high and low level

Supply pipe

Distribution pipe

Temporary distribution pipe connection to permit cleansing of system

▲ Linked cisterns in series

Care needs to be taken when linking cisterns in order to avoid stagnation and hence *contamination* occurring in parts of the cistern. The diagram shows a method of cistern linking which minimises the risk of stagnation taking place.

lint
The light matter, such as dust, hairs, fluff, etc., that gathers on ventilators, meshes and air filters.

lint arrestor
A fibre-based pad or mesh filter installed to prevent dust and debris from entering the airways of a gas burner.

lintel
A supporting beam installed above openings in walls, for example windows, door openings, *builder's openings* and *fireplace recesses*; it is designed to prevent wall collapse.

liquefied petroleum gas (LPG)
Commercial *propane* or *butane* is used as a fuel for burners, heaters and gas torches. LPG has a very low *lower flammability level*, so very small quantities can create an explosive mixture with air. One litre of LPG in its liquid form becomes 250 litres of gas at temperatures above –42°C. LPG cylinders must be kept upright in secure open-air compounds. Draw-off rate must be limited; if too high, the control valve may freeze, causing leaks. LPG is heavier than air, so any leaked LPG will sink, forming an explosive concentration, so it must be handled with care.

liquid
Any fluid substance which takes the shape of the vessel it is contained in.

liquid-expansion thermostat/mechanical thermostat
A type of mechanical thermostat that is most likely to be used in gas cookers. It senses the temperature through a remote liquid-containing phial. When the liquid in the phial expands, due to heat, the bellows expand and close the gas valve, cutting off the supply of gas to the burner. There is a bypass which supplies a small amount of gas to keep the oven burner lit. When the oven cools, the liquid in the phial contracts, the bellows contract, and the gas valve opens.

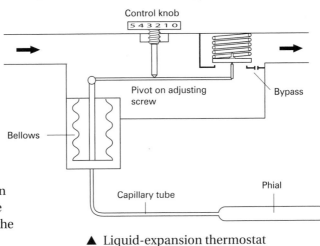

▲ Liquid-expansion thermostat

A
B
C
D
E
F
G
H
I
J
K
L
M
N
O
P
Q
R
S
T
U
V
W
X
Y
Z

A
B
C
D
E
F
G
H
I
J
K
L
M
N
O
P
Q
R
S
T
U
V
W
X
Y
Z

liquid vapour flame supervision device

A type of mechanical *flame supervision device* that can be used in room heaters, water heaters and ovens. The following example is based on the device's operation in an oven. When the oven is turned on a small amount of gas is permitted to bypass the device and flow into the oven. This small amount of gas ignites a pilot flame, usually by a *piezoelectric* ignition device. The *pilot light* plays on to the sensing probe of the device, causing the liquid to expand which in turns moves the bellows, allowing the full gas rate to the burner. If the phial cools, the valve closes to the bypass rate, preventing large amounts of gas from entering the appliance.

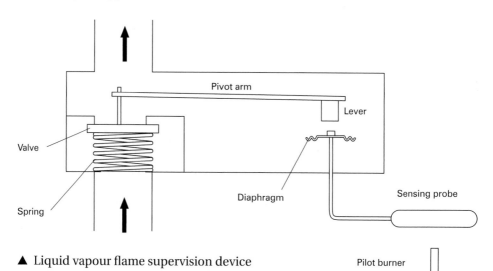

▲ Liquid vapour flame supervision device

litre

A metric unit of capacity (volume) equal to the volume of 1 kilogram of pure water at 4°C – the maximum density of water.

live fuel effect gas fires

See *Decorative fuel-effect gas appliance; Inset live fuel effect gas fire*

loading unit

Loading units are used to calculate the water-flow rate required in hot- and cold-water systems. The loading unit for a particular appliance is an estimate relating to the flow rate at the terminal fitting (tap or valve), the period of time in use and the frequency of use. The *British Standards Institution* provides a table showing the loading units for various appliances. See *Flow rate*

Outlet fitting	Design flow rate (l/s)	Minimum flow rate (l/s)	Loading units
WC cistern – dual or single flush	0.13	0.01	2
WC trough cistern	0.15 per WC	0.01	2
Wash basin – ½" size	0.15 per tap	0.01	1½ to 3
Spray tap or spray mixer	0.05 per tap	0.03	–
Bidet	0.20 per tap	0.01	1
Bath tap – ¾" size	0.30	0.20	10
Bath tap – 1" size	0.60	0.40	22
Shower head	0.20 hot or cold	0.10	3
Sink tap – ½" size	0.20	0.10	3
Sink tap – ¾" size	0.30	0.20	5
Washing machine – ½" size	0.20 hot or cold	0.15	3
Dishwasher – ½" size	0.15	0.10	3
Urinal flushing cistern	0.004 per position	0.002	–

▲ Loading units for different appliances

localised hot-water system

A water-heating system which heats water at the point at which it is required, for example an *instantaneous electric shower*.

locknut

See *Backnut*

lockout

A fail-safe control function in a plumbing component; for example if a fault occurs then a *pressure-jet burner* goes to lockout and the operation of the burner ceases.

lockshield

A type of head on a valve that prevents an unauthorised person from making an adjustment to it.

lockshield radiator valve

A type of radiator valve that has a tamper-proof cover over the valve mechanism. The plastic cap covers a lockshield head which can be opened only with a special key or pliers.

▲ Lockshield radiator valve with drain-off facility

A
B
C
D
E
F
G
H
I
J
K
L
M
N
O
P
Q
R
S
T
U
V
W
X
Y
Z

169

A
B
C
D
E
F
G
H
I
J
K
L
M
N
O
P
Q
R
S
T
U
V
W
X
Y
Z

lockup
A condition in a *gas meter* where, at zero flow conditions, the *regulator* closes off.

London sink
A white sink with no overflow, made of heavy-duty fireclay and used in domestic and commercial properties. The London sink takes a 1½" threaded waste and usually has *bib taps*, but *pillar* or *monobloc* taps can be fitted.

long radius bend
A type of bend with a very long radius. Long radius bends are typically used in drainage systems to minimise resistance to the passage of water and sewage.

longscrew connector
A type of coupling joint to a *low-carbon steel* pipe that can be made with a minimum gap between the two pieces of pipe being joined together.

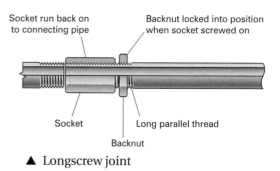

Socket run back on to connecting pipe

Backnut locked into position when socket screwed on

Socket

Long parallel thread

Backnut

▲ Longscrew joint

loose ball slow ignition device
A device used in *gas-fired instantaneous water heaters* to let the gas in gradually when the heater is turned on, preventing noisy ignition. The slow ignition device also allows the main burner to light safely and quietly, and closes the burner down quickly. The loose ball slow ignition device is usually located in the low-pressure side of the diaphragm. The amount of water that can bypass the ball is controlled by screwing the device in or out: this adjusts the rate at which the diaphragm lifts.

Valve opening

Loose ball

Valve fully open

Loose ball

Low-pressure duct

Low-pressure duct

▲ Slow ignition device, loose ball type

low-carbon steel (LCS)/mild steel

An alloy manufactured from iron and carbon. LCS tube is available in three grades: light, medium and heavy; it is colour-coded brown, blue and red respectively. The outer diameter is similar, but the internal bore and wall thickness varies. Light LCS is used for conduit, medium and heavy LCS tubes are used for water-supply services. For domestic water supplies (now used on a limited basis owing to corrosion issues) the LCS must be *galvanised*.

low-level bath traps

These are designed to fit into tight spaces under baths and shower trays. The seal depth is normally 38–50 mm. The 50 mm seal depth is the minimum required for connection of a bath to the discharge stack.

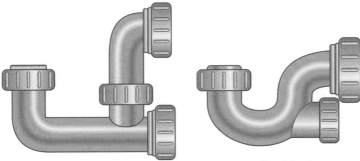

▲ Low-level bath traps

low-level flushing cistern

See *Water closet*

low pressure – natural gas

A gas inlet pressure to the *meter* not exceeding 75 mbar.

low pressure cut-off valve

A valve that can be fitted to a gas-supply system which, in the event of an open pipe end or a large gas leak, closes the supply to the system and prevents a major gas escape. This type of valve is becoming increasingly popular in rented accommodation to guard against theft of gas appliances.

low pressure hot-water heating system

A wet *central-heating system* that is open to atmosphere; it is *open-vented*.

low water-content boilers

A space-saving modern boiler with a small *heat exchanger*. Low water-content boilers need a greater water circulation through them to prevent *boiler noise* or *kettling*, which can also cause the *overheat thermostat* to trip.

lower flammability level

See *Flammability level*

LPG

See *liquified petroleum gas*

A
B
C
D
E
F
G
H
I
J
K
L
M
N
O
P
Q
R
S
T
U
V
W
X
Y
Z

macerator WC

A macerator is a special unit fitted to allow a WC to discharge its contents below drain level, or where there is an excessive distance to the main *soil stack*. A macerator WC can only be installed in the second bathroom of a property where the first bathroom has a WC with a traditional soil connection. The wiring for a macerator is regulated by BS 7671 and an unswitched electrical supply point should be installed near the point of connection by a qualified electrician. The unit is usually connected to 19 mm discharge pipework which may increase in size dependent on the vertical lift of the

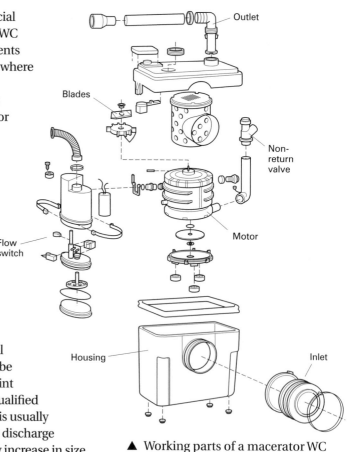

▲ Working parts of a macerator WC

pipework and the length of run. The pipework from a macerator should incorporate long radius bends or $2 \times 45°$ angled bends where 90° changes of direction are required. There are many parts to the macerator WC, as shown in the diagram.

m&f elbow

A *low-carbon steel elbow* with a *male thread* at one end and a *female thread* at the other.

magnetic water conditioner

See *Water conditioner*

magnetite

A black-coloured *sludge* found in wet *central-heating systems*. It is the oxide (rust) that occurs as a result of system *corrosion*. Excessive magnetite build-up in the system can lead to system inefficiency, potential system noise and, in the worst case, blockage of components. Excessive magnetite build-up can be avoided in the first instance by correct system design and installation (a system that constantly aerates or has leaks in it will suffer from an increased level of magnetite deposits). The proper treatment of the central-heating water on *commissioning* by the addition of a *corrosion inhibitor* will reduce the opportunity for magnetite to form.

main earthing terminal

An earthing terminal installed at the electrical point of entry to a property, usually the main distribution board.

main equipotential bonding

The main *bonding* conductor to water or other services that should be installed as near to the point of entry of the service as possible, in order to provide

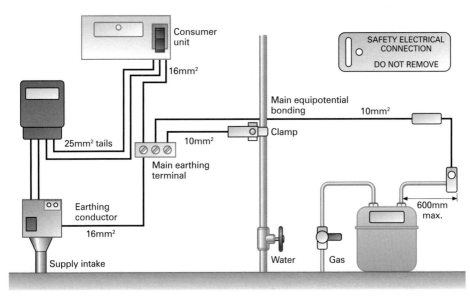

▲ Earth-bonding conductors

A
B
C
D
E
F
G
H
I
J
K
L
M
N
O
P
Q
R
S
T
U
V
W
X
Y
Z

protection in the event of electrical contact with the metallic services. Bonding to the gas supply must be within 600 mm of the meter. Bonding the pipework, as shown in the diagram, is called 'main bonding'. The main bonding conductor is usually sized at 10 mm² in a domestic property. The clamp should be labelled 'Safety electrical connection – do not remove'.

mains

The main services (supplies) into a building – water, gas or electricity.

mains connection

New water mains are PVC, old mains may be *asbestos cement*, steel, PVC or *cast iron*, and these will eventually be replaced with PVC. The water company is responsible for the connection to the mains operating under live pressure. This requires specialist equipment; the connection to a steel or cast-iron main is made using a mains tapping machine, as shown in the illustration, which drills, threads the pipe and inserts a *ferrule* to make a live connection.

Body rotates between spindles

Ratchet spanner

Spindle holding drill

Spindle holding ferrule

Seal

Casing clampe onto main usir chain

Ferrule

Drill and tap

▲ Mains tapping machine

making good

This involves, for example, repairing and finishing off brickwork, blockwork and concrete, pointing any disturbed brickwork joints, or finishing the gap around a pipe sleeve penetration with either mortar or, for pipework, mastic sealant.

male thread

An external thread that is cut on to pipes and fittings. The male thread screws into a *female thread*.

malleability

The ability to be worked into shape without fracturing. Lead is the most malleable metal that plumbers use and is readlily worked using hand tools by a process called *lead bossing*. Lead can be formed into quite complex shapes, or 'dressed' to fit the many types and shapes of roof tiles.

malleable iron

This is a result of *annealing* cast iron to make it less brittle. Malleable iron can be used in the process of producing *low-carbon steel*.

mallet

See *Leadworking tools*

manhole

A term largely replaced by *inspection chamber*. It is still commonly used for larger type inspection chambers into which people can climb to gain access to the *sewer* system.

manifold for microbore system

A larger pipe fitting, usually 22 mm or 28 mm in diameter, that contains a range of smaller diameter pipe connections for a *microbore heating system* feeding 8 mm or 10 mm pipework to the radiators. See *Linear (spider) manifold*

▲ Microbore pipework manifold

manipulative compression joint/ type B joint

See *Compression joint*

manometer

A device used to measure pressure and test for leaks. A manometer is a U-shaped device filled with coloured water that establishes the pressure in a system, usually measured in millibars, and can be used, once the system is pressurised, to measure any drop in pressure over a specified test period in order to establish whether the pipework is leaking. Manometers come in a range of tube lengths dependent on the system being tested.

manual handling

See *Lifting*

masonry drill

A drill bit used for making holes in masonry materials such as brick or concrete. The cutting tip is made from tungsten carbide bonded to a spiralled steel shaft.

▲ Manometer being used during a gas tightness test

mass

The amount of matter in an object or substance. Weight can change, according to gravity, but mass stays the same.

MCB

See *Circuit breakers*

MDPE pipe

A medium-density polyethylene pipe used extensively for below ground water and gas service pipework, it is colour-coded blue for water and yellow for gas.

A
B
C
D
E
F
G
H
I
J
K
L
M
N
O
P
Q
R
S
T
U
V
W
X
Y
Z

A
B
C
D
E
F
G
H
I
J
K
L
M
N
O
P
Q
R
S
T
U
V
W
X
Y
Z

mechanical services

The trades in the building services industry which deal with mechanical installation work, namely: plumbing, heating and ventilation, gas fitting, refrigeration and air conditioning.

mechanical thermostat

See *Liquid-expansion thermostat*

mechanical ventilation

A type of forced draught ventilation to a room or a building using a fan to either pump air into the room or extract it from the room in order to achieve a desired *air change* rate.

medium pressure – natural gas

A type of gas system where the inlet pressure to the *gas meter* is not less than 75 mbar but does not exceed 2 bar.

meniscus

The curve of the water surface in a tube or beaker brought about by the *cohesion* of water *molecules*.

meter

A device used to measure the quantity of a fluid flowing through it.
See *Gas meter; Water meter*

meter box

A compartment designed to house a *meter* and its associated controls. A meter box is commonly sited external to the main building in new properties.

meter pressure

See *Gas pressure*

meter regulator

A meter regulator (governor) that is fitted between the *emergency control valve* and the *gas meter* to regulate the supply of gas to the property. See *Gas governor*

meter union

A fitting used to connect a *gas meter* to the installation pipework in the property.

methane

A colourless, odourless gas formed naturally by the decomposition of organic matter. It is the major constituent of *natural gas*.

metric system

A set of standard units now used in the UK in which the quantities of a substance or an event can be expressed. The core units of the metric system are:

Length	metre	m
Mass	kilogram	kg
Time	second	s
Electric current	ampere	A
Temperature	kelvin	K

microbore heating system
A heating system incorporating circulating pipework to radiators normally within the size range of 6 mm to 12 mm outside diameter.

micropoint connections
Special fittings which provide a neat finish to the ends of a gas pipework installation. Some micropoint connections include an *isolation valve*. Small-diameter rigid pipes or flexible hoses are used to connect from the micropoint to the appliance.

micro-switch
A small electrical switch found in components. A *motorised valve* to a heating system usually contains an auxiliary switch (micro-switch) which is used to power the electrical supply to the boiler and pump, and is essential in forming *boiler control interlock* controls.

▲ Micropoint (rigid connection)

mid-position valve
A three-port mechanical/electrical valve used on a fully-pumped heating system which permits the hot water and heating circuits to work independently of each other or to operate together. See *Types of fully pumped central-heating*

▲ Mid-position valve

mild steel
See *Low-carbon steel*

milled sheet lead
See *Lead*

miniature circuit breaker (MCB)
See *Circuit breakers*

mirror test
See *Alignment test*

mixer tap
A tap which houses the hot and cold controls in the one unit and distributes mixed water at the outlet of the tap. There are a variety of mixer taps available, including single-tap hole (monobloc), twin-tap hole and three-tap hole. The single-flow-outlet type permits mixing of hot and cold water inside the body of the tap. When the cold water is provided from the *supply pipe* a *backflow prevention device*, in the form of a single-*check valve*, must be fitted to each of

A
B
C
D
E
F
G
H
I
J
K
L
M
N
O
P
Q
R
S
T
U
V
W
X
Y
Z

the hot and cold pipes supplying the mixer in order to prevent *backflow* of the contaminated mixed water. The twin-flow outlet does not allow water to mix inside the tap outlet, therefore the backflow devices are not required with this type of mixer tap.

mixing valve

A valve which mixes hot and cold water to achieve a mixed water temperature. See *Shower mixer valve; Thermostatic mixing valve*

mobile scaffold tower

Mobile scaffold towers are commonly used for services installation work as they permit temporary long-term access to work at heights; they are therefore the preferred method of medium- to long-term working as opposed to the *ladder*, as they are more safe to use. Mobile scaffold towers may be constructed using basic scaffold components or using specially designed light alloy tube components. The base section is fitted with lockable wheels, and sections are slotted together to reach the required height. If the working platform of the tower is 2 m or more above the ground, hand rails, guardrails (knee rails) and toe boards must be fitted. The hand rail should be approximately 910 mm above the working platform. The guardrail must have two horizontal bars fitted 0.4 m and 0.7 m above the working platform. The wheels must be locked when the platform is in use. All people, tools and equipment must be removed before the wheels are unlocked and the tower is moved. If the tower is higher than 9 m it must be secured to the building. A ladder should be securely fastened inside the tower to provide access to the working platform. The mobile scaffold should only be used on firm level ground.

modified stack system

See *Types of sanitary pipework system*

modular boiler

A heating system that contains two or more boilers with a similar heat output. The operation of the boilers is usually controlled by a modular control system where the operation of the boilers is activated by the demand from the system. In low-load conditions (mild weather) only one boiler may be activated, whereas in high-load conditions (colder weather) all the boilers may be activated.

modulating burner

A type of burner that is now commonly used on gas appliances where the burner is provided with a varying gas flow rate from the *multi-functional control valve*, based on the heat demands from the system; for example in lower-load conditions the gas flow is reduced and hence the flame size reduced.

moisture penetration

The movement of water and dampness through walls, due to *capillary action*. Solid-wall constructions are at risk of moisture penetration, but the cavity wall has a gap which prevents capillary flow. Solid walls need a *damp-proof course*

(DPC) to prevent moisture penetration and solid floors need a *damp-proof membrane* (DPM).

molecules

Every known substance is made up of molecules, a combination of two or more *atoms* joined together by electrical bonds. When molecules are densely packed the substance formed is a solid (e.g. ice) when they move more freely the molecules form a liquid (e.g. water), and unrestricted movement of molecules forms a gas (e.g. water vapour or steam). See *Change of state*

momentum

See *Trap seal loss*

monobloc taps

A type of *mixer tap* in which the hot- and cold-water controls and the outlet are housed in the one unit. Monobloc taps are also known as single tap hole assemblies.

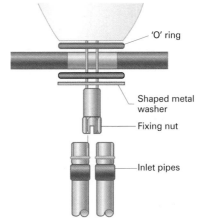

motorised valve

A mechanical/electrical central-heating control used for controlling the flow of water to heating or hot-water circuits. Motorised valves used in *central-heating systems* may be in the form of *two-port valves*, *mid-position valves* (three-port) or *diverter valves* (three-port).

▲ Monobloc connections

moulded seals

These seals are fitted between the waste flange and the appliance on *pop-up wastes* and *combined waste* and overflow fittings used on baths, plastic washbasins and sinks.

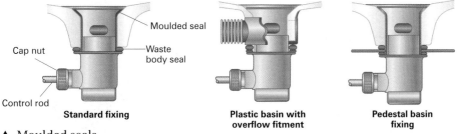

▲ Moulded seals

mountings

The fixing arrangements usually for larger plumbing components such as *boilers* or cylinders.

multifunctional control valves

A combination of several gas control devices contained in one unit and usually fitted on to boilers. A multifunctional control valve may include: the main control *cock*, an adjustable *gas governor*, a *solenoid valve*, a *thermocouple connection*, a *thermostat connection* and an *ignition device*.

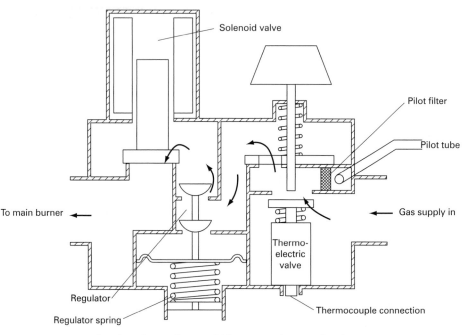

▲ Section through a multifunctional control valve

multimeter

A multifunctional electrical test instrument designed to take a number of different test readings, including: *voltage*, *current* flow, *resistance* and *earth continuity*. The operative using the multimeter needs to be properly trained in its use. The test dial is moved to the correct position in order to take key electrical readings. The multimeter is commonly used in fault finding; other test instruments are used for full electrical testing.

multipoint instantaneous water heaters

See *Gas-fired instantaneous water heater*

▲ Multimeter being used to test for continuity

natural draught burner

Also known as an atmospheric burner, this type of burner draws all its air for combustion purposes by natural means. The alternative to the natural draught burner is the *forced draught burner* which uses a fan to provide combustion air to the burner.

natural draught flue

A type of flue which uses the natural draught created by *convection* currents to remove the *products of combustion*. See *Open flue; Room sealed flue*

natural gas

A hydrocarbon gas that is usually obtained from underground sources, often in association with petroleum and coal deposits. Natural gas generally contains a high percentage of *methane* plus other inert gases.

natural ventilation

Natural ventilation is used in buildings to provide the required *air change* rate. Natural ventilation occurs through cracks in building components, through openable windows and through ventilators such as *air bricks*. Natural ventilation usually takes place through building openings owing to *convection* currents established between the warm air in the room and the cooler outside air. See *Mechanical ventilation*

neoprene

A type of rubber manufactured to make *gaskets* or sealing rings.

neutral flame

A flame which is supplied with equal amounts of oxygen and acetylene at the welding blowpipe. A neutral flame is used in the *lead-welding* process.

A
B
C
D
E
F
G
H
I
J
K
L
M
N
O
P
Q
R
S
T
U
V
W
X
Y
Z

neutral point

The point at which the *cold-feed pipe* joins a pumped heating system; at this point the pressure in the system changes from positive to negative. This is caused by the static pressure created by the *head* of water in the cold-feed pipe. The pressure from the base of the *feed and expansion* (F&E) cistern to the point of cold-feed connection is greater than the pressure created by the pump at that point. An external pressure is therefore exerted which causes a pressure change from positive to negative.

neutral water

A water supply that is neither *alkali* nor *acid*, that is, it is neutral. Neutral water has a pH of 7. See *pH value*

newton

The newton (N) is the SI unit of force, named after Sir Isaac Newton in recognition of his work on mechanics.

nipple

A short piece of *low-carbon steel* pipe with two *male threads* on the end, or a gas pressure test point for the purpose of connecting a *manometer*.

nitrogen

An odourless, gaseous element that makes up 78 per cent of the Earth's atmosphere, and is a constituent of all living tissue. Nitrogen is sometimes used to create the charge pressure in an *expansion vessel*.

noise in systems

Noise in water-based systems, including *water hammer*, *flow noise* and *expansion noise*.

nominal capacity

This is the capacity of a *storage cistern* if it is completely filled to the top. In practice, cisterns are not fully filled because of the overflow and *float-operated valve* fitments, in which case the actual capacity of the cistern is the quantity of water to the waterline.

non-aerated burner

A type of gas burner in which the air is mixed with gas at the point that it leaves the burner. Non-aerated burners are not commonly used in gas appliances.

non-aerated flame

See *Post-aerated flame*

non-combustible

A material which will not easily burn.

non-concussive tap (valve)

A self-closing tap or valve that is fitted to sanitary appliances such as wash basins in public conveniences. The non-concussive tap is a water-conservation device. The tap works on the principle that once the head is depressed it will provide a quantity of water through it for washing or drinking purposes. Over time the tap gradually closes shutting off the supply. The tap may need proper adjustment on installation to ensure that it does not shut off too rapidly, as this will cause inconvenience to users and may result in *water hammer* in the system.

▲ Non-concussive tap

non-domestic sanitary appliances

Special sanitary appliances used in commercial kitchens, laundries, laboratories, hospitals, hotels, etc.

non-ferrous metal

A metal or *alloy* which does not contain iron, for example copper and lead.

non-manipulative joint/type A joint

See *Compression joint*

non-return valve

A valve which allows water to flow in one direction only. An *anti-gravity valve* and a *check valve* are both types of non-return valve.

non-self-resetting thermal cut-out

See *High-limit thermostat*

nozzle

A projecting part with an opening, as at the end of a hose, pipe or fitting, for regulating and directing a flow of *fluid*.

nucleus

The centre of an atom, consisting of non-electrically-charged neutrons and positively charged protons around which *electrons* orbit, forming the main mass.

nuisance discharge

An undesired discharge of water from a plumbing component such as an *overflow pipe*, *warning pipe* or the discharge pipe from an *unvented hot-water system*.

A
B
C
D
E
F
G
H
I
J
K
L
M
N
O
P
Q
R
S
T
U
V
W
X
Y
Z

ABCDEFGHIJKLMN **O** PQRSTUVWXYZ

O ring

A type of round rubber ring used to make a seal between two parts of a plumbing component such as a plastic *push-fit joint* or the spout of a *mixer tap* to the tap body.

obstruction test

See *Alignment test*

offset bend

Two fittings or a double bend both with angles less than 90° used to shape pipes around obstacles. An offset is commonly used at the top of a *rainwater pipe* to connect the *eaves gutter* to the pipe. In terms of *copper* and *low-carbon steel* (LCS) tube bending, the first set is bent to the angle required to offset the pipe around the obstacle. The pipe is then reversed, returned to the machine and the offset is made to make the pipe continue parallel to its initial line.

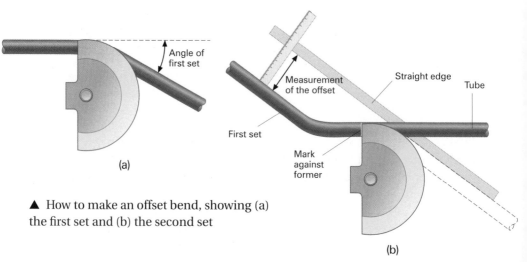

▲ How to make an offset bend, showing (a) the first set and (b) the second set

ohm

A unit of electrical resistance used to measure a material's resistance to the flow of electric current. See *Resistance*

Ohm's Law

Ohm's Law states that *voltage* (V) is equal to the *current* (I) multiplied by the *resistance* (R). The equation is written: $V = I \times R$. It can also be written as: $I = V/R$ and $R = V/I$. The Ohm's Law Triangle is used to help remember the equation. If you know two of the quantities, you can find the third. If you know the current (I) and resistance (R) of a circuit and want to find out the voltage, cover the V of the triangle and it shows that you need to multiply the current by the resistance. If you know the voltage (V) and resistance (R) but want to find the current, cover I and the triangle shows that you now need to divide the voltage by the resistance.

▲ Ohm's Law Triangle

oil appliance commissioning procedures – pressure jet boilers

The first stage in the *commissioning* process is to carry out a visual inspection, checks and tests on points such as the:

- location of the storage tank and correct assembly of its control devices
- oil storage line
- flue termination, routing and materials and the provision of adequate ventilation
- correct installation of the appliance itself and the correct assembly of all its components such as the provision of the correct oil nozzle.

The next stage in commissioning the appliance is to establish the correct fuel supply to the appliance:

- With a *pressure jet burner* this includes fixing the *oil-pressure gauge* to the *oil pump* and connecting the oil line and purging it of air via the gauge manifold. Check the operation of the safety controls by running the burner for a few minutes, then disconnect the solenoid coil which should result in the burner going to *lockout* after approximately 15 seconds. After 60 seconds reconnect the solenoid coil and press the reset button; the burner should light up as normal. Fire the burner, check and adjust the pump pressure to meet manufacturer's requirements.

The next stage is to carry out a *combustion analysis* test on the appliance:

- After the burner has been running for approximately 10 minutes carry out a preliminary check on combustion using a *smoke pump* at the appliance test port, adjusting the air shutter at the fan to give a smoke reading, usually of between 0 and 1.
- Commence the *combustion efficiency* test by running the appliance up to operating temperature and, with *open-flued* appliances, taking a flue draught reading using a flue draught gauge or *inclined manometer*.

A
B
C
D
E
F
G
H
I
J
K
L
M
N
O
P
Q
R
S
T
U
V
W
X
Y
Z

- Take a percentage carbon dioxide (CO_2) reading with a *carbon-dioxide indicator*, fine tuning the adjustment of the air shutter to give the correct CO_2 sample. Carry out a further smoke test to make sure that the smoke reading is adequate.
- Take the flue gas temperature using a *flue gas thermometer*, recording the maximum temperature reached. Also take a reading of the *ambient air temperature* entering the appliance (with open-flued appliances this is usually at the base on entry to the fan).
- The combustion efficiency of the appliance is determined by deducting the ambient air temperature from the flue gas temperature. Using tables the resultant temperature reading and the CO_2 reading are used to determine the combustion efficiency of the appliance, which must meet manufacturer requirements. An alternative to the manual combustion analysis kit is to use an *electronic portable gas analyser*.

oil filter

A type of filter fitted in the oil line between the storage tank and oil-fired appliances to prevent any foreign material in the tank from entering the supply pipes and blocking components such as oil nozzles.

oil-fired boilers

There is a wide range of oil-fired boilers available, including: combination, condensing, traditional, wall-mounted internal (room sealed or open flue), wall-mounted external, floor-mounted internal (room sealed or open flue), floor-mounted external. Modern oil-fired boilers use *pressure-jet burners* to burn the fuel, older oil-fired boilers used *vaporising burners*, which are still fitted to oil-fired cookers and small room heaters.

oil-pressure gauge

A device used in the commissioning of pressure-jet oil-fired appliances to set the *oil pump* pressure.

oil pump

A device fitted to an oil-fired *pressure-jet burner* to raise the oil to high pressure, when it is then forced through a fine nozzle to atomise the oil ready for combustion on exiting the nozzle.

▲ Oil-pressure gauge

oil-supply system

There are three main types of oil-supply system used in domestic properties:

- The single-pipe gravity system, where the bottom of the oil tank is sited at least 300 mm above the burner. The oil is supplied by gravity to the burner.
- There are two types of sub-gravity system, where the bottom of the oil tank is sited below the burner:
  - The single-pipe sub-gravity system with de-aeration device; the oil feed line is still single-pipe to the *de-aerator*, the purpose of which is to remove air from the oil line during pumping. A two-pipe line is taken from the de-aerator to the burner.

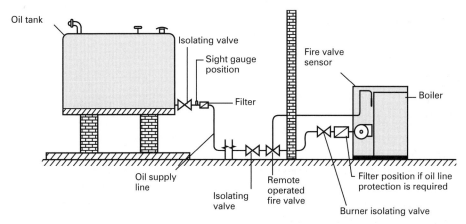

▲ Single-pipe gravity system

  - Two-pipe sub-gravity system, which has two pipes, a flow to the oil pump and a return from the oil pump to the tank. The oil pump needs to be modified to permit two-pipe operation. (See diagram overleaf.)

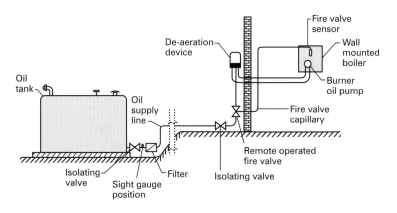

▲ Single-pipe sub-gravity system with de-aeration device

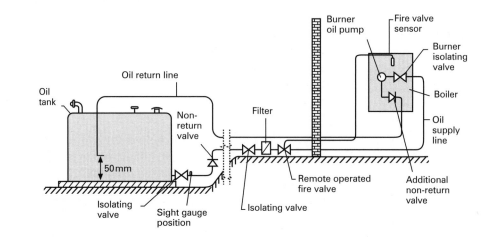

▲ Two-pipe sub-gravity system

oil tank

A component installed for the purposes of storing heating oil. The tank is sized to suit the size of heating system installed in the property so that it does not require to be replenished at too short an interval. The minimum size of tank is 1250 litres. Tanks which are rectangular in shape can be manufactured from steel, though *plastic* tanks now tend to be more popular for domestic premises and are available in a variety of shapes.

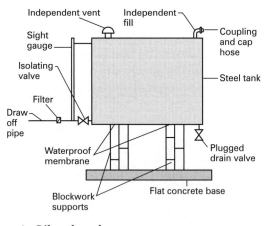

▲ Oil tank and components

There are detailed restrictions on the positions in which the tank may be sited in terms of its proximity to combustible material, although it is possible to site the tank internally or externally. Regulations also lay down specific requirements in relation to the tank's proximity to drains and water-courses, in which case a *catchpit* may have to be installed around the tank to collect any oil in the event of leakage; this is also a likely requirement if the tank is sited indoors. The tank is usually sited within 30 m of the normal fill point; in the event that this cannot be achieved then an extended fill pipe is installed to bring the fill point within 30 m. Key components on the tank are:

- 50 mm diameter fill point with coupling and cap
- 75 mm tank vent, to prevent pressurisation in the tank and venting of air during filling
- Plugged drain valve for the purposes of cleaning the tank in the event of build-up of foreign matter (*sludge*)
- Isolating valve – the main isolation valve from the tank to the appliances
- Sight glass or contents gauge – to check on the oil level in the tank, in order that a fresh supply may be ordered if the tank is running low
- Filter – the main filter usually positioned at the tank to prevent any foreign material from entering the pipework system
- A steel tank is usually rested on two or more brick or block piers with a *damp-proof membrane* on top of the piers to prevent contact between the masonry material and the tank in order to avoid *corrosion*. Plastic tanks must be fully supported across their entire base.

olive
See *Compression ring*

one-pipe circulation
A type of unwanted circulation that takes place in a single hot-water or heating pipe. An example of possible parasitic circulation taking place is when a long vertical section of pipe is connected to the hot-water draw-off of a hot-water cylinder. *Convection* currents can occur in the long vertical pipe causing a circulating effect within it, resulting in heat being lost from the cylinder. To avoid this the cylinder connection is usually made with a bent *union connector* and a horizontal length of pipe at least 450 mm.

one-pipe oil-supply system
See *Oil-supply system*

one-pipe semi-gravity central-heating system
A superseded system that might be found in older properties. It is a system where the primary circuit to the hot-water storage cylinder is fed by *gravity circulation*. The heating circuit is in the form of a one-pipe ring, that is, the flow pipe from the boiler is also the return pipe connecting back to it. This configuration was popular in early systems in domestic properties.

A
B
C
D
E
F
G
H
I
J
K
L
M
N
O
P
Q
R
S
T
U
V
W
X
Y
Z

A
B
C
D
E
F
G
H
I
J
K
L
M
N
O
P
Q
R
S
T
U
V
W
X
Y
Z

There are however a number of disadvantages:

- The water returning from the first radiator forms the flow to the next so the temperature of water supplied to the first will be higher than the last; radiators at the end of the circuit will therefore need to be larger in comparison to those at the beginning for a given heat output.
- The radiators cannot be sited too far from the ring, otherwise the system cannot be effectively *balanced* as the resistance will be too great through the radiator circuit.

See *Two-pipe central-heating system*

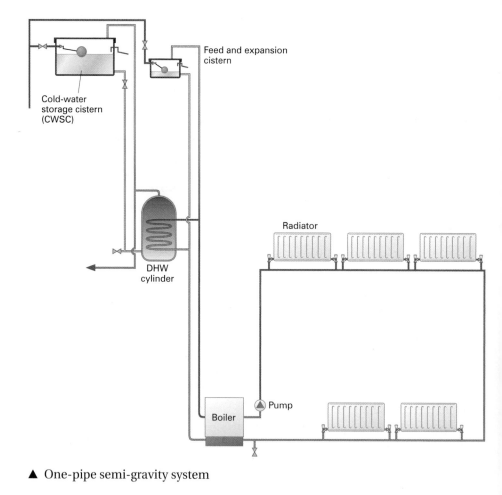

Feed and expansion cistern

Cold-water storage cistern (CWSC)

Radiator

DHW cylinder

Pump

Boiler

▲ One-pipe semi-gravity system

open flue

A *flue* that draws its air for *combustion* from the room in which the appliance is sited and discharges the *products of combustion* to outside air. Appliances may draw their air for combustion through a combination of *adventitious ventilation* and openable windows for smaller appliances, or adventitious ventilation and permanent ventilation through *air vents* for larger appliances. The flue itself works on the principle of *convection* with the warm heated air resulting from the combustion process rising in the flue and being replenished by the cold unheated air at the base of the appliance. There are however a number of key issues that need to be taken into account to ensure that the flue works effectively:

- Flue height is critical – if the flue is too short or too high then the flue draught created may be too poor to completely remove the products of combustion.
- A flue should be kept warm throughout its length in order to avoid undue cooling nearer to the outlet which will reduce the flue draught.
- The number of *bends* should be kept to a minimum, and bends should not be sharper than 135°.
- The flue termination must be in an acceptable position where it will not be adversely affected by wind pressure in the form of *down draught*.

The diagram shows the key parts of an open flue system to a boiler; with modern boilers the primary flue and draught diverter are usually integrated within the appliance itself.

open vent pipe

See *Vent pipe*

open-vented

A system with a vent pipe which remains open to the atmosphere at all times.

open-vented heating system

A heating system which is open to atmosphere and includes a *feed and expansion (F&E) cistern*.

operating pressure

The gas pressure to which a manufacturer requires a *range rated* gas-burning appliance to be set; that is, the *operating pressure* may be variable dependent on the output of the appliance.

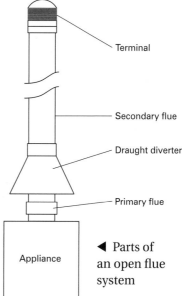

Terminal

Secondary flue

Draught diverter

Primary flue

Appliance

◄ Parts of an open flue system

A
B
C
D
E
F
G
H
I
J
K
L
M
N
O
P
Q
R
S
T
U
V
W
X
Y
Z

OPSO/UPSO valve

An over-pressure/under-pressure valving arrangement is fitted to a *liquefied petroleum gas* installation to protect against over-pressurisation of the system should the *regulator* fail, and under-pressurisation of the system should a large leak occur.

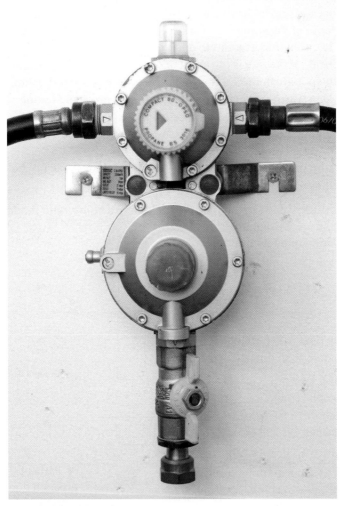

▲ OPSO/UPSO valve

optimiser
A type of central-heating control that is fitted to larger heating systems in commercial and industrial properties. The optimiser varies the start-up time for the heating system based on the outside weather conditions; that is, the heating system will take less time in milder weather for the rooms to reach their desired temperature than in colder weather when a longer period of time will be required. The optimiser is therefore an *energy conservation* device.

orifice
An opening in a component. More specifically, a *float-operated valve* contains an orifice through which the water discharges and against which the washer seats to close the valve.

outlet pipes
Outlet pipes are those that take the water from an appliance such as *cold feed* and *distribution pipes*.

outlet plugs/waste plugs
All baths, wash basins, sinks or similar appliances must have a watertight plug fitted to the waste outlet in order to avoid wastage of water. Most outlet plugs are plastic or rubber push-in types which are connected to the appliance with a metal chain. Modern *pop-up wastes* are available with *mixer taps*. Appliances with low-flow taps do not require outlet plugs; these appliances include: wash basins with *spray mixer taps* or *self-closing taps*, *shower trays* and drinking-water fountains.

over-rim bidets
A type of bidet that includes a tap which discharges above the *spill-over level* of the bidet. This type of bidet can incorporate a *tap gap* as its *backflow prevention device* and therefore presents less of a *contamination* risk than the *ascending spray bidet*, and can usually be fitted to a *supply pipe*. Over-rim bidets with a flexible hose connection, however, cannot be fitted to a supply pipe as the flex and head can be dropped into the bidet, and so represent a similar risk to the ascending spray type. See *Ascending spray bidet*

overcloak
The jointing of sheet-weathering components. The overcloak is the piece of lead that lies on top of another piece of lead at the joint known as the *undercloak*.

overcurrent protection device
A device installed in an electrical system to protect against high electrical *current* passing through wires that are not designed to carry such current. High currents lead to overheating of the wires and a possible fire risk. The overcurrent protection device must therefore be properly sized to suit the system or component being protected. A standard *fuse* and a *miniature circuit breaker* are examples of overcurrent protection devices.

A
B
C
D
E
F
G
H
I
J
K
L
M
N
O
P
Q
R
S
T
U
V
W
X
Y
Z

overflow pipe

A pipe installed to discharge excess water from *cisterns*, safely. A fault, for example in the *float-operated valve*, may cause water in a cistern to rise above a preset level. The overflow pipe is used to discharge the water to a location which will not cause any damage. Larger cisterns incorporate both an *overflow* and a *warning pipe*.

overheat thermostat

See *High-limit thermostat*

oxidation

The chemical process of oxygen combining with an element or compound (e.g. the oxidation of iron to form rust).

oxide

The result of a chemical element, such as lead, copper or iron, combining with *oxygen*. The oxide of a substance forms a coating or protective layer on *ferrous* and *non-ferrous metals*, sometimes known as a *patina*, that guards against *corrosion* of the metal beneath.

oxidising flame

A flame which has an excess of oxygen at the blowpipe. An oxidising flame is typically used when *hard soldering* or *brazing*.

oxyacetylene flame

See *Carburising flame; Neutral flame; Oxidising flame*

oxygen

A colourless, odourless, tasteless, gaseous element which makes up 21 per cent of the air we breathe and that is vital to life.

oxygen-depletion device (ODD)

See *Atmosphere sensing device*

P trap

These are usually made from *polypropylene* to BS 3943 and are used on above ground discharge system pipework and appliances. They are available in *brass* for use on *copper* pipework. The P *trap* is the most common type of trap used with sanitary appliances; the standard trap in a *WC pan* is a P trap.

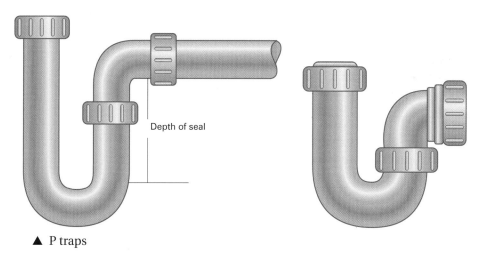

Depth of seal

▲ P traps

packing-gland nut

A nut used on *valve* spindles to compress packing and make the spindle completely watertight.

pad saw

A *hand tool* that comprises a handle into which a thin blade is inserted. The pad saw is used to cut holes in tight places; one common application is to cut the holes in a plasterboard ceiling to accept pipework.

A
B
C
D
E
F
G
H
I
J
K
L
M
N
O
P
Q
R
S
T
U
V
W
X
Y
Z

pan connector

A *sanitary pipework* system fitting that connects a *WC pan* to the *branch discharge pipe*. Pan connectors come in various patterns: straight, bent, angled and flexible.

panel radiator

See *Radiator*

parallel branch

A branch fitting or junction in which the branch connection is parallel with the main flow of water into the junction.

parallel thread

A thread that is cut on to a pipe or fitting that has a uniform depth of cut across its length. This type of thread is used with components such as *float-operated valves* which require a *backnut* to run down the complete length of the valve connection to make the joint with the *cistern* surface. The alternative to the parallel thread is the *tapered thread*, where the thread is cut such that the cut is deeper at the beginning of the thread than at the end; it is the common thread type used with pipes and fittings where, because of the taper, the pipe slowly tightens as it is screwed into the fitting.

parapet gutter

A type of *gutter* sited between a parapet wall and a flat or pitched roof surface.

parasitic circulation

See *One-pipe circulation*

part-house central heating

See *Types of central heating*

partial vacuum

See *Vacuum*

partially separate drainage system

See *Types of drainage system*

pascal

The pascal (Pa) is the SI unit of pressure. It is equivalent to one newton per square metre. The unit is named after Blaise Pascal, the eminent French mathematician, physicist and philosopher.

passover offset bend

A type of pipe bend used to clear small obstacles, such as another pipe. The measurements for a passover offset are taken using the

Measurement of offset

▲ Passover offset

same method as for an ordinary offset. The angle of the first set is calculated to clear the obstacle that the pipe has to pass over.

PAT tests/portable appliance test

All portable electric power tools of 110 or 230 volts must be PAT tested to show that they are safe to use. Records should be kept showing all testing, maintenance and repairs to portable equipment, ensuring that all tools are safe and in good condition. A PAT test for tools used on construction sites is usually recommended to take place at three-monthly intervals.

pathogenic organisms

These are micro-organisms capable of causing illness, especially in humans. Pathogenic organisms include bacteria, viruses or parasites, for example salmonella, vibrio cholera and campylobacter. Micro-organisms are transported through faecal matter, animal waste and body fluids.

patina

A protective *oxide* coating or barrier which forms on metals; for example lead very gradually develops a non-soluble silver-grey patina. Patination oil can be applied to lead to prevent staining by the formation of white lead carbonate.

peak demand

A term used in the design of mains services such as gas and water. It is the period in the day when a maximum demand will be placed on the service, usually in the early evening in water terms when people are bathing, using washing machines, etc.

pedestal wash basin

See *Wash basin*

penetrating damp

The transfer of moisture from the outside face of an external wall to the inside face of an internal wall, by *capillary action*. Cavity-wall construction prevents this as the capillary path is broken by the cavity. At locations where the cavity is bridged, for example at window and door reveals and lintels, the inside wall is protected with a *damp-proof membrane* (DPM). A DPM is applied when *air bricks* are used for suspended-floor construction.

performance test

A performance test is undertaken on a system as part of the *commissioning* process to confirm that it is working effectively.

- With wet *central-heating systems* this includes *balancing* the circuits to ensure the correct heat outputs from the *heat emitters*. This is carried out by measuring flow and return temperatures at the heat emitters and balancing or throttling the circuits accordingly to achieve system design temperatures.
- With hot- and cold-water systems pressures, temperatures and flow rates are measured at outlet points (taps and valves) to check that they meet the requirements of the system design.

A
B
C
D
E
F
G
H
I
J
K
L
M
N
O
P
Q
R
S
T
U
V
W
X
Y
Z

A
B
C
D
E
F
G
H
I
J
K
L
M
N
O
P
Q
R
S
T
U
V
W
X
Y
Z

- With *above ground sanitary pipework* systems a range of tests are carried out to ensure that the *trap* seal is retained at a minimum depth of 25 mm during the tests. Key tests include:
  - Filling sanitary appliances to their overflow level and discharging them then measuring the trap seal depth retained; this tests for *self-siphonage*.
  - Filling the sanitary appliance furthest away from the *discharge stack*, then releasing the water and checking the *trap seal depth* in other traps on the pipe run; this test checks for *induced siphonage*.
  - A selection of sanitary appliances are discharged simultaneously down the main discharge stack to check for induced siphonage created in the stack that may affect appliance traps or *trap seal loss* at the base of the stack.

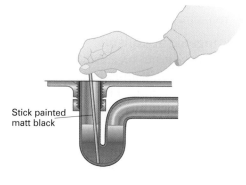

Stick painted matt black

▲ Performance test to a trap

permanent hardness

A type of *hard water* that occurs when water is brought into contact with or permeates through ground containing magnesium sulphate or calcium sulphate. As with all hard waters, a lather cannot be readily obtained with soap. The magnesium or calcium salts cannot be removed from the water when it is heated; this type of hard water does not lead to sizable scaling of hot-water components, as distinct from *temporary hard water* with which there can be considerable *scale* build-up.

permanent pilot

A gas *pilot light* which, once lit, remains permanently lit in order to provide an ignition source for the main burner. Permanent pilot lights do not now tend to be that popular on new appliances as they are wasteful of energy. See *Intermittent pilot*

permeation

This is caused when a liquid or gas passes through the walls of a container, such as a pipe, and contaminates the contents. For example, some *plastic* pipes and fittings can be permeated by petrol and oil which soften and weaken the plastic and cause *contamination*. Gas and fumes can also permeate through the walls of plastic pipes, making the water in the pipes smell or taste strange. If water fittings and pipework are at risk of contamination by oil or petrol, materials other than plastic, and resistant to permeation must be used. *Barrier pipes* made with a cross-linked *polyethylene* to BS 7291 can prevent some permeation. These must be used for *open-vented* and *sealed systems* to prevent the ingress of air.

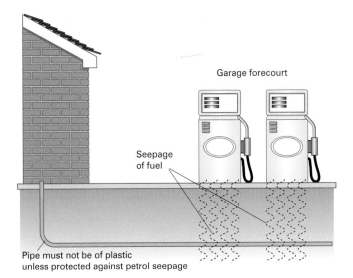

Garage forecourt

Seepage
of fuel

Pipe must not be of plastic
unless protected against petrol seepage

▲ Permeation

Personal Protective Equipment (PPE)

The Personal Protective Equipment (PPE) at Work Regulations 1992
provides guidelines for protective clothing in the workplace. PPE includes all
equipment worn or held to protect against a Health and Safety risk, and includes
eye, hand, foot, head and full-body protection.

pervious

A material or substance that will permit water to pass through it. See *Impervious*

pet cock

A type of valve that is used to regulate the flow of water into an *automatic
flushing cistern*. A pet cock for this application contains a simple screw that is
turned against a valve seating to reduce or enlarge an *orifice*, so regulating the
quantity of water flowing into the cistern which in turn impacts on the flushing
intervals of the cistern.

petrol interceptor

A series of *inspection chambers* are used to prevent petrol or similar flammable
liquids from entering the main *sewer*. It is commonly used to prevent any spillage
from garage forecourts or industrial processes from entering the drainage
system. It works on the principle that petrol, which is lighter than water, will rise
to the surface in the chambers where it will evaporate and be discharged safely
away to atmosphere via a *vent pipe*.

A
B
C
D
E
F
G
H
I
J
K
L
M
N
O
P
Q
R
S
T
U
V
W
X
Y
Z

A
B
C
D
E
F
G
H
I
J
K
L
M
N
O
P
Q
R
S
T
U
V
W
X
Y
Z

pH value

The acid or alkaline levels of a substance. Pure water has a neutral pH value, but the dissolved minerals may cause this to change. The acidity or alkalinity of water can cause *corrosion* in materials, appliances and components, especially those made from metal. The pH of a liquid can be tested using special indicator paper such as litmus paper which changes colour in contact with water of differing pH values.

The pH scale of acidity

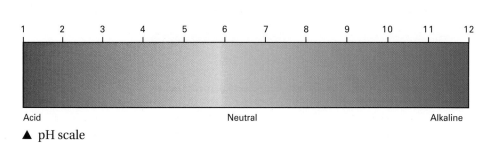

| 1 | 2 | 3 | 4 | 5 | 6 | 7 | 8 | 9 | 10 | 11 | 12 |

Acid   Neutral   Alkaline

▲ pH scale

photoelectric cell

An electrical device found in an oil-fired *pressure-jet burner* that is capable of detecting light from a burning flame. The photoelectric cell is a key safety device which is used to detect the presence of a flame in the appliance. In the event that no flame is present the cell causes the burner to go to *lockout* which prevents any further quantities of oil being discharged at the burner until it has been reset.

piezo igniter

A device that creates a spark using mechanical stress to produce a high *voltage* in a crystal. The piezo igniter is commonly used to ignite gas burners.

pillar tap

A widely used tap sometimes fitted with *ceramic discs* used in *quarter-turn taps*. Pillar taps have a long vertical thread which is passed through pre-drilled holes in the appliance and secured with a *backnut*. A tap connector is used to attach the *supply pipe* to the thread. An *air gap* or *tap gap* must be maintained above the appliance *spill-over level* in order to prevent the possibility of *backflow* occurring from the appliance when fitted directly to a *supply pipe*.

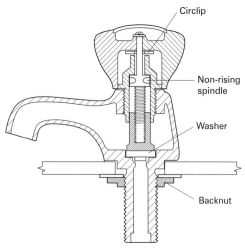

▲ Pillar tap with non-rising spindle

pilot hole

A small hole that is drilled prior to drilling a large hole. The pilot hole is used as a guide to ensure the correct positioning of the large hole.

pilot light

A small gas-burner jet and flame used to light the main burner to a gas appliance. Pilot lights may be intermittent or permanent. See *Intermittent pilot; Permanent pilot*

pipe bending

The process of bending pipe to fit around obstacles or building components.

- *Low-carbon steel* (LCS) tube and large diameter *copper* tube are bent using a *hydraulic pipe bender* which is more suited to bending pipes with thicker wall diameters.
- Medium and small diameter copper tubes can be bent using a *stand bender*, smaller diameter tubes can be bent using a *hand bender* or by *spring bending*.
- Heat bending copper and LCS tube which was sand loaded to support the bend has now largely been superseded by machine bending owing to the length of time it takes to complete the bend.

pipe clips

A range of fixing devices to secure pipework to the surface of building components in order to prevent damage to the system and the potential for knocking noise in pressurised systems. In domestic properties *plastic* and *copper* pipe clips are commonly used. In industrial/commercial buildings more heavy-duty clips tend to be used. LCS tubes tend to be fixed with heavy-duty brackets made from *malleable* iron. See *Clips*

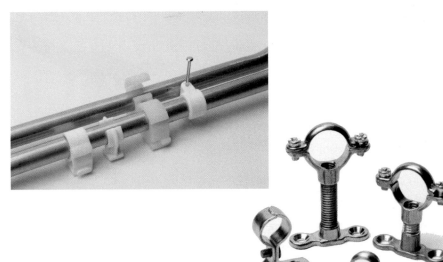

▲▶ Selection of metal and plastic pipe fixings

A
B
C
D
E
F
G
H
I
J
K
L
M
N
O
P
Q
R
S
T
U
V
W
X
Y
Z

pipe cutters

Tools used for cutting pipe lengths. There are a number of different types of cutters:

* Roller cutter – this uses a cutting wheel and a number of rollers which do not form a burr on the outside of the pipe. These are the commonly used cutters for small-diameter copper and stainless-steel tube; larger roller cutters can also cut *low carbon steel* (LCS) tube.

▲ Roller cutters for copper   ▲ Large roller cutter for LCS

* Wheel cutter – this type of cutter has three or more cutting wheels and is particularly useful when cutting pipes in confined spaces as it does not need to be fully rotated around the pipe.
* Link cutter – these are used to cut brittle pipes such as *cast iron* and *clayware*; they consist of a series of links that can be extended or shortened to suit the pipe diameter.
* Chain cutter – this consists of a chain-type device incorporating cutting edges. The chain is slowly tightened around the pipe by leverage and the cutting action causes the pipe to snap cleanly. This type of cutter is used for brittle pipe types such as cast iron and clayware.
* Plastic pipe cutter – a type of cutter with a scissor-blade-type action used for cutting *polybutylene* pipe for hot, cold and central-heating purposes.

▲ Plastic pipe cutter

Care must be taken when using wheel or roller cutters in order to avoid *tracking* along the pipe, which damages the pipe surface.

A
B
C
D
E
F
G
H
I
J
K
L
M
N
O
P
Q
R
S
T
U
V
W
X
Y
Z

pipe-freezing equipment

This equipment is used during activities such as branching into a live *supply pipe* where it is impossible to isolate the main water supply, for example the supply cannot be turned off owing to the building occupancy or as an *isolation valve* is defective. One of the golden rules of pipe freezing is to remember that only cold pipework with no water flow may be frozen. So central-heating pipes must be cool before being frozen otherwise an unpredictable ice plug may be formed that will melt too early. There are several types of refrigerant gas used in the freezing process, including *carbon dioxide* or liquid *nitrogen* in canisters or bottles. Carbon dioxide tends to be the most commonly used for freezing applications:

- Throw-away canisters – these tend to be used by the DIY market or by plumbers who do not carry out the process very often; they are suitable for small-diameter pipes only. A bag is supplied which is attached to the pipe and the refrigerant gas is injected through a narrow tube from the canister to the bag.
- Gas bottles containing carbon dioxide – a bag is again attached to the pipe which is directly connected by a tube to the carbon dioxide bottle. Liquid carbon dioxide is released from the bottle into the bag; on release, the liquid gas turns to a solid known as dry ice which freezes the pipe. Care needs to be taken to avoid contact with the dry ice because it causes extensive freeze burning if contact is made. Carbon dioxide bottles can be used to freeze much larger diameter pipes.

▲ Pipe freezing

pipe interrupter

A type of *backflow prevention device*. There are two types of pipe interrupter:

- Type DB with atmospheric vent and moving element – this provides protection against a *fluid risk category* 4 and is typically used to provide backflow protection with garden irrigation systems and porous hoses.
- Type DC with permanent atmospheric vent – this provides protection against a fluid risk category 5 and is typically used to provide backflow protection with the use of *pressure flushing valves* to *WC pans* and *urinals*.

▶ Type DB pipe interrupter with atmospheric vent and moving element

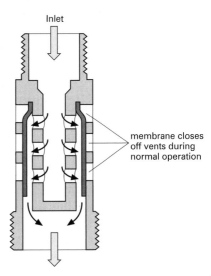

Inlet

membrane closes off vents during normal operation

A
B
C
D
E
F
G
H
I
J
K
L
M
N
O
P
Q
R
S
T
U
V
W
X
Y
Z

pipe sizing
The process of correctly sizing pipework and fittings to provide a desired flow rate and pressure to components and appliances. Pipework in key services such as hot and cold water, central heating, fuel supplies and sanitary pipework systems need to be correctly sized so that the desired performance is achieved from plumbing components.

pipe thermostat
A thermostat used in conjunction with a *frost thermostat* to reduce energy wastage. The pipe thermostat is a simple mechanical/electrical switch that is wired in series between the outlet from the frost thermostat and the connection to the *motorised valve* and usually set to between 40 and 50°C.

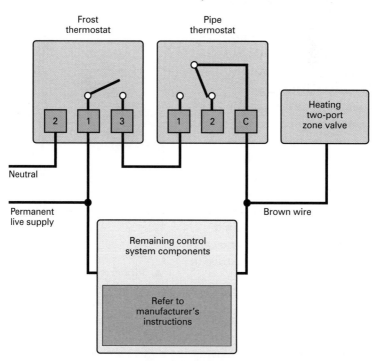

▲ Frost thermostat and pipe thermostat wiring detail

pipe-threading machine
An electric threading machine that forms a thread on *low-carbon steel* (LCS) pipes. A pipe threader may be combined into an all-in-one machine, with a *pipe cutter*, de-burring reamer, and *stock head and dies* that is rested on a stand. Smaller diameter LCS tubes may be threaded using a portable pipe-threading machine.

▲ Portable electric pipe-threading machine

pipe vice

A type of vice used to secure *low-carbon steel* (LCS) tube while cutting or threading it. There are essentially two types of vice used: the jaw-type vice where an upper jaw is lowered on to the lower jaw to grip the pipe, and the chain-type vice where a chain is tightened across the pipe surface to clamp the pipe.

▲ Pipe vice in use

pipeline switch

See *Flow switch*

pipework colour coding

The *British Standards Institution* requirements for the colour coding of pipework are blue for cold water service pipes, yellow for natural gas and white (plastic coating) for central-heating pipework in solid floors.

pipework materials

Pipes are made from either metal or plastic; materials are selected according to the ability to withstand a particular situation or condition. Variations that affect the choice of materials include: pressure, type of fluid, cost, bending and jointing method, *corrosion* resistance, *expansion* and appearance. Metals commonly used for pipes are copper and steel. *Thermoplastics* are used for pipe as they have strong resistance to *acids* and *alkalis*, low *specific heat capacity*, and poor *heat transfer*.

pitched roof

A roof with a steep-angled fall from top to bottom.

pitcher tee – swept tee

See *Swept tee*

plant

Expensive building site equipment and vehicles such as cranes, excavators, earthmoving equipment, forklift trucks and power access equipment.

A
B
C
D
E
F
G
H
I
J
K
L
M
N
O
P
Q
R
S
T
U
V
W
X
Y
Z

plasterboard fixings

Used to fix components to plasterboard stud partitions when there is no solid backing on the plasterboard. Plasterboard fixings include spring toggles, rubber-nut fixings, and collapsible anchor bolts.

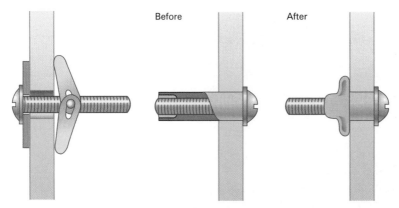

Before   After

▲ Spring toggle and rubber-nut fixing for plasterboard

plastic

Plastics are polymers manufactured as a by-product of the oil industry. Crude oil produces ethene, and molecules of ethene link into long chains to form polythene (poly + ethene, also known as ethylene or polyethylene). Ethene can be modified by the replacement of one of the hydrogen atoms with another atom or molecule, and when these link together a different type of plastic is produced. In the plumbing industry *thermosetting plastics* are used for mouldings, for example WC cisterns, and *thermoplastics* are used for pipework materials.

plastic tubes and fittings

Plastic tubes and fittings are made from two main categories of plastic. The first group is made by the polymerisation of ethers and includes *polythene* (polyethylene) and *polypropylene*. These are used for service supply, hot water and hot-water heating pipework. The second group includes unplasticised polyvinyl chloride (UPVC or PVC-u) and acrylonitrile butadiene styrene (ABS). These are used mainly for waste distribution pipework and cold-water installations.

For fitting types see *Compession joint, electrofusion welding, push-fit fittings* and *solvent welding.*

plastic wall plugs

Plastic plugs for use with screws are available in a range of colour-coded gauges. The chart shows how to select the correct drill, plug and screw.

Screw size (gauge)	Drill size (mm)	Plug colour code
6–8	5	Yellow
8–10	6	Red
10–14	7–8	Brown
14–18	10	Blue

▲ Table showing screw gauges, drill size and plug colour code

plasticity
The properties of a material that allow it to be shaped and to retain its shape.

pliers
A type of *hand tool* used to grip components such as valve spindles. Common types used by the plumber are:
- engineer's pliers – everyday uses such as balancing *lockshield radiator valves*
- gas pliers – developed for working with small nuts on gas appliances
- gland nut pliers – originally designed for tightening *gland nuts*, they are widely used to work on a variety of different nuts.

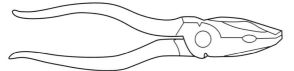

Engineer's combination pliers

Gas pliers

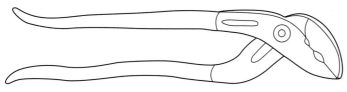

Gland nut pliers (water pump pliers)

▲ Common types of pliers

A B C D E F G H I J K L M N O P Q R S T U V W X Y Z

A
B
C
D
E
F
G
H
I
J
K
L
M
N
O
P
Q
R
S
T
U
V
W
X
Y
Z

plug cock
See *Cock*

plugging chisel
See *Chisels*

plumb line
A line with a heavy weight such as a plumb bob on the end, that is used to establish a vertical line when fixing plumbing components such as *rainwater pipes*. The heavy weight keeps the line taut and perfectly vertical.

plumbo solvent
The ability of water to take lead into solution. The level of plumbo-solvency that takes place is usually dependent on the *pH value* of the water.

pluming
This is the clouds of water vapour that are seen discharging from a *flue terminal*. Pluming occurs when the water vapour in the *products of combustion* is reduced to the *dew point* temperature of air. Pluming occurs when a boiler is started up, that is, when the flue gases are colder. It can also take place throughout the operating period of a *condensing appliance* owing to the lower flue gas temperatures that are produced. Pluming can sometimes be considered to be a nuisance with condensing boilers, and care must be taken to site their flue terminals in a location that may not cause offence to others.

plunger
See *Force cup*

pneumatic test
See *Air test*

point-of-use backflow prevention devices
These are *backflow prevention devices* that are either in-built into an appliance or sited in close proximity to the appliance. In the UK all plumbing components are protected by an individual point-of-use backflow prevention device in order to prevent contamination of supply pipework. See *Zone backflow prevention devices*

polarity testing
An electrical test undertaken to ensure that phased conductors are not crossed, for example the neutral from the mains connected to live and vice versa (reversed polarity). The system can still function in this situation, but when isolated from a switch, the system would be dangerous.

polybutylene
A plastic produced by the polymerisation of ethers, commonly used for above ground hot, cold and central-heating pipework.

polyethylene/polythene
A plastic produced by the polymerisation of ethers, commonly used for below ground water and gas pipework.

polymerisation
The process of plastic formation from *ethene* (ethylene). See *Plastic*

polypropylene
A *thermoplastic* commonly used for producing components such as waste *traps*.

polythene pipe – compression joint
This pipe is used for underground services (colour-coded blue) and for internal use on cold-water services (colour-coded black). Joints in *polythene* (polyethylene) pipe are made using gunmetal, brass or plastic fittings. The pipe is cut and de-burred and the nut and compression ring put in place. A liner is inserted into the pipe to ensure the compression ring makes a watertight seal. Ensure that the pipe is properly inserted into the fitting and tighten with an adjustable grip or spanner.

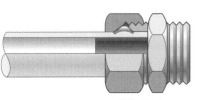
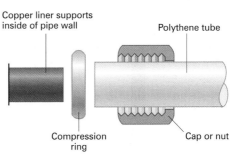

Copper liner supports inside of pipe wall

Polythene tube

Fitting body

Compression ring

Cap or nut

▲ Typical polythene pipe fitting

polyvinyl chloride (PVC)
A type of polyvinyl chloride which has had a plasticiser added to it to remove its brittleness. It is less susceptible to damage from heavy blows and is therefore more flexible than unplasticised PVC. See *Unplasticised polyvinyl chloride*

ponds/pools
All ponds or pools must have an impervious lining or membrane fitted to prevent water leakage. Ponds or pools made of concrete must comply with BS 8007 – Design of Concrete Structures for Retaining Aqueous Liquids. Under the *Water Regulations* a pond or pool (other than a swimming pool) must never be permanently or directly connected to a *supply* or *distribution pipe*.

A
B
C
D
E
F
G
H
I
J
K
L
M
N
O
P
Q
R
S
T
U
V
W
X
Y
Z

pop-up waste

These are wastes that are available for washbasins, baths, bidets and sinks, instead of a traditional plug on a chain. The pop-up plug is raised by twisting or pulling a circular knob projecting through the tap assembly. The height of the plug lift can usually be raised or lowered by an adjusting screw.

porous-hose systems

See *Irrigation systems*

Portsmouth ball valve

A type of *float-operated valve* that was commonly installed in the UK. Its use however is primarily restricted to maintenance work. It has largely been replaced by the use of the *diaphragm ball valve* owing to its bottom entry water outlet which presents an increased risk of *backflow*. If used on a new installation then the valve would have to be fitted with a *backflow prevention device*.

'O' ring
ring plug unit
strainer
Nut and stem
waste body
Shackle
Screw
Control
port seat

▲ Pop-up waste fitting

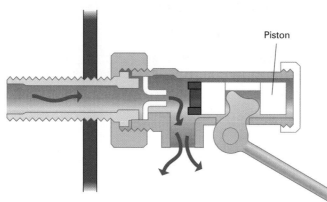

Piston

▲ Portsmouth ball valve

post-aerated flame

A gas flame produced in a non-aerated burner where the air for *combustion* is mixed with the gas on exiting the burner, that is, mixing at the flame.

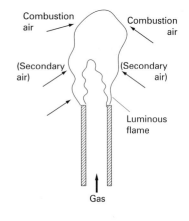

Combustion
air
Combustion
air
(Secondary
air)
(Secondary
air)
Luminous
flame
Gas

▶ Post-aerated flame

potable water
A term that is now largely superseded. See *wholesome water*

potential difference
This is an electrical term for the measure of energy in joules used when one *coulomb* flows between two points in a circuit.

power drills
Used for drilling holes for items such as small fixings through to a hole capable of accommodating a *room-sealed flue* system. The capability of each type of power drill depends on its power rating which is governed by the size of the motor; power ratings range from 620W to 1400W. Power drills may have variable speed, reversible action and/or hammer action.

power saw
A saw power-driven by a motor. They may be used for taking up floorboards or chipboard sheets to install pipework under floors. Key checks are that the cutting depth is exactly the same as the thickness of the floor and the cut avoids nails and screws. Power saws for cutting floor boards usually require a tungsten carbide tipped cutting blade. Most power saws run off 110V; battery-operated circular saws with an 18V motor are also available.

power tools – safety
When using power tools:
* inspect for damage before use – never use damaged power tools
* check that electric tools are double insulated or include an earth cable
* use battery-powered tools instead of mains-operated tools, if possible
* use 110V tools when using the mains or a temporary power supply
* check that cables and plugs are not damaged or worn
* check the PAT test label
* make sure that you have been instructed properly on the correct use of each power tool.

See *PAT test*

pozidrive screwdriver (PZD)
See *Screwdrivers*

pre-aerated flame
A flame supplied with a mixture of gas and air prior to ignition, as in most domestic gas appliances which use an *aerated burner*.

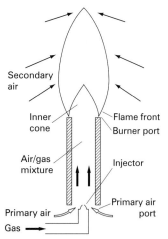

▶ Pre-aerated flame

A
B
C
D
E
F
G
H
I
J
K
L
M
N
O
P
Q
R
S
T
U
V
W
X
Y
Z

pre-cast concrete flue blocks

Specially designed blocks for building into walls of domestic properties during construction. Gas flue blocks must conform to BS 1289, and be fitted exactly to the manufacturer's instructions. All excess cement must be removed and no air gaps left. There must be a thorough visual inspection of the flue system and adequate *spillage* tests made prior to handover. The top flue block is usually connected to a ridge terminal by means of a *twin-wall metal flue pipe*.

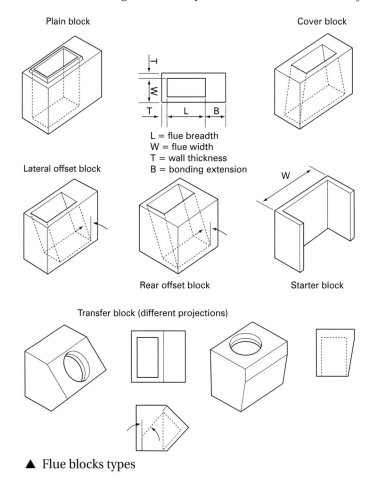

Plain block

Cover block

L = flue breadth
W = flue width
T = wall thickness
B = bonding extension

Lateral offset block

Rear offset block

Starter block

Transfer block (different projections)

▲ Flue blocks types

pre-payment meter

A type of *gas meter* where tokens are purchased and the gas is paid for as it is used. See *Credit meter*

prefabrication

A plumbing component that has been made or assembled away from its installation location. Sheet-lead components are often prefabricated for ease of production then lifted for installation to roof level. Prefabrication of components can make the job easier and less time-consuming.

press-fit fitting

A pipe fitting to copper or steel pipe that uses a butyl rubber seal. The fitting is permanently fixed on to the pipe by the application of a special machine; once fitted into position, the fitting cannot be removed. This type of fitting is commonly used in industrial/commercial hot- and cold-water systems.

pressed steel

Steel sheet that is pressed into its required shape. Baths can be manufactured from pressed steel; they are then coated with *vitreous enamel* to give the desired finish.

pressure

Pressure is a measure of the concentration of force applied over a unit area. Measurements of pressure may be expressed as:

- newtons per square metre (N/m^2), or pascals (Pa)
- bars: one bar = 100,000 N/m^2
- pounds per square inch (lbs/in^2): one lb/in^2 = 6894 N/m^2

Exerting pressure will increase force, for example if you press the end of a water hose the force of the jet of water increases.

pressure-flushing cistern

A special flushing device used in WCs where the pressure of water within the cistern supply pipe compresses air and increases the pressure of water available.

pressure-flushing valve

See *Flushing valve*

pressure gauge

A gauge which shows the pressure level in a system. Pressure gauges must be fitted to *sealed heating systems* to assist with filling and top-up. The pressure gauge should have a scale from 0 to 4 bar and should be installed near the *expansion vessel*.

pressure governor (pressure regulator)

See *Gas governor*

pressure-jet boiler

Pressure-jet oil-fired boilers are available in wall-mounted or floor-standing models and may be traditional, *condensing, combination* (floor-standing only) or condensing-combination types. These boilers are fully controllable, and new installations and replacements are governed by Part L of the *Building Regulations*. See *Pressure-jet burner*

pressure-jet burner

A type of oil-fired appliance where oil is forced at high pressure from an oil pump through a very fine nozzle or atomiser, producing a fine spray of oil which ignites easily when combined with the correct amount of air which is supplied through a fan. The jet of oil is lit by spark electrodes and continues to burn as long as air

A
B
C
D
E
F
G
H
I
J
K
L
M
N
O
P
Q
R
S
T
U
V
W
X
Y
Z

and fuel are provided through the nozzle. The correct size of nozzle must be used and placed at the correct angle, and the distance from the nozzle to the spark electrodes must also be correct. It is also essential that oil is delivered at the right pressure and flow rate. The sequencing of the burner is operated by a control box which contains a number of relay devices. The burner has key fail-safe controls in the form of a *solenoid valve*, which does not open until the pump pressure is established, and a *photoelectric cell*, which detects the presence of a flame.

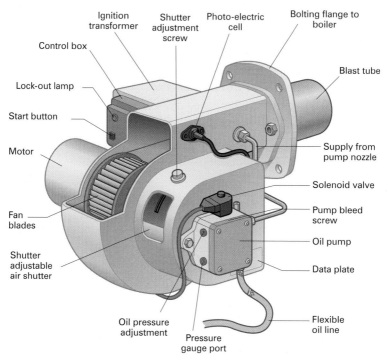

▲ Pressure-jet burner

pressure-limiting valve

A type of *pressure-reducing valve* containing a spring-loaded mechanism that was used with early *unvented hot-water systems* to control the inlet pressure to the cylinder. The valve does not provide as close a tolerance as a standard pressure-reducing valve and therefore is not now that widely used.

pressure loss

The pressure lost in a system either when multiple appliances are used together and the pressure in the system reduces, or when the pressure loss is created by *frictional resistance* as the fluid passes through the pipework, fittings and components.

A
B
C
D
E
F
G
H
I
J
K
L
M
N
O
P
Q
R
S
T
U
V
W
X
Y
Z

pressure-reducing valve

A pressure-control valve (governor) which ensures a fixed maximum water pressure in a system. When there is no water flow the outlet pressure overcomes the spring pressure on the diaphragm, causing it to rise. The linkage joining the diaphragm and seat holds the seat closed so that *downstream* pressure cannot increase. When water is flowing the outlet pressure drops until the spring overcomes the pressure, causing the diaphragm to move the linkage down. The seat opens and water flows through the valve. A pressure-reducing valve may be incorporated as part of a *composite valve*. A pressure-reducing valve can be fitted to water-based systems to restrict the water supply to a fixed pressure. It must be fitted to an *unvented hot-water system* to ensure that a fixed water pressure is provided that will not affect other components in the system, typically set at 3 to 3.5 bar pressure. The pressure-reducing valve in an unvented system must be of the non-adjustable type.

▲ Pressure-reducing valve

pressure regulator

The component fitted to oxyacetylene cylinders to regulate the supply pressure to the *blowpipe*.

pressure-relief valve

A valve used in all *sealed heating systems* to replace the safety features of the *open vent pipe*, which is not used. In domestic systems this valve must be non-adjustable and preset to discharge when the system reaches a maximum pressure of 3 bar. The valve should include a manual test device and have a connection for a full-bore metal discharge pipe that should terminate safely to waste. The valve should be installed inside the boiler or on the flow pipe close to the boiler. An *unvented hot-water system* incorporates an *expansion valve*, which is a type of pressure-relief valve; the pressure setting however is usually much higher.

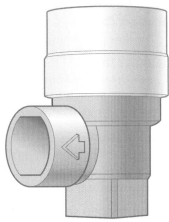

▲ Pressure-relief valve to a sealed heating system

pressure switch

A type of electrical switch used in cold-water systems and fan-assisted gas boilers. The switch senses pressure established in a component or system to activate controls such as a *pump* or a *multi-functional control valve*:
• High- and low-pressure switches can be used in a *boosted cold-water system* to control the operation of the pump set.

A
B
C
D
E
F
G
H
I
J
K
L
M
N
O
P
Q
R
S
T
U
V
W
X
Y
Z

- A pressure switch is used as a safety device in a gas boiler with a fan draught flue system; the switch senses the operation of the fan owing to the change in pressure inside the appliance created by the fan and in turn opens the multi-functional control valve permitting the main burner to light; if the fan fails to operate, the switch prevents the valve from opening.

pressure testing (water systems)

Guidance on testing, flushing and disinfection of water installations is covered by *British Standards Institution* requirements and the *Water Regulations*.

British Standards provide separate test procedures for *copper*, *steel* and *cast-iron* systems that contain no *plastics* and for systems that do contain plastic pipes and fittings. The test pressure applies to all tests and all installations regardless of installation size, whether the installation is new or a replacement, or whether the installation is above or below ground. See *Soundness test – water systems*

primary circuit

An assembly of water fittings in which water circulates between a boiler or other heat source and a water-to-water *heat exchanger* such as an *indirect cylinder*. An example of a primary circuit is the flow and return pipework from the boiler to the cylinder in an *indirect hot-water system*. See *Secondary circuit*

primary circulation

The water that flows around the *primary circuit* either by pumping in a fully-pumped system or by *gravity circulation*.

primary flow

The flow pipe from the boiler to the cylinder in a *primary circuit*.

primary flue

A short length of pipe that leaves an *open-flued* boiler and connects to the *draught diverter*. In new boilers the primary flue is usually incorporated inside the boiler together with the draught diverter.

primary meter

A gas meter connected to the gas service and which measures the amount of gas used. The meter is read periodically by the gas supplier and bills for supply sent to the customer.

primary open safety vent

A primary open safety vent is installed in an *open-vented heating system* and provides a safety outlet if the system overheats owing to component failure; it makes sure that the system is kept safely at or near *atmospheric pressure*. The minimum diameter allowed is 22 mm, and it must not contain a valve. In a fully-pumped system, the *open vent pipe* should rise to a minimum height of 450 mm above the level of the water in the *feed and expansion* (F&E) cistern.

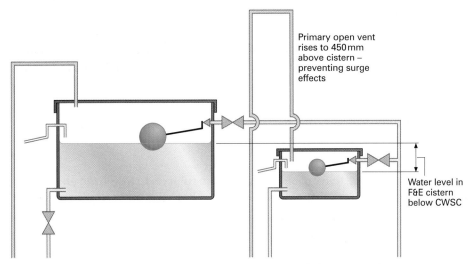

Primary open vent
rises to 450mm
above cistern –
preventing surge
effects

Water level in
F&E cistern
below CWSC

▲ Open safety vent to feed an expansion cistern in a fully-pumped system

primary return
The return pipe from the *cylinder* to the *boiler* in a *primary circuit*.

primary ventilated stack system
See *Types of sanitary pipework system*

printed circuit board (PCB)
A thin board on to which electronic components are soldered. The leads from different components may pass through holes in the board or be surface mounted. The PCB is designed to control multiple functions in a set sequence in appliances such as boilers.

private sewer
See *Sewer*

products of combustion
These are the flue gas products that should be produced on burning fuel in an appliance. If *complete combustion* has taken place then the products should predominantly be water vapour, *carbon dioxide* and *nitrogen*. If *vitiated air* is supplied to the appliance then *incomplete combustion* may occur which may produce the deadly gas *carbon monoxide*.

programmer
A timing device used to control *central-heating systems* with extra switching functions controlling two or more circuits (usually the hot water and heating circuits). The programmer automatically controls the independent operation of each circuit by having separate timing and switching functions.

A
B
C
D
E
F
G
H
I
J
K
L
M
N
O
P
Q
R
S
T
U
V
W
X
Y
Z

prohibited zones – flues

Areas on or adjacent to buildings where *flues* are not allowed to terminate. Regulations aim to prevent the *products of combustion* from entering a building (due to down draught and reversal of flue-pipe operation) and prevent the positioning of the flue pipe in relation to building components and openings.

propane gas

A type of gas used for heating purposes. Plumbers use it extensively for fuelling *blowtorches*. See *Liquefied petroleum gas*

protected shaft

A shaft in a building that enables persons, air or objects to pass from one room or compartment to another that is enclosed within a fire-resistant structure.

protective multiple earthing (PME)/TN-C-S system

The TN-C-S system stands for:

T – terra (earth)

N – exposed metalwork is connected to the main earthing terminal

C – the functions of the neutral and earth conductors are combined in a single common conductor for part of the system (supply)

S – the functions of neutral and earth are performed by separate conductors for part of the system (consumer).

This is the most commonly installed electrical earthing system for new-build dwellings. The main safety rules involve the neutral conductor and are as follows:

- The neutral conductor must be earthed at a number of points.
- The neutral and phase conductors must have the same cross-sectional area and be made of the same material.
- The neutral conductor must not be fitted with any neutral link or device that could break the neutral path.

proving unit

This is a low-voltage, inverted direct-current testing device used in an electrical safe isolation procedure to confirm that an approved voltage indicating device is working correctly.

PTFE tape

Short for *polytetrafluoroethylene*, this is a sealing material used in the making of threaded joints in gas and water based systems. The PTFE tape should be applied sparingly to the pipe and in such a direction on the pipe that the tape will not be removed from the thread as it is screwed into the fitting.

public sewer

See *Sewer*

pump

An electromechanical device that uses pressure to move water from one point to another, such as in a *boosted cold-water system*, or to circulate water around a system, such as a *circulating pump* in a *central-heating system*.

pump-overrun thermostat

A thermostat fitted to a boiler which ensures that the pump keeps running until the boiler has cooled down. In *low water-content boilers*, there may be a problem when the boiler shuts down because of the residual heat in the *heat exchanger* continuing to heat the water to near boiling point. A pump overrun thermostat allows the pump to continue to remove the residual heat from the heat exchanger to the rest of the system in order to cool it down.

purging

The process of ensuring that all air is removed from a gas pipe on the first filling of a gas system prior to its use or after maintenance work has taken place.

push-fit joint

Push-fit joints are made from plastic or metal and can be used on a variety of metallic and plastic plumbing systems, including sanitary pipework systems, hot- and cold-water systems and central-heating systems. The diagram shows a fitting that can be used on hot, cold and central-heating pipework that uses a grab ring to lock the pipe in place, and a neoprene 'O' ring to make the joint watertight.

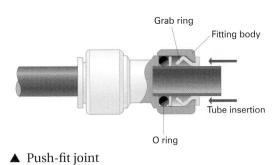

▲ Push-fit joint

putlog

A temporary horizontal beam projecting from a gap in a wall (usually the brick joint) to tie scaffolding in to the building.

putlog scaffold

A putlog scaffold is attached to the brickwork of a building by putlogs or tubes with putlog adaptors. This type of scaffold is commonly used for new-build properties as the putlogs are built into the mortar joints as the building is constructed. See *Independent scaffold*

PVC

Polyvinyl chloride

PVC channel

A PVC channel or conduit is used to protect cable runs from damage when they are installed in cement or plaster.

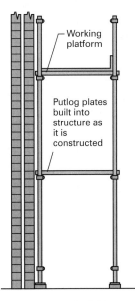

▲ Putlog scaffold

PVC heat-resistant flexible cords

Heat-resisting flexible cords which may be used in ambient temperatures up to 85°C, for example connection to a circulating pump or an immersion heater. PVC heat-resisting flexible cords have plain copper flexible conductors insulated and sheathed (white) with heat-resisting PVC.

PVC-insulated and sheathed cables

Flat-wiring cable is used for domestic and industrial service wiring where there is a low risk of mechanical damage. It is available with two, three or four cores. Multi-strand cable is used for surface wiring with low risk of mechanical damage, for example in meter tails, which connect the *consumer unit* or distribution board to the public electricity supply meter, or as single core for *conduit* and trunking runs where conditions are difficult.

quarter bend
Term for a 90° bend.

quarter-turn tap
A type of tap that is opened and closed by making a quarter turn of the tap head, often by a lever. These taps are commonly used in hospitals and with the elderly or infirm as they are easier to operate. Quarter-turn taps are also now widely used as luxury taps in domestic properties, the tap mechanism often using *ceramic discs*.

quantity surveyor
A member of the construction management team who deals with controlling expenditure (labour and materials) on large construction projects.

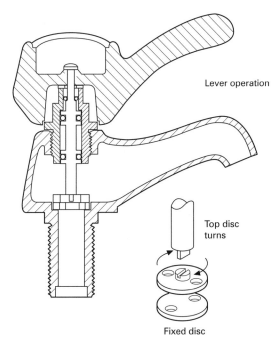

Lever operation

Top disc turns

Fixed disc

▲ Quarter-turn tap with ceramic discs

ABCDEFGHIJKLMNOPQ **R** STUVWXYZ

radiant

A component forming part of a gas appliance and designed to become *incandescent* when heated by a gas.

radiant convector gas fire

A gas fire designed to emit heat by both *radiation* and *convection*. Radiant convector gas fires must conform to BS 5871 Part 1; the *open-flued* model is most common with a minimum flue size of 125 mm across the axis. These fires should be installed in front of a *closure plate* fitted to a *fireplace opening*. Fires with up to 7 kW input will not usually require additional ventilation. The radiating surface may feature *radiants* or an imitation fuel giving a live-fuel effect. Air from the room can circulate around the *firebox* and become heated, giving the bonus of convected heat.

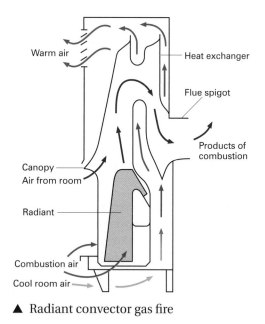

▲ Radiant convector gas fire

radiant gas fire

A gas fire designed to emit heat by radiation. Radiant gas fires must conform to BS 5871 Part 1. These fires usually have a decorative outer casing, an inner *firebox* containing the *radiants* and a firebrick and a canopy leading to the *flue spigot*. Radiants may be surrounded by reflector panels, increasing the heat output to the room and keeping the fire casing cool; they have similar ventilation requirements to *radiant convector gas fires*.

radiant heater

A type of *heat emitter* that tends to be used in industrial/commercial properties. Heating occurs by *radiation* direct to the body rather than by conventional methods where the air in the room is heated up. Radiant heaters can be direct fired (gas or electrically heated) or operated by warm water circulated via a heating system. They can also be in the form of wall panels (similar to radiators), skirting panels or ceiling mounted. Care must be taken when siting the panels to ensure that they will effectively heat the human body.

radiation (thermal)

The transfer of heat from a hot object by infrared waves. The waves travel through the air until contact is made with a cooler object which can absorb the heat. Thermal radiation is the heat you feel from a fire or from the sun. Dull surfaces absorb thermal radiation more efficiently than shiny surfaces.

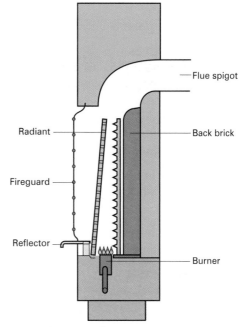

▲ Radiant gas fire

radiator

A type of *heat emitter* installed in a *central-heating system* to heat the rooms. The radiator heats the room by a combination of *radiation* and, mostly, *convection*. Radiators are now mostly of the panel type made from pressed steel; low surface temperature radiators are available to protect vulnerable persons such as the young, elderly or infirm from potential burning.

Traditional column type radiators are still available and are often used in the refurbishment of designer or historic properties.

▲ Panel radiator

▲ Column radiator

A
B
C
D
E
F
G
H
I
J
K
L
M
N
O
P
Q
R
S
T
U
V
W
X
Y
Z

radiator key
> See *Air tap key*

radiator valves
> A type of valve fitted to either end of a radiator. One end has a *lockshield radiator valve* for the purpose of *balancing* the radiator during *commissioning*. The other end has a *wheelhead radiator valve* or a *thermostatic radiator valve*, which are both user controls for the purpose of controlling the water flow into the radiator. The isolation of both valves will permit the radiator to be removed without draining the whole system down for the purpose of decorating.

rafter bracket
> A type of *eaves gutter* bracket used to make screwed fixings to a roof rafter.

rainwater
> Water arising from natural precipitation (rainfall) that has not been contaminated by other sources.

rainwater cycle
> Rainwater falls and flows into streams, rivers, lakes, wells, and into the sea. Water vapour is produced from heated surface water and through the transpiration of plants, and rises into the air to forms clouds. Water precipitates as rain from these clouds and falls back to earth.

rainwater head
> See *Hopper head*

rainwater pipe
> The pipe which connects the outlet of a *gutter system* to the *drainage system*. As the rainwater pipe is run externally to the building the joints are not fully sealed. Care must be taken when using *plastics* materials to ensure that room for *thermal movement* is provided.

rainwater shoe
> A rainwater fixing fitted at the lower end of a *rainwater pipe* to discharge the water away from the building and usually into a *gully*.

range
> A type of appliance that is used for cooking purposes. Some designs can include a *boiler* for the purposes of heating a hot-water *storage cylinder* and a low number of *radiators*.

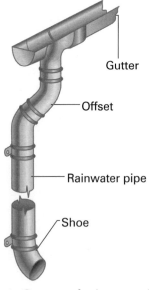

Gutter

Offset

Rainwater pipe

Shoe

▲ Gutter and rainwater pipework

range rated

A gas appliance such as a boiler in which the gas pressure to the burner can be adjusted to suit a range of heat loadings from the appliance, for example a range-rated gas boiler with heat output from 12 kW to 15 kW.

rasp

A type of *file* used for removing excess material such as wood or plastic. A rasp is often used for chamfering the ends of plastic pipe prior to making a joint with a *push-fit joint*.

reaction zone

The part of a flame from a *pre-aerated burner* in which combustion occurs; the gas is not completely burned in the reaction zone. The hottest part of the flame is just to the far end of the zone.

recovery period

The amount of time required to reheat the water in a plumbing component such as a hot-water *storage cylinder*. The recovery period could be described as the time taken to reheat the cylinder from, say, 10°C to 60°C.

recovery position

This position is used for unconscious casualties of accidents. Before moving the casualty into the position, check that there is no injury to the back, as moving the person may cause further damage to the spine. The recovery position ensures that the tongue cannot block the airway and reduces the risk of accidental fluid inhalation. An unconscious casualty may be left unattended in the recovery position if you have to leave to get help.

▲ The recovery position

rectification

See *Flame conduction and rectification*

recycled water

Waste water from baths, basins etc. that is then treated and re-used, for example for watering gardens and flushing toilets. Systems for dealing with recycled water make a significant contribution to water conservation, but great care must be taken to prevent *cross-connection* and *backflow*.

A
B
C
D
E
F
G
H
I
J
K
L
M
N
O
P
Q
R
S
T
U
V
W
X
Y
Z

reduced-pressure zone (RPZ) valve

A *backflow prevention device* that protects against *fluid risk category* 4 applications. RPZ valve installation requires a contractor's certificate and the *water undertaker* must be notified. The valves should be inspected and tested annually to ensure correct operation.

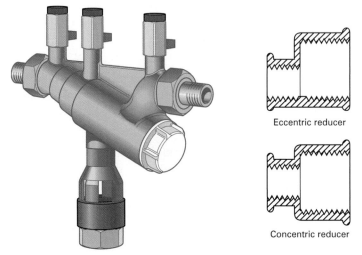

▲ RPZ valve

Eccentric reducer

Concentric reducer

▲ Concentric and eccentric reducer

reducer

A pipe fitting used to joint two pipes of different sizes, for example 15 mm and 22 mm. There are two types of reducer:

- Concentric reducer – the connection of the smaller diameter pipe is centralised across the diameter of the larger pipe.
- Eccentric reducer – this is used to avoid the possible build up of air or foreign matter at the point at which the reduction occurs, such as an eccentric reducer to a *soil stack* component.

reflection test

See *Alignment test*

register plate

A fire-resistant plate sealing the opening at the base of a *chimney* where a *flue pipe* enters. The plate is normally used with *open-flued* gas appliances.

regulator

Another name for a *gas governor* or similar device for regulating (reducing) the gas pressure to a fixed supply pressure.

relative density

The relative density of a substance or object is a comparison of the mass per unit volume of the substance to the mass per unit volume of water. The relative density of water is therefore 1.0. A cubic metre of water has a mass of 1000 kg and a cubic metre of mild steel therefore 7700 kg. Thus mild steel has a relative density of 7.7. Relative density is also known as specific gravity.

relay

An electrical device which can be used in heating circuits to feed multiple circuits. Backfeed to individual circuits is avoided by the relay which usually consists of a switch which is energised, making the contacts of another switch.

relay valve

A type of gas control device that is not now commonly used; it is a type of mechanical gas valve usually operated by a rod-type *thermostat* for the purposes of controlling the gas flow to an appliance.

relief vent

A type of *ventilating pipe* connected to a *discharge stack*, such as the base of the stack, in order to relieve excessive pressure build-up in the stack.

Reporting of Injuries, Diseases and Dangerous Occurrences Regulations (RIDDOR)

Under these regulations, plumbing companies must report certain dangerous situations (including major injuries and fatalities) to the Health and Safety Executive (HSE) for investigation. The HSE will report on the nature and scale of the problem and decide on appropriate action and regulation.

resealing traps (anti-siphon traps)

A type of *trap* designed to retain its seal should negative (suction) pressure be created in the pipeline that would ordinarily remove the trap seal. There are several types of resealing trap design, with the *anti-vacuum valve* type now being the most popular. On a partial vacuum being created at the trap outlet, air is introduced into the waste system via the anti-vacuum valve to equalise the pressure in the system and prevent the trap seal from being lost. A resealing trap is used when the installation cannot conform to key design requirements, such as when the maximum length of acceptable *branch discharge pipe* has been exceeded or its fall is too steep.

▲ Anti-vacuum type resealing trap

A
B
C
D
E
F
G
H
I
J
K
L
M
N
O
P
Q
R
S
T
U
V
W
X
Y
Z

reseating tool

A tool that is used, primarily, to re-cut the seat of a tap. Taps can sometimes suffer erosion or *cavitation* at their seat, causing the washer not to seat properly and water to pass between the washer and the seat, that is, it passes water when turned off. If minimal damage has occurred, the seats of standard *bib taps* and *pillar taps* can often be re-cut with the reseating tool rather than replacing them.

▲ Tap reseating tool

residual current device (RCD)

A unit that can detect very small changes in the electrical current between different electrical conductors in a system. The RCD will disconnect the circuit automatically if even the slightest change occurs. The RCD provides significant protection to high-risk areas such as plug-socket outlets and electric showers. The operating current for a typical RCD is about 30 mA or 0.03 A.

resistance

The amount of opposition to the flow of an electric current in a device or substance.

respiratory protection

Respiratory protective devices include dust masks and respirators. These guard against inhaling dust, mist or fibre particles (e.g. loft insulation particles or dust and soot) and toxic gas (e.g. lead fumes). In extreme circumstance, for example in *sewers*, full breathing apparatus is required.

rest bend

A type of bend which has a foot or a number of rests formed into the bend to give support at the base of a soil stack. It is normally used with cast-iron stacks to give additional surface area (contact with the ground) at the stack base to prevent the downward pressure of the stack from moving the bend and its connecting drainage pipework.

restrictor elbow

A type of gas fitting that includes an *isolation valve* for use in connecting exposed gas lines to gas fires. The gas supply may be taken from a restrictor elbow, which is usually installed at one side of the chimney breast. A small-diameter chrome-plated tube is fitted to the restrictor and to the inlet of the fire.

retention ports

The ports on a *gas burner* which produce small flames to help to prevent *flame lift*.

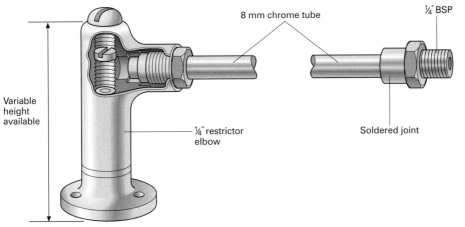

▲ Restrictor elbow and connecting pipe

return bend

A U-shaped bend designed to return the flow of water in the same direction from which it came.

return pipe

A pipe in a *heating* or *primary* hot-water *circuit* in which water is returned to a boiler or circulator for reheating.

reverberation

See *Water hammer*

reverse circulation

A problem that occurs in a *fully-pumped* central-heating system when the primary return connection from the hot-water *storage cylinder* is not the last connection to the common return before the boiler; *radiators* are therefore heated even when the circuit is isolated, such as during summer months. The solution is to re-pipe to ensure the correct configuration or to install a *non-return valve* to the affected pipeline to prevent *reverse circulation*.

reversed return

A method of designing and installing a *two-pipe central-heating system* which includes the installation of additional return pipework to ensure that the pipe lengths (flow and return) to each individual *radiator* are exactly the same, the *frictional resistance* to each is the same, and the system therefore does not require *balancing*.

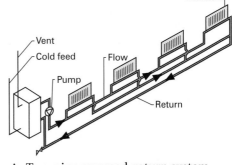

▲ Two-pipe reversed-return system

A
B
C
D
E
F
G
H
I
J
K
L
M
N
O
P
Q
R
S
T
U
V
W
X
Y
Z

RIDDOR

See *Reporting of Injuries Diseases and Dangerous Occurrences Regulations*

ridge

The high point of a pitched roof, usually where the two sides (slopes) of the roof intersect.

ridge piece

See *Saddle piece*

▲ Ridge terminal

ridge terminal

A type of *flue terminal* that terminates at the *ridge* of a roof.

ring main circuit

The sockets used in domestic properties for portable appliances, such as televisions and stereos, are usually 13 amp sockets on a continuous ring circuit. The cables circulate from the consumer unit round each socket and return to the *consumer unit* forming a ring. The cables used are 2.5 mm twin and earthed *PVC* cable and the ring main circuit is protected by a 32 amp *MCB* or a 30 amp *fuse*.

ring spanner

See *Spanner*

rippling

A rippling defect at the throat of a bend created when a *bending machine* has not been correctly adjusted.

riser

The vertical fire-fighting pipe rising through a building; it can be of the *dry-riser* type or the *wet-riser* type.

risk assessment

A checking system designed to increase safety by evaluating the possible hazards of performing a specific work task before the work begins. The assessment involves a careful examination of tasks to assess those that could cause harm to workers, to other people or to equipment and materials. Then safety control measures need to be identified to bring the risk down to the lowest practicable level. Risk assessment legislation is covered by the Management of Health and Safety at Work Regulations.

rodding eye

A capped access point to a *sanitary pipework system* or a *drainage system*.

roll

A type of *expansion joint* used on flat and pitched roof surfaces covered with sheet lead. See *Hollow roll; Solid roll*

rolled sheet lead

See *Lead*

roller

See *Bending machine*

roof ladder

A roof ladder is used by plumbers to access chimneys and to carry out short jobs such as small repairs to *sheet weatherings* and installing *chimney* liners. For work of longer duration a *scaffold* must be used. To position a roof ladder correctly, turn the wheel side to the roof, push the ladder until the top is just above the ridge tiles, then turn it over and lower it so that the hook rests over the ridge tiles. Make sure that the roof ladder supports rest on the roof surface and that the roof *ladder* is long enough for the job. The ladder used to access the roof ladder must be securely fastened at

▲ Roof ladder

the top and placed adjacent to the roof ladder. Always work with a partner to assist with handing you the tools and equipment required for the job.

roof weatherings

The material used to weatherproof the roof of a building to keep it watertight. Sheet lead can be used for roof weatherings. See *Sheet weatherings*

room heater

A *solid-fuel* heater which is designed to burn solid-fuel materials for the purposes of heating a room. A room heater, often called a stove, is an *open-flued* appliance. It may also include a boiler for the purpose of heating water to feed radiators in a central-heating system. The rate of burning in the *firebox* in the heater is controlled by the opening/closing of an air flap, which is regulated by the temperature readings from a *thermostat* which measures the air temperature in the room (if heating the room only) or the water temperature in the boiler (if feeding a central-heating system).

▲ Solid-fuel room heater

A
B
C
D
E
F
G
H
I
J
K
L
M
N
O
P
Q
R
S
T
U
V
W
X
Y
Z

A
B
C
D
E
F
G
H
I
J
K
L
M
N
O
P
Q
R
S
T
U
V
W
X
Y
Z

room-sealed flue (balanced flue)

This is a gas- or oil-fired appliance that draws its combustion air from a point adjacent to the point at which *products of combustion* are discharged to outside air. The inlet and outlet are sited so that wind effects are largely balanced. A room-sealed appliance is safer than an *open-flued* appliance as there is no risk of any *down draught* from a *chimney* causing products of combustion to spill into the room. The illustration shows an example of a room-sealed wall heater.

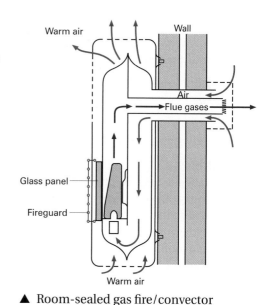

▲ Room-sealed gas fire/convector

room thermostat

A device which measures the air temperature within an area or zone, and controls the heating circuit. The thermostat is a switch with a live connection which may activate a *circulating pump* or *boiler*, or operate a *motorised valve*.

rotary vaporising burner

A type of oil-fired *vaporising burner* in which a rotating distributing tube is driven by a motor at speed inside a circular-shaped boiler. A circular wall of flame occurs around the boiler surfaces when the oil/air mixture is ignited, caused by the circular motion of the distributing tube. This type of vaporising burner is not now commonly available.

run-off

The water that is discharged or run off from a surface such as a roof.

rungs

The horizontal steps of a ladder.

running traps

These *traps* are installed where there is a series of untrapped wash basins, for example in public toilets. In some cases a running trap may be used on a domestic installation where a *P* or *S trap* cannot be fitted; they should not be sited too far away from the appliance waste outlet as smells can be produced. They may also be used with a washing machine or dishwasher waste outlet.

▲ Running trap

ABCDEFGHIJKLMNOPQR **S** TUVWXYZ

S trap

A *trap* used where the waste discharge pipe has to run vertically from the trap through a floor or into a horizontal waste pipe from another appliance. They are often used with wash basins as they can be hidden within the pedestal. *Trap seal loss* by *self-siphonage* can be a real problem with this type of trap owing to the steep vertical drop in the pipework. If an S trap is used then it should normally be of the *resealing trap* type in order to eliminate the possibility of trap seal loss.

▲ S trap

sacrificial anode

A piece of more easily corroded metal fixed to a metal water-containing vessel to prevent *corrosion* of the vessel. *Cylinders* can include a sacrificial anode inside, made from magnesium to guard against pitting corrosion and to protect the lifespan of the cylinder. See *Cathodic protection; Electrolytic action (corrosion)*

saddle piece

A sheet-lead weathering component used where the two sides of a pitched roof meet adjacent to an abutment such as a chimney or a wall.

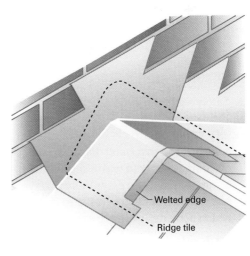

Welted edge

Ridge tile

▲ Saddle piece

safety cut-off devices (gas)

See *Atmospheric sensing device (ASD)*; *Flame conduction and rectification devices*; *Oxygen-depletion device (ODD)*; *Thermoelectric devices*; *Vapour-pressure flame failure devices*

safety helmets

See *Head protection*

safety signs

Some safety signs give workers and visitors helpful information, such as the locations of first aid-kits and fire extinguishers. Other signs warn about possible dangers in the area. The four types of safety sign are:

- prohibition signs – warning that a certain activity is banned
- mandatory signs – showing that certain precautions are absolutely essential
- warning signs – showing hazards and danger
- general safety information signs.

	Prohibition signs	Mandatory signs	Warning signs	Information or safe condition signs
Shape:	Circular	Circular	Triangular	Square or rectangular
Colour:	Red borders and cross bar. Black symbols on white background	White symbol on blue background	Yellow background with black border and symbol	White symbols on green background
Meaning:	Shows what must NOT be done	Shows what must be done	Warns of hazard or danger	Indicates or gives information on safety provision
Example:	No smoking	Wear eye protection	Danger electric shock risk	First-aid equipment

▲ Safety signs

safety valve

A valve fitted to a water-based system such as cold, hot or central heating, which discharges water to waste should the pressure or the temperature increase in a system. There are essentially two types of safety valve: the *temperature-relief valve*, which activates owing to excess temperature, and the *pressure-relief valve*, which activates owing to excess pressure in the system.

sand-loaded heat bending

An outdated method used for bending pipes.

sanitary accommodation

A room or cubicle that contains *water closets* or *urinals*.

sanitary appliances

See *Domestic sanitary appliances*; *Non-domestic sanitary appliances*

sanitary equipment – access for people with disabilities

The requirements for *sanitary accommodation* for people with disabilities is covered in Approved Document M of the Building Regulations, which can be downloaded at www.communities.gov.uk. Details regarding the size of the accommodation and the layout and positioning of the WC are given for wheelchair and non-wheelchair access. The details also include the types of fittings and grab-bars to be installed.

sanitary equipment – spacing

Spacing of sanitary equipment must be suitable for the user. Body size is a key element in establishing appropriate spacing arrangements for sanitary equipment.

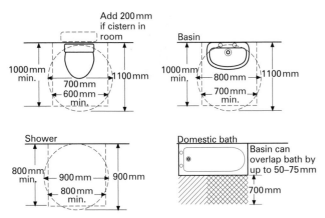

▲ Recommended spacing requirements of sanitary equipment for average-sized people

sanitary equipment – ventilation

The ventilation requirements for sanitary accommodation are covered by Part F of the *Building Regulations*. This is usually the responsibility of the builder or contractor, but you should understand what level of ventilation meets the Building Regulations requirements, for example *mechanical ventilation* (an extractor fan) will be required in most rooms containing a *water closet* under the Regulations.

sanitary pipework

An arrangement of *discharge pipework*, with/without *ventilating pipes*, that is connected to a *drainage system*. See *Types of sanitary pipework system*

A
B
C
D
E
F
G
H
I
J
K
L
M
N
O
P
Q
R
S
T
U
V
W
X
Y
Z

sanitary ware

The *sanitary appliances* used in buildings which fall into the category of either *soil appliances* or *waste appliances*. Sanitary ware is manufactured from materials that are non-absorbent, easily cleaned and will not corrode, such as *vitreous china*, *vitreous-enamelled* pressed steel, *stainless steel* or *plastics*.

SAP rating

See *Standard assessment procedure*

scaffolds

See *Independent scaffold*; *Mobile scaffold tower*; *Putlog scaffold*

scale

Temporary hard water contains calcium and magnesium carbonate; these compounds can precipitate out of the water, especially in appliances that boil the water, such as kettles. The carbonates form a layer called scale, or lime scale, on the surface of the fitting or appliance. Hard scale can accumulate inside boilers and circulating pipes, restricting the flow of water, reducing efficiency, causing damage and resulting in system failure.

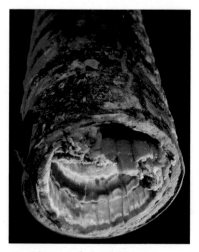

▲ Lime scale build-up in pipework

scale reducer

See *Water conditioner*

screwdown stop valve

The most common type of *stop valve* used in domestic properties, this is manufactured to BS 5433 and approved for above or below ground use up to 50 mm diameter.

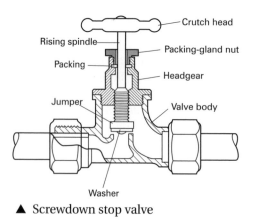

▲ Screwdown stop valve

screwdrivers

A plumber may use several different types of screwdriver dependent on the screw type, screw size and space available, including stubby, *pozidrive (PZD)*, supa drive (SDV), Philips and slotted or normal screwdrivers. Check the handle before use; do not use a screwdriver with a defective handle.

▲ A selection of screwdrivers

screwdriver-operated spherical plug valve

A type of *service valve* approved for use on above ground components in hot- and cold-water systems, the valve is operated by a screwdriver rather than a lever, which is provided on some valve types. See *Lever-operated spherical plug valve*

screws

Plumbers use a variety of screws, categorised by length and gauge. You may need to make decisions about the length and gauge of screw required for a particular task. For general work, steel countersink screws are appropriate, such as for fixing clips and radiator brackets. For situations where a screw may be exposed to moisture, *brass* or *alloy* screws should be used. Self-tapping screws are the best type for fixing into metal sheet. There are also special screws for chipboard fastenings. Where the outward appearance is important, mirror screws are the best type to use.

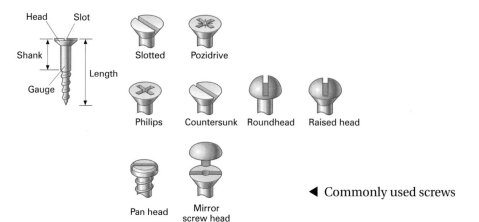

◀ Commonly used screws

SE duct

A duct which rises through a building, with an opening at the base for drawing in air for combustion and which removes the *products of combustion* from specially adapted *room-sealed flued* appliances by *convection* via a roof-level termination. The SE duct system is used in multi-storey high-rise buildings.

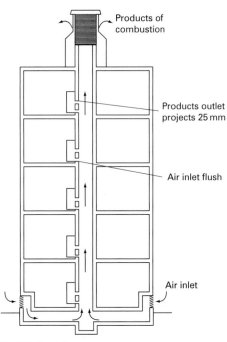

▲ SE duct flue system

sealed heating system

A wet *central-heating system* which is not open to atmosphere but which incorporates an *expansion vessel, pressure-relief valve, pressure gauge* and a method of filling, typically a *filling loop*. The system is normally charged to above *atmospheric pressure*, in domestic properties usually between 1–1.5 bar pressure. This type of system is now very popular and is commonly used with *combination boilers*.

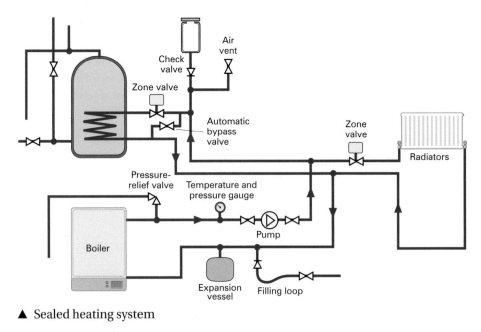

▲ Sealed heating system

seating

The part of a valve, such as a *screwdown stop valve* or a *float-operated valve*, through which the water discharges and against which the washer seats to form a watertight seal. In float valves the size of seat can be varied based on the supply pressure to the property.

second fix

The second stage of plumbing installation work which takes place when the building is watertight. The second fix includes the installation of fixtures and appliances such as bathroom fittings and radiators. See *First fix*

secondary air

Air supplied to a *pre-aerated flame* after the fuel has been ignited.

secondary circuit

The pipework circuit in an *indirect hot-water system* that supplies water from the *hot-water storage vessel* to the hot water outlets (taps). The secondary circuit in the indirect hot-water system is kept totally separate from the *primary circuit* (from which it is heated) by means of a *heat exchanger* sited in the hot-water vessel.

secondary circulation

An installation method for hot-water pipework where a return hot-water pipe is fitted near the top of the *cylinder*. Secondary circulation is used to overcome the problem of '*dead legs*', that is, long lengths of hot-water pipe which are wasteful of energy and water drawn off. A flow-and-return loop feeds all the appliances, and the water is kept circulating by *gravity* or more likely using a *circulating pump*. As an energy conservation measure, the operation of the pump is usually controlled by a timing device so that circulation in the system ceases at night time or when the building is unoccupied. The return pipe is connected in the top third of the cylinder, preventing the lower, cooler water from mixing with the hot water. A *non-return valve* is fitted in the pipeline to prevent reverse circulation in the pipework when water is drawn off. A *WRAS*-approved *bronze* circulating pump must be used as the hot water is aerated and will corrode *ferrous* components.

◀ Secondary circulation

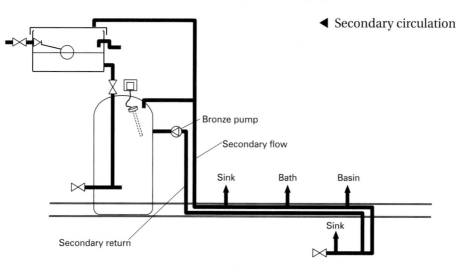

Bronze pump

Secondary flow

Sink   Bath   Basin

Sink

Secondary return

A
B
C
D
E
F
G
H
I
J
K
L
M
N
O
P
Q
R
S
T
U
V
W
X
Y
Z

secondary flue

The section of an open flue system running from the *draught diverter* up to the *terminal*. See *Open flue*

secondary ventilated stack system

See *Types of sanitary pipework system*

secret gutter

A type of concealed gutter that is built into either a flashing to an abutment or into a *valley gutter* system. A secret gutter is commonly used to minimise the amount of sheet lead on view.

sectional boiler

A type of boiler that is commonly used in industrial/commercial properties. The boiler *heat exchanger* is provided in a number of sections that are bolted together on site. A sectional boiler is used where access to the boiler location may make it difficult to lift the boiler into position or access through doorways may be difficult.

sectional tank

A cold-water *storage cistern* or tank that is provided in sections that are assembled on site. Sectional tanks are used where very large quantities of water are required. Modern tanks tend to be manufactured from reinforced glass-fibre components that are bolted together. Internal bracing of the sections is normally required to prevent collapse of the tank once filled with water.

Sector Skills Council

SummitSkills is the Sector Skills Council for plumbing, heating, ventilating, air conditioning, refrigeration and electrical installation. The organisation is responsible for links with government and for the training and development needs of the different trades that form the building services industry. See *SummitSkills*

SEDBUK rating (Seasonal Efficiency of Domestic Boilers in the UK)

An efficiency rating of different types of domestic *boiler*. The rating is given as a percentage, and percentage ranges are assigned a letter, as shown in the table. For example, a boiler classified in band C has a SEDBUK rating of 82–86 per cent. SEDBUK ratings for most boilers may be found at: www.boilers.org.uk

Continuous (or single step) flashing

65

15 max

Welt

75

Gutter depth: 25 min

▲ Abutment flashing with secret gutter

The SEDBUK band rating ranges are as follows:

A 90% and above
B 86–90%
C 82–86%
D 78–82%
E 74–78%
F 70–74%
G below 70%

Under Part L of the *Building Regulations*, boilers in domestic properties must now meet a minimum specified SEDBUK rating in order to be installed in new properties and be used as replacements in existing properties. In domestic properties, oil and gas boilers from bands A to B are now required to be installed which must be of the *condensing* type.

self-cleansing gradient

This is the gradient to which a horizontal discharge pipe or drain run is laid. It is the optimum gradient to which the pipe is laid in order that the solid material waste is transported with the flowing water and not left behind to form a blockage. Too shallow a gradient and the water flow will not be capable of carrying the solid waste along with it or too steep a gradient and the water will leave the solid waste behind.

self-closing tap

See *Non-concussive tap*

self-sealing valve

The self-sealing (HepvO) valve is manufactured by Hepworth Building Products and may be used as an alternative to a *trap*. The HepvO valve uses a tough, collapsible membrane to make a seal in the waste pipework system. The membrane is open when water is discharged down the valve and returns to an airtight seal when the water has discharged. *Back pressure* forces the membrane

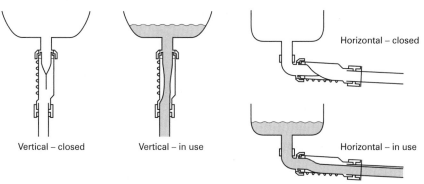

Vertical – closed   Vertical – in use   Horizontal – closed   Horizontal – in use

▲ The HepvO valve in its closed state and its operating state. It can be sited either horizontally or vertically.

A
B
C
D
E
F
G
H
I
J
K
L
M
N
O
P
Q
R
S
T
U
V
W
X
Y
Z

to close ensuring that no water or noxious smells discharge back into the appliance; the problems associated with *trap seal loss* are therefore avoided. HepvO valves are useful for very long pipe runs, steep pipe falls or trap seal depth issues and systems where combined waste pipes are required. The pipework system from the self-sealing valve must, however, be laid to a minimum fall in order to ensure a *self-cleansing gradient* is achieved and blockage does not occur.

self-siphonage
See *Trap seal loss*

semi-counter top basin
See *Wash basin*

sensible heat
Heat energy that causes a rise or fall in the temperature of a gas, liquid or solid when heat is added or removed from that material. Sensible heat changes the *temperature* by changing the speed at which the *molecules* move. See *Change of state; Latent heat*

sensor
A device that is designed to sense variations such as temperature or lighting levels. An *infrared sensor* may be used to control the operation of sanitary appliance taps and valves in public conveniences to ensure that water is not wasted.

separate drainage system
See *Types of drainage system*

septic tank
A method of *sewage* disposal that is used in rural areas where the property is not connected to the main drainage system. The septic tank consists of two chambers. *Sludge* settles in the first chamber and is mostly broken down by anaerobic bacteria; the chamber must however be periodically pumped out. Untreated water is discharged from the second chamber via land drains into the surrounding soil. This untreated water must not be discharged to rivers or streams as it is *contaminated*. Septic tanks may be manufactured in sectional concrete pieces or, more likely for new properties, from reinforced glass fibre.

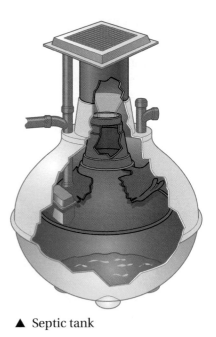

▲ Septic tank

service

A thorough check of a system conducted at regular intervals to ensure optimum functioning and serviceability of components.

service pipe (gas)

The pipe that connects a service from the central distribution main or gas storage vessel to the consumer's property. The service pipe terminates at the *emergency control valve* in most circumstances.

service pipe (water)

The pipe that connects from the water supplier's main to the property. The pipe is in two sections: the *communication pipe*, which is the responsibility of the water supplier, and the *supply pipe*, which is the property owner's responsibility. See *Cold-water supply*

service valve

A valve used for shutting off the water supply so that maintenance or service work can be done. Service valves should be positioned in a readily accessible location and must, as a minimum, be included on every *float-operated valve* and on the outlets from *storage cisterns* such as cold feed pipes and distributing pipes (with the exception of a cold feed pipe to a *primary circuit*).

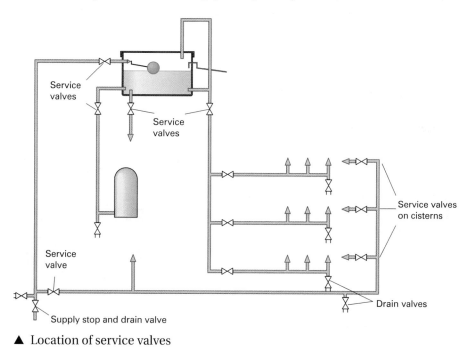

▲ Location of service valves

setting-in stick

See *Leadworking tools*

sewage

A combination of liquid wastes which may include chemicals, house wastes, laundry wastes, human excreta, animal or vegetable matter in suspension or solution, and other solids in suspension or solution, which is discharged from a dwelling, building or other establishment, usually for treatment at a treatment works.

sewer

The main drain which collects *sewage* from drainage pipes to individual properties. Sewers may be either a private sewer, which is a section of pipework that collects sewage from two or more properties but which runs across private land, in which case the private sewer is the shared responsibility of the property owners, or a public sewer, where the main drainage system serves two or more properties that runs on public land, for example under roads, in which case the public sewer is the responsibility of the local authority.

shallow seal trap

A *trap* with a *trap seal depth* of 38 mm. This type of trap must only be used if the waste discharge pipe discharges to a *trapped gulley*. A shallow seal trap cannot be used with a sanitary appliance connected to a *discharge stack*. See *Deep seal trap*

shared flue

It is possible to design a *flue system* in a multi-storey property which can accept the flue products from several appliances. The *SE duct* and *U duct* systems are examples of a shared flue system.

shave hook

A tool used for cleaning the edges of lead sheet and lead filler strips prior to *lead welding*.

sheet weatherings

The sheet lead components used to cover building details, such as roofs and the edges of abutments, in order to make the building watertight.

shock arrestor

A device such as a mini-*expansion vessel* which is installed in a pipeline in order to minimise the effects of *water hammer*. An example of the use of a shock arrestor is its installation near to a *quarter-turn* type *ceramic disc tap*; because the tap can be rapidly turned off there is a tendency for water hammer or a banging noise to occur

▲ Mini-expansion vessel used as a shock arrestor

when the tap is turned off quickly. The shock arrestor absorbs the *back pressure* surge created in the pipeline when the tap is tuned off and minimises the banging effect.

short radius bend

A type of bend which has a very short or tight radius, which creates a greater *frictional resistance* to the passage of *fluids*. Short radius bends are not advisable on sanitary and drainage pipework systems as they can lead to blockage.

shower booster pump

Water is pumped from storage to supply domestic showers using either a single- or a double-impellor *pump*. The single impellor version is installed between the mixer outlet and the *shower head*; the double-impellor pumps both hot and cold water and is installed before the mixer. The double-impellor provides a greater performance at the shower mixer. A pumped shower supply must have the right size of pump and *storage cistern*. The pump location should produce the minimum noise levels, which may be further reduced using *anti-vibration mounting*. The pipework connections should be flexible, pump- inlet connections must have *strainers* to prevent damage to the pump, and the shower mixer should be thermostatic. The operation of the pump can be controlled by either a *flow switch*, in which case there must be a minimum of 150 mm *head* between the water level in the cistern and the top of the shower rose to make the switch operate correctly, or a *pressure switch*, in which case the shower rose can be above the height of the water level in the cistern. Make sure that all relevant regulations and manufacturer's recommendations are followed for wiring and earthing the shower system. See *Shower mixer valve*

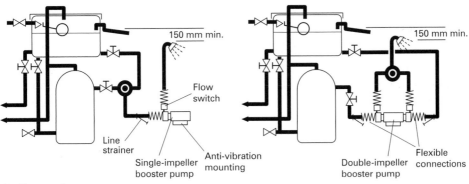

▲ Shower booster pumps

shower – gravity fed

Low-pressure gravity-fed showers operate by the head of water created between the water level in the *cistern* and the *shower head (rose)*. Manufacturers usually require a minimum distance of 1 m between the base of the cistern and the shower rose for there to be sufficient head for the shower to work correctly. The

A
B
C
D
E
F
G
H
I
J
K
L
M
N
O
P
Q
R
S
T
U
V
W
X
Y
Z

shower should be fed from independent dedicated distributing pipes in order that the supplies to the shower are not affected when other outlets in the system are opened. If dedicated distributing pipes are used then a manual shower mixer can be used. See *Shower mixer valve*

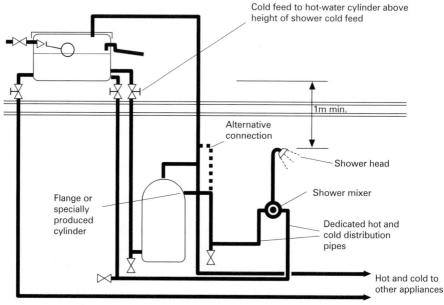

Cold feed to hot-water cylinder above height of shower cold feed

1m min.

Alternative connection

Shower head

Shower mixer

Flange or specially produced cylinder

Dedicated hot and cold distribution pipes

Hot and cold to other appliances

▲ Gravity-fed shower

shower head (rose)

The part of a shower where water is issued in the form of a spray.

shower mixer valve

There are essentially two types of shower mixer valve:

- Manual mixer – the user adjusts the rate of water flow (either hot or cold) to give the desired water pressure and temperature. This type of shower should only be used on low-pressure gravity-fed systems with independent dedicated distributing pipes where there is little chance of a reduction of the hot- and cold-water supply flow rates or pressures during operation.
- Thermostatic mixer – these can be used on low pressure and higher pressure systems (a different valve may be required for a low- or high-pressure system). High-pressure mixers can accept *unbalanced pressures* from hot and cold pipework within manufacturer tolerances. The advantage of a thermostatic mixer is that, if a reduction in the cold-water flow rate and pressure occurs, the shower maintains the mixed water supply at a constant temperature and scalding therefore cannot occur.

All high-pressure and low-pressure systems that are not fed with independent dedicated distributing pipes should be fitted with a thermostatic mixer, including showers fed off *combination boilers* and those fed from shower pumps.

Showers mixers connected to the *supply pipe* may require *double-check valves* built into the shower mixer or in the connecting hot and cold pipework to protect against the *backflow* risk associated with dropping the shower head in contaminated water in either a bath or shower tray.

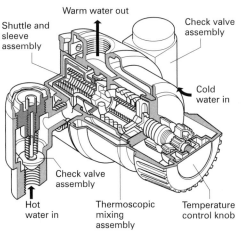

Warm water out

Shuttle and sleeve assembly

Check valve assembly

Cold water in

Check valve assembly

Hot water in

Thermoscopic mixing assembly

Temperature control knob

▲ Thermostatic shower mixer valve

shower tray

There are a variety of shapes of shower tray on the market, with trays usually manufactured from a range of materials such as *plastic*, resin-bonded plastic and *fireclay*. The tray is the base of what should form a watertight cubicle. The wall surfaces in the cubicle should therefore be waterproofed, usually by tiling. The front opening to the cubicle may include a shower door which rests on the tray or a shower curtain. The edges between the shower tray, tiling and any door frame must be fully sealed using *silicone sealant* to prevent leakage. The *trap* to the shower tray, when fitted, should be accessible for maintenance and repair.

SI (Système Internationale) units

The standard international measurement system using metric measurements. Most measurements in the plumbing trade are made in metric units, but older components may be measured in feet and inches (distance) or pounds and ounces (weight); these units are known as imperial measurements.

side flashings

Weathering for areas of a roof where brickwork adjoins the tiles or slate.

sight gauge

A clear gauge fitted to the side of plumbing appliances, such as oil tanks, in order to be able to determine the level of fluid in the component. The gauge provides a clear indication when the component needs refilling.

A
B
C
D
E
F
G
H
I
J
K
L
M
N
O
P
Q
R
S
T
U
V
W
X
Y
Z

A
B
C
D
E
F
G
H
I
J
K
L
M
N
O
P
Q
R
S
T
U
V
W
X
Y
Z

silencer tube

A short tube connected to a *float-operated valve* which discharges water from the valve below the surface of the water level in the *cistern* in order to avoid noise and splashing. A silencer tube is not now permitted to be installed unless it is of the collapsible bag type, because it presents a risk of *backflow*.

silicone lubricant

A type of lubricant supplied in tubs or aerosol cans that is used to lubricate the rubber rings in plastic push-fit sanitary and drainage fittings in order to ease the jointing process.

silicone sealant

A sealant material supplied in applicator tubes, used in plumbing for making watertight joints between sanitary appliances and finished wall surfaces, for example the bath edge to a tiled wall surface.

silver soldered joint

A type of *hard soldered* joint which does not need the application of a *flux*. There are two types of solder used: silflos and sibralloy. The silflos solder creates a stronger joint owing to its higher silver content. As part of the jointing process pipes and fittings should be cleaned prior to applying heat with an *oxyacetylene flame*. The melting point of the solder is dependent on the solder being used but ranges from about 650°C to 750°C. The solder penetrates the close-fitting surfaces of the pipe and fitting by *capillary action*.

single-check valve

See *Check valve*

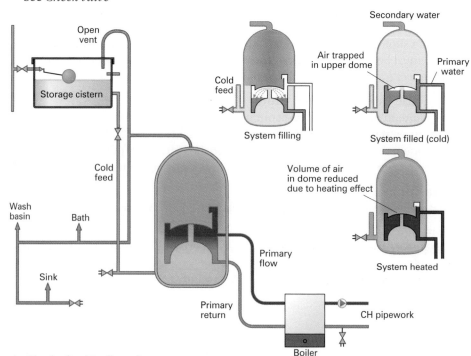

▲ Single-feed indirect hot-water storage system

single-feed indirect cylinder

An *indirect hot-water system* with a single-feed self-venting cylinder in which there is no need for a separate feed and expansion cistern. The *primary* and *secondary circuits* are separated by an air bubble. The system must be very carefully installed, to ensure that the trapped air is retained during normal operation. The single-feed cylinder has special holes at the top of the vertical pipe under the upper dome for water to enter the primary circuit. The system releases air through an air-vent pipe as the primary circuit fills. When the primary circuit is full, filling of the secondary circuit proceeds, and when this is full two air seals are formed maintaining a seal. Owing to the ease in which the trapped air may be lost, the single-feed indirect cylinder is not now widely used. See *Double-feed indirect cylinder*

single-point instantaneous water heater

See *Instantaneous water heater*

sinks

See *Belfast sink; Kitchen sink; London sink*

sinks – air gap requirements

Sinks are considered a *backflow fluid risk category* 5. The minimum protection required is a type AUK 3 air gap/tap gap. See *Tap gap*

siphon

A tube through which a liquid is lifted over a high-level vessel by the pressure of the atmosphere and is then emptied at a lower level. For the siphon to work it must have a short leg and a longer pipe leg. To start the siphon, air must first be eliminated from the short leg, which can be achieved by pressure created from the lungs. The elevation over which a siphon will lift a liquid is limited by the *atmospheric pressure*. The siphon must discharge at a level lower than that of the liquid at the intake, that is, a longer leg will be required. Once water has been dragged over the crown of the siphon the pressure created by the water dropping down the long leg will continue to draw water from the upper vessel until such time as the air breaks the siphonic action at the entry to the short leg.

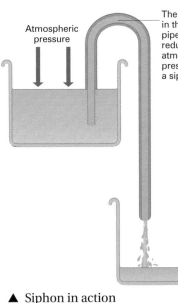

Atmospheric pressure

The air pressure in the crown of pipe has to be reduced to below atmospheric pressure to create a siphon effect

▲ Siphon in action

A
B
C
D
E
F
G
H
I
J
K
L
M
N
O
P
Q
R
S
T
U
V
W
X
Y
Z

siphon – WC

A type of manual flushing device fitted to a *flushing cistern* that works on the principle of a *siphon*.

siphonic WC pan

A WC pan that uses the principle of a *siphon* to flush the contents of the pan. Siphonic pans do not tend to be that popular although they have been extensively installed in the past. There are two types of siphonic pan:

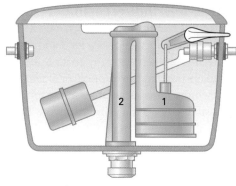

▲ WC siphon

- Single trap – siphonic action is created by a reduction in the outlet of the pan which causes the pan to momentarily fill to a higher level, then the contents are cleared by siphonic action between the higher pan and lower outlet levels.
- Double trap – the pan has a double trap and a pressure-reducing fitting is installed between the cistern and the pan. As water discharges down through the pressure-reducing fitting, air is sucked from between the traps, creating a partial vacuum which draws the water from the upper trap and commences siphonic action to clear the contents out through the second trap. Once the flush ceases, air is reintroduced and the remaining water reseals the traps in the pan.

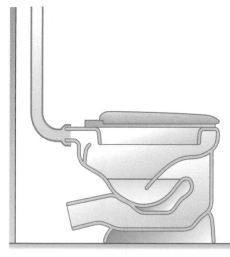

▲ Single trap siphonic WC pan

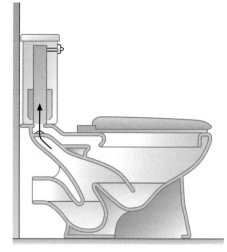

▲ Double trap siphonic WC pan

skeleton flashing

Another name for a *continuous step flashing*. See *Lead flashing*

skirting heater

A natural *convector heater* installed at the skirting of a wall. Heat is conducted from water circulating in a heating pipe in the heater, which has fins attached to it providing a large surface area for heat output. Cool air passes over the fins and

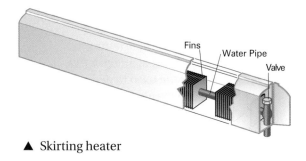

▲ Skirting heater

as the air is heated it rises through the louvres at the top of the heater and into the room.

slab urinal

See *Urinal*

sleeves

Pipes passing through solid walls must be protected by a pipe sleeve to prevent damage to the pipework from movement in the wall or the corrosive effects of wall construction materials. The pipe sleeve should be constructed using material that will not cause *corrosion* to the pipe; *plastic* is commonly used. For water pipes the space between the sleeve and the pipe should be sealed with a non-setting compound at either end of the sleeve. For gas pipes the space between the pipe and the sleeve should be sealed on the inside wall with a fire-resistant non-setting material. The pipe sleeve should be continuous, with no splits, and should span the width of the wall, and vent to external air. The outside edge at each end of the sleeve should be sealed with mortar.

slip coupling

A type of coupling which has no middle divider. The coupling is used to connect two pipes where there is no lengthways movement available with either pipe. The coupling is slipped on to one pipe end, the pipes are then married together, and the coupling is then partially drawn back from the first to slip over the second. The joint can then be made.

slotted waste fittings

A waste fitting that contains a number of slots in order to receive discharge from an overflow. A slotted waste is therefore a type of waste fitting that is used with sanitary appliances which have an integral overflow such as a *wash basin*.

slow ignition device

See *Loose ball slow ignition device*

sludge

The solid matter which settles in the bottom of plumbing and heating components such as *cisterns* and *cylinders*.

A
B
C
D
E
F
G
H
I
J
K
L
M
N
O
P
Q
R
S
T
U
V
W
X
Y
Z

smallbore central-heating system

A heating system including circulation pipework normally within the size range of 15 mm to 35 mm outside diameter.

smoke pellets

These are used for *flue-flow testing* to confirm the soundness of an *open flue*. The smoke pellets are used to determine whether there is any leakage from the flue and that it correctly discharges to atmosphere at the correct *terminal*. The pellets also indicate whether the *chimney* is generating sufficient flue pull in order to remove the flue gases. See *Flue-flow testing*

smoke pump

A device used in the *commissioning* of oil-fired appliances. It is used to determine the concentration of smoke arising from the *combustion* process, a key indicator of the correct fuel to air mix. See *Oil appliance commissioning procedures*

▲ Smoke pump

smoke test

A type of *soundness test* for sanitary and drainage pipework systems. The pipe ends are sealed with stoppers and smoke is introduced to the system via a smoke machine (not the same as a *smoke pump*). The system is filled with smoke and partially pressurised during the process. A leak in the system will be shown by a fall in the dome on the machine. Smoke testing must not be carried out on *plastic* pipework systems as it can degrade the plastic. It has largely been superseded by *air testing* for *sanitary* and *drainage pipework systems*.

SNIPEF

This is the Scottish and Northern Ireland Plumbing Employers Federation. It represents the interests of its members to key organisations, such as government, and provides a range of essential services in support of running an effective plumbing business.

soakaway

A hole in the ground sited well away from a building, it is designed to receive *surface water* from a property. The soakaway is filled with coarse material such as hardcore. The water discharged into the soakaway is then drained away into the surrounding subsoil. A soakaway must only be used in locations where the subsoil is capable of absorbing the water, so use in clay soils is not permitted as it tends to hold the water. It is designed for use in rural areas where there is no *drainage system* or access to a local stream.

soaker

A piece of lead (usually code 3) which forms part of the weathering to abutments with slates or traditional roof tiles. The soaker is used in association with a *cover flashing* when making *abutment flashings* to plain tiled or slated roof surfaces. One side of the soaker fits between the slates or tiles and the other side is turned flush with the side of the abutment. The soakers are covered with a cover flashing, providing a waterproof seal between the roof and the chimney. A soaker is formed from sheet lead with a minimum width of 175 mm – 75 mm for the upstand and 100 mm for the projection under the slate or tile. The length of soakers for a specific roof is determined by the formula: gauge of the tile + the overlap of the tile + 25 mm, where the gauge is the distance between the roof battens and the lap is the overlap of one tile over the other. See *Lead flashing*

socket

A *low-carbon steel* (LCS) fitting with *female threads* designed to join two pieces of straight pipe with *male threads* or a fitting secured at the end of a pipe designed to receive another pipe in forming a joint.

socket expander

A tool used with copper pipework to form a socket on a plain pipe end which can receive another pipe for the purposes of making a *capillary joint*. The socket expander is a cost-effective method of making a straight coupling between two copper pipes.

▲ Socket expander

sodium hypochlorite

This is diluted chlorine used for disinfection of water systems. The *British Standards Institution* gives recommendations for flushing and disinfecting systems. Chemicals for disinfecting drinking-water installations must be one of those listed by the Drinking Water Inspectorate in the *Water Fittings and Materials Directory* published by the *WRAS*. Unless a specific chemical disinfectant is specified, sodium hypochlorite can be used.

soffit

A timber or *PVC* board secured to the underside of the rafters on an overhanging pitched roof.

soft solder

The standard solder used to make *capillary joints* in domestic properties has a melting point of around 450°C. The solder is said to be softer and the joint will have lower strength than a hard-soldered joint which is used in industrial/commercial applications and which has a much higher melting point. Soft solder used in hot- and cold-water fittings must be of the lead-free type.

A
B
C
D
E
F
G
H
I
J
K
L
M
N
O
P
Q
R
S
T
U
V
W
X
Y
Z

A
B
C
D
E
F
G
H
I
J
K
L
M
N
O
P
Q
R
S
T
U
V
W
X
Y
Z

soft water

This is water which does not contain salts such as carbonates and sulphates which would ordinarily lead to *hard water*. Soft water readily makes a lather when used with soap. It also tends to be slightly *acidic*, brought about by the absorption of gases during rainfall or by the water running through materials such as peat. Water can also be softened by the use of a *water softener*.

soil appliances

These are the appliances designed to remove human waste in the form of faecal matter or urine; they include *water closets* and *urinals*. See *Waste appliances*

soil manifold

See *Collar boss*

soil stack

See *Discharge stack*

solar collector

A type of *heat exchanger* designed to collect radiated heat from the sun in order to heat water circulated through it.

solar heating

A system which collects radiated energy from the sun to heat domestic hot water. There are several methods of heating hot water by solar energy, including *direct* and *indirect* hot-water storage *cylinders* and pre-heating water to a *combination boiler*. In terms of a system featuring an indirect hot-water storage cylinder it is popular to use a twin-coil cylinder in which water from the solar collector runs through one coil and water from a conventional heating system runs through the other coil. Key components in the system are:

- *Solar collector* – the heat exchanger in which radiated heat from the sun is converted to hot water.
- *Circulating pump* – pumps the heated water around the solar circuit.
- Heat transfer fluid – a water/anti-freeze/*corrosion inhibitor* mixture which transports the heated water from the collector to the cylinder. The addition of anti-freeze and inhibitor prevents freezing of the system and the effects of *corrosion*.
- Differential temperature controller – monitors the temperature of the water at the collector and in the cylinder near the solar coil. If the collector temperature is higher than the cylinder temperature then the pump is activated, if it is lower then the pump does not operate.
- The solar heating system is commonly sealed, rather than being an open-vented system, therefore requiring the key components as laid down for a *sealed heating system*.
- The boiler or auxiliary heater circuit through the other coil provides for heating the hot water during winter months when the energy that can be produced from the sun is at a lower level.

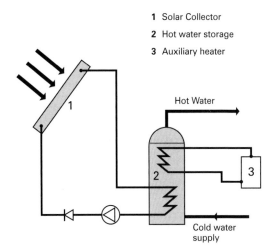

1 Solar Collector
2 Hot water storage
3 Auxiliary heater

◀ Solar-heating system with indirect twin-coil cylinder

solder

A material used for jointing water fittings. The *WRAS* guidance document specifies the types of jointing materials approved for use. Solders containing lead must never be used on domestic hot- and cold-water pipework. Lead-free solders for *capillary jointing* of *copper* or copper *alloy* water fittings include: type 23 or 24 tin/copper alloy; type 28 or 29 tin/silver alloy BS EN 29453; silver solder or silver brazing metal. See *Hard soldering; Silver soldering; Soft soldering*

solder ring capillary joint

See *Capillary joint*

solenoid valve

An on/off valve which works in conjunction with electrical *thermostats* or switches to control the flow of gas or water. The valve opens when electric current flows through the coil as this magnetises the soft iron core, lifting it against the spring. When the current is off, the valve springs to the closed position. Solenoid valves are used in multifunction controls and in gas lines to burners. A solenoid valve can also be used in a water system to control the flow of water to an *automatic flushing cistern* for a *urinal*.

solid

The state of a substance which is not liquid or gaseous and has a stable shape.

solid fuel

These are solid materials used as a fuel, for example coal, wood, cokes such as anthracite, and environmentally friendly pelleted waste products.

solid roll

Also known as a wood-cored roll, this is a type of *expansion joint* used in sheet lead roofwork laid with the fall of the roof. The solid roll is used on flat roofs which may be subject to pedestrian traffic. The wood roll which is fixed to the

A
B
C
D
E
F
G
H
I
J
K
L
M
N
O
P
Q
R
S
T
U
V
W
X
Y
Z

roof surface protects the joint from being squashed flat under foot as would be the case with a hollow roll. See *Hollow roll*

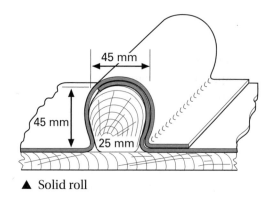

▲ Solid roll

solvent/solvent power

A liquid with the capability of dissolving certain substances.

solvent welding

A solvent welded cement is used to joint plastic pipework such as PVC-u/UPVC and ABS, primarily for use in pipework to soil and waste systems. The solvent weld cement bonds the two surfaces of the pipe and fitting. To make an effective joint the pipe and fitting must first be wiped clean then further cleaned by the use of a cleaning solution. The solvent cement is carefully applied to the fitting surfaces, the joint assembled and left to stand for a period of 10 to 15 minutes, before being moved. The joint will then take up to a further 24 hours to fully set.

soundness test – water systems

The *Water Regulations* lay down the requirements for testing hot- and cold-water systems as part of new installation work and when major modifications or extensions to existing systems are required. Soundness testing is usually carried out using *hydraulic test equipment*. There are different testing procedures prescribed for metallic and non-metallic pipework systems.

The procedure for testing rigid pipes (e.g. copper):
* Make sure any open-ended pipes are sealed, for example, *vent pipes*.
* Once the system has been filled, it should be allowed to stand for 30 minutes to allow the water temperature to stabilise.
* The system should be pressurised, using the hydraulic test equipment, to a pressure of 1.5 times the system working pressure.
* Leave to stand for 1 hour.
* Check for visible leakage and loss of pressure. If sound, the test has been satisfactorily completed.
* If not sound, repeat the test after locating and repairing any leaks.

The procedure for testing plastic pipes:

BS 6700 has two test procedures for plastic pipes: procedures A and B (see Water Regulations for more details).

Test A procedure:
* Apply test pressure, which is maintained by pumping for a period of 30 minutes, and visually inspect for leakage.
* Reduce pressure by bleeding water from the system to 0.33 times maximum working pressure. Close the *air tap*.

- Visually check and monitor for 90 minutes. If the pressure remains at or above 0.33 times working pressure, the system can be regarded as satisfactory.

Test B procedure:
- Apply test pressure (1.5 times maximum working pressure) and maintain by pumping for a period of 30 minutes.
- Note the pressure and inspect visually for leakage.
- Note the pressure after a further 30 minutes. If the pressure drop is less than 60 kPa (0.6 bar), the system can be considered to have no obvious leakage.
- Then visually check and monitor for 120 minutes. If the pressure drop is less than 20 kPa (0.2 bar), the system can be regarded as satisfactory.

space heating
The heating of one or more rooms, or other spaces, to produce a desired *temperature* in those rooms or spaces.

spacer nipple
A short piece of *low-carbon steel* pipe with *male threads* at either end. A spacer nipple may be purchased or made from a short length of pipe.

spanners
A type of *hand tool* used by plumbers for tightenting/ untightening nuts. There are four main types of spanner: ring spanner, open-ended spanner, box spanner and adjustable spanner. Ring, open-ended and box spanners are described as fixed-head spanners, that is, they are non-adjustable. Non-adjustable spanners tend to be the preferred option if correctly selected, as they do not tend to slip off the nut as easily when used. Adjustable spanner are, however, commonly used by plumbers.

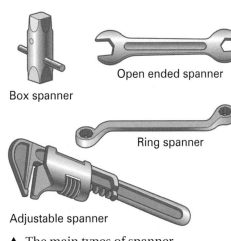

Box spanner

Open ended spanner

Ring spanner

Adjustable spanner

▲ The main types of spanner

sparge outlet/sparge pipe
A chromium-plated pipe with a number of holes drilled into it, used to direct water on to the face of slab *urinals*. The sparge outlet is mounted on the face of the urinal and washes the face of the slab and the channel. The sparge outlet should supply the correct amount of water to clear the urinal channel.

spark igniters
A type of *ignition device*, of which there are two main types: piezo-electric and mains transformer or battery. In the piezo-electric spark igniter, a push button

A
B
C
D
E
F
G
H
I
J
K
L
M
N
O
P
Q
R
S
T
U
V
W
X
Y
Z

A
B
C
D
E
F
G
H
I
J
K
L
M
N
O
P
Q
R
S
T
U
V
W
X
Y
Z

activates crystals to produce about 6000 volts at the igniter. These igniters are used on gas fires and for lighting pilots on boilers and water heaters. Mains transformer spark igniters have a step-up transformer connected to an electrode which provides the spark; they can provide pulse sparks at up to 8 sparks per second of 15,000 volts.

specific gravity

See *Relative density*

specific heat capacity

The amount of heat required to raise 1 kg of a material by 1°C. The specific heat capacity is different for each type of material. For example, the specific heat of water is 4.186 kJ/kg°C and the specific heat of *copper* (at the same starting temperature) is 0.385 kJ/kg°C. Therefore, the amount of heat required to raise the temperature of copper for a given weight is less than that required to heat water.

specification

A document which describes the materials, components and standards of work for a particular job. For large installations a *bill of quantities (B of Q)* is produced to specify how the work will be carried out, as well as the quality and quantity of the materials.

spherical plug valve

See *Lever-operated spherical plug valve; Screwdriver-operated spherical plug valve*

spider manifold

See *Linear (spider) manifold*

spigot

The plain end of a pipe that fits into a socket or coupling.

spillage testing

This test is used to determine whether the *products of combustion* from an *open-flued* appliance are effectively being drawn up the flue. A smoke match is used to test the draw while the appliance is running. All doors and windows must be closed and any fans switched to maximum. The appliance is turned on to the full setting, the smoke match is lit and the *draught diverter* or *canopy* checked for spillage according to the manufacturer's instructions. The smoke should be drawn into the flue. If this is not the case, the appliance is dangerous and must be disconnected. Signs of past spillage include staining around the draught diverter and above the point of burning on appliances.

▲ Spillage testing

A
B
C
D
E
F
G
H
I
J
K
L
M
N
O
P
Q
R
S
T
U
V
W
X
Y
Z

spill-over level

The level at which water would begin to spill over or spill out of a plumbing appliance such as a basin or a cold-water *storage cistern*. The spill-over level of an appliance is sited above the height of any overflow that an appliance may have.

splashback

The protective (watertight) wall covering at the back of a plumbing appliance such as a bath or basin. A splashback will usually be formed by a tiled surface; other materials such as plastics can however be used.

split pin

A type of pin which has split ends for the purpose of securing plumbing components. A split pin is commonly used in a *float-operated valve* to secure the lever arm to the valve body. The pin is kept in place by the opening of the two ends.

spray mixer tap

A type of tap commonly used on *wash basins* in public buildings. The spray tap is a water conservation device significantly reducing water consumption. Key features of the tap are:

- It should be provided with equal or balanced water pressures to work effectively.
- The mixer tap is usually of the single-flow type; when connected to the *supply pipe*, protection against *backflow* will be required owing to the mixing of water taking place in the valve body.
- The spray mixer tap must not be supplied from a long hot-water *dead leg* as it will take an extremely long time for warm water to discharge at the outlet.

spreader

A type of fitting fixed to the lower end of a *flushpipe* to a *urinal*; its purpose is to spread the water across the face of the urinal for cleansing purposes.

spring bending

See *Bending spring*

sprinkler head

Sprinkler systems for fire-protection purposes consist of overhead pipes fitted with sprinkler heads. Each head is held closed independently by heat-sensitive seals. These seals prevent water flow until a design temperature is exceeded by the individual sprinkler heads. Seals may be broken by melting (fusing) of metals with a low melting point (often bismuth *alloys*), or may be glass bulbs that break from pressure differences when heated.

sprinkler, pop-up

See *Irrigation systems*

sprinkler systems

See *Dry-pipe sprinkler system; Wet-pipe sprinkler system; Sprinkler systems – backflow prevention*

A
B
C
D
E
F
G
H
I
J
K
L
M
N
O
P
Q
R
S
T
U
V
W
X
Y
Z

sprinkler systems – backflow prevention

Wet sprinkler systems with no additives, fire-hose reels and hydrant landing valves are all *fluid risk category* 2 and require a *single-check valve*. Wet sprinkler systems with additives (e.g. to prevent freezing) and systems that contain *hydropneumatic accumulators* are fluid risk category 4. These systems must have a verifiable backflow prevention (RPZ or type BA) or be fitted with a type AA air gap or similar device.

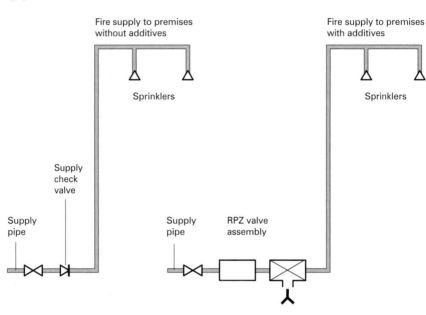

▲ A sprinkler system (no additives used) with a single-check valve installed, and a system (additives used) with a type BA (RPZ) valve

spur outlets

A method of connecting a low-loaded fixed electrical appliance, or system such as a *central-heating system*, or an appliance such as a *macerator WC*, to the *ring main circuit* in the property.

square bend

Another name for a 90° bend.

square entry

An equal branch junction used in a *sanitary pipework* or *drainage system* that is more than 45° or has a centre line radius less than the internal pipe diameter.

stabiliser to flue

See *Draught stabiliser*

stability device

A device used to ensure that appliances with a flexible connector, for example a cooker, are firmly secured to the wall or floor.

stack offset

The non-vertical part of a discharge stack. Offsets in discharge stacks (the wetted portion of the soil system) should be avoided under *Building Regulations* requirements wherever possible.

stack vent

The extension of a vertical discharge pipe above the highest *branch discharge pipe* connection that terminates in an open end to atmosphere. See *Types of sanitary pipework system*

stainless steel pipe

Stainless steel is a complex alloy used to make strong, *corrosion*-protected pipe used for water services, especially exposed pipework. The composition of stainless steel is: approximately 70% iron, with 18% chromium, 10% nickel, 1.25% manganese, 0.6% silicon, 0.08% carbon, and traces of sulphur and phosphorus. Stainless steel pipe is about 0.7 mm in thickness and available in a range of bores from 6 mm to 35 mm. Stainless steel is also used to manufacture sinks and urinal units.

stall urinal

See *Urinal*

stand bender

See *Bending machine*

stand pipe

A vertical pipe with a *stop valve* and tap for the purposes of temporarily drawing water from the main. A stand pipe is typically used as a temporary water supply for use on a construction site.

Standard Assessment Procedure (SAP)

A compulsory energy rating for new houses, specified in Part L1 of the Building Regulations. The energy efficiency performance of a house is estimated and rated on a scale of 1 to 100, with 100 being the top energy efficient rating. The SAP is also used to calculate the carbon index to show that houses comply with Part L1 and to predict heating and hot-water costs. SAP calculations are often made using a computer program approved by the Building Research Establishment. The calculation is based on: the size of the house, the amount of insulation and ventilation, and the types of heating and hot-water systems.

standards

The standards and regulations on the installation of plumbing components and fittings and the standards to which plumbing components and fittings should be manufactured from a quality perspective.

See *British Standards; European Standards (EN); International standards; Water Regulations Advisory Scheme (WRAS)*

A
B
C
D
E
F
G
H
I
J
K
L
M
N
O
P
Q
R
S
T
U
V
W
X
Y
Z

standing pressure
> See *Gas pressure*

stat
> A shortened version of 'thermostat'; it is widely used.

static head
> This is the pressure created by the vertical height (or head) of water in a system when it is at rest. Static head is usually expressed in metres.

statutory instrument
> A legal document outlining regulation requirements. A statutory instrument is used to make new *Building Regulations* and amendments to those regulations.

steel
> An alloy of iron and carbon, steel is usually classified as low, medium or high in respect of its carbon content. See *Low-carbon steel*

steel wool
> Bundles or pads that are made up from thin strands of steel; it is used in the process of cleaning pipe ends and fittings for the purpose of making *capillary joints* to copper pipework.

step and cover flashings
> See *Lead flashing*

step flashings
> See *Lead flashing*

step ladders
> These are free-standing *ladders* which need to be placed with all four legs resting on firm, level ground before use. Steps and ropes or stabilisers must be checked to be in good condition. When using them, never work with your knees higher than the top step.

stiles
> The uprights of a *ladder*; the *rungs* (horizontal steps), are connected to the stiles.

stillson
> A type of *wrench* used primarily when making joints to low-carbon steel pipework.

stocks and dies
> A tool used to create a thread on a *low-carbon steel* (LCS) pipe. Dies are held in a stock which is rotated around the pipe, cutting a thread into it. There are a number of different types of stocks and dies:

▲ Stillson wrench used to make an LCS joint

- Chaser dies with interchangeable heads – non-adjustable heads are dropped into the lever mechanism, these are usually used for smaller pipe diameters.
- Chaser die stock – this has an adjustable stock to suit a range of different pipe sizes; if excessive force is placed on the pipe during the cutting process with this type of stocks and dies, crushing of the pipe can occur.
- Receder die stock – this overcomes the problem of pipe crushing as it has an integral clamping device, that moves as the thread is cut, to support the pipe.

Stocks and dies usually cut a *tapered thread* (to make the threading process easier) for the first part of the cut, leading to completion of the thread with a *parallel thread*. Cutting compound is applied to the end of the pipe before using stocks and dies to ease the cutting process and prevent the threads from being ripped. The thread is usually cut 1.5 to 2 threads longer than the length of the inside of the fitting, then the excess cutting compound is wiped off. An electric *pipe-threading machine* is commonly used as an alternative to using stocks and dies, as the work is much quicker and the threads are often of better quality.

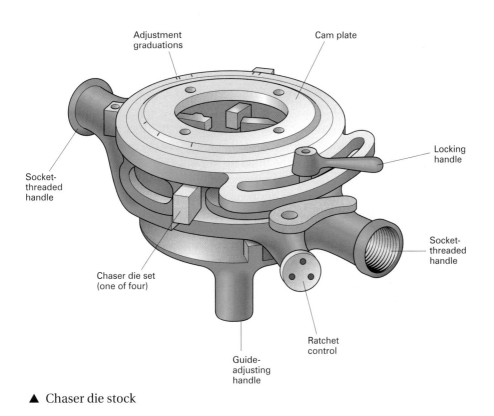

▲ Chaser die stock

stoichiometric mixture

The ideal mixture of gas and air for complete combustion. The correct stoichiometric mixture for natural gas is approximately 10 volumes of air for every volume of gas, to ensure *complete combustion* takes place.

stop valve (stop tap)

A valve for shutting off the flow of water, usually the mains supply, to a system for isolation purposes. For below ground installations, stop valves manufactured from *corrosion*-resistant material must be used. Paragraph 10(1) of the *Water Regulations* states that water supply pipework to separate premises must have stop valves installed to allow the supply to each of the premises to be shut off without affecting the other. Stop valves should be positioned on the *supply pipe*, as close as possible to the point of entry to the premises and above floor level, so that it is accessible to the occupier if the supply needs to be closed off, for example if there is a leak. See *Screwdown stop valve*

storage cistern

An open-topped protected stage vessel for the purpose of storing *wholesome water* for hot- or cold-water supply purposes. Key requirements of a cistern for wholesome water are that it must be:

- fitted with an effective inlet-control device such as a *float-operated valve* to maintain the correct water level
- fitted with *service valves* on inlet and outlet pipes
- fitted with a screened (filtered) *warning* or *overflow pipe* to warn against impending overflow
- supported to avoid damage or distortion that might cause them to leak
- outlet pipes to be sited as low as possible in the cistern (preferably bottom entry) in order to minimise the build up of *sludge*
- installed so that any risk of *contamination* is minimised, and arranged so that water can circulate and stagnation will not take place
- covered to exclude light or insects, and insulated to prevent heat losses and undue warming
- *corrosion*-resistant and watertight and must not deform unduly, shatter or fragment when in use
- unobstructed and have space above them of not less than 350 mm for servicing purposes.

For a domestic property with a *direct cold-water system*, the cistern will usually have a minimum capacity of 100 litres (higher if a gravity fed shower system is used). With an *indirect cold-water system* the cistern will usually have a minimum capacity of 200 litres.

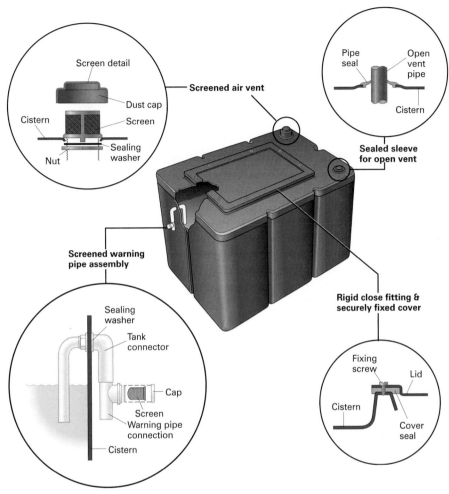

Screen detail

Cistern

Nut

Dust cap

Screen

Sealing washer

Screened air vent

Pipe seal

Open vent pipe

Cistern

Sealed sleeve for open vent

Screened warning pipe assembly

Sealing washer

Tank connector

Cap

Screen

Warning pipe connection

Cistern

Rigid close fitting & securely fixed cover

Fixing screw

Lid

Cistern

Cover seal

▲ Features of a protected cistern for storing wholesome water

storage cylinder

A hot-water storage component usually made from *copper* or *stainless steel*. A *sacrificial anode* may be required to prevent *corrosion*. Information on thermal insulation and the surface area of the heating coil in storage cylinders is covered by Approved Document L1 of the *Building Regulations*. See *Hot-water storage vessel*

A
B
C
D
E
F
G
H
I
J
K
L
M
N
O
P
Q
R
S
T
U
V
W
X
Y
Z

storage heater

A gas storage heater is a self-contained hot-water storage system that is directly heated by a burner with an open flue which terminates externally. Storage heaters may be fed indirectly by a cistern or they may be of the *unvented* type fed by main supply. Electric storage heaters are also available.

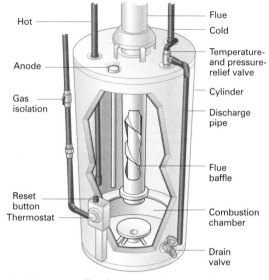

▲ Direct gas-fired unvented storage heater

stored water contamination

Paragraph 16.5 of the *Water Regulations* refers to contamination of stored water. All cisterns should be installed to minimise contamination risk; a protected cistern will achieve this, especially domestic water supply. The cistern must also be an appropriate size, reducing the risk from legionella bacteria, and should have the connections positioned to allow good circulation; this prevents stagnation. The outlet connections should be installed as low as possible, preventing sediment build-up in the base of the cistern. See *Linked cisterns; Storage cistern*

straight-through trap

Another term for an *S trap*.

strainer

A device fitted over the inlet or outlet of an appliance, or fitted in a pipeline, designed to prevent unwanted matter entering the pipeline or appliance. As an example, a line strainer is fitted in an *unvented hot-water system*. This strainer prevents any debris in the water supply from entering the system. Grit and other debris can block system controls, causing malfunction.

strap-on boss

A type of fitting used to make a plastic waste connection to a *discharge stack*. A hole is cut into the discharge stack using a hole saw and the strap-on boss is jointed to the stack using gap-filling cement.

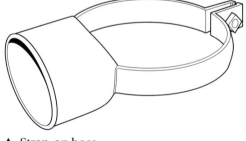

▲ Strap-on boss

stratification

Hot water rises and cooler water falls, therefore in a hot-water storage vessel there are layers of water of different temperatures, with the hottest at the top. This is called stratification and assists the storage vessel in efficient operation. For the best stratification effect, the storage vessel should be cylindrical and installed in a vertical position with the cold-feed connection entering on a horizontal plane. The hot water can be drawn off from the top of the vessel with no interference with the incoming cold feed. This reduces the need for frequent reheating of the storage vessel, saving energy and money.

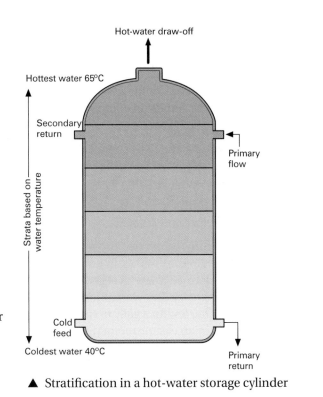

▲ Stratification in a hot-water storage cylinder

strength

The strength of a material is a measure of its ability to withstand pressure without breaking. The pressure may be compression force, tensile or stretching force, or shear force, and materials are described as having compressive, tensile or shear strength. *Cast iron*, stone and brick can withstand high compression, which is why they are good for building, but they have low tensile strength. *Steel* has high tensile strength and for this reason it is used to reinforce buildings in earthquake-prone regions.

striking back

See *Lighting back*

stub stack

A short length of capped pipe rising above floor level to connect the ground-floor sanitary appliances in a property and which must be connected to a ventilated drain. Stub stacks are often found in a second bathroom if the first bathroom is at the head of the drain with a properly ventilated stack. Without an *air-admittance valve* the highest waste connection allowed is 2 m above the invert of the drain, or 1.3 m for a WC. See *Types of sanitary pipework system*

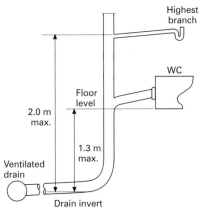

▲ The stub stack system

stud partition

A hollow-boarded internal wall.

stuffing box

Another name for the *gland* where the packing is positioned to make a watertight seal to the spindle in components such as *bib taps* and *screwdown stop valves*.

sulphuric acid

A corrosive and toxic chemical that has been used for unblocking drains. Given the dangers of its use, other forms of drain clearance, such as jetting, are now considered to be a much safer alternative.

SummitSkills

See *Sector Skills Council*

sump pump, electric

A type of *pump* used to lift water from a purpose-designed sump hole. The sump hole is formed at low level in order to collect water in areas that may be prone to flooding, such as underground *cistern* chambers and cellars, and where the floor level is too low for a gully to connect into the *drainage system*. The sump pump driven by an electric motor raises water out of the sump hole and prevents flooding.

supatap

An older type of tap which requires a special washer. The key feature of the tap is that it incorporates a self-closing mechanism if the tap nozzle is removed.

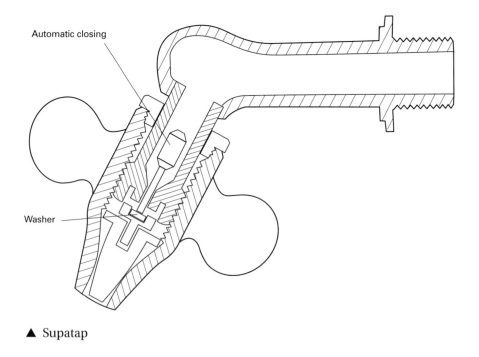

▲ Supatap

supplementary bonding
See *Bonding (equipotential bonding)*

supply pipe
The pipework in the property operating under the influence of the *water undertaker's* main, that is, working at mains pressure.

surcharging
A drain or sewer that has insufficient capacity to cope with the volume of water passing down it. Flooding will therefore usually occur at points in the system such as a gully.

surface tension
The *cohesion* of water *molecules* creates surface tension and forms a thin skin, called a *meniscus*, on the top surface of water in a vessel.

surface water
Rainwater collected in lakes, streams, rivers, and collected from roofs via the rainwater system.

swaging tool
A tool that can be used in flaring the pipe end when making a *manipulative compression joint*.

swan neck
Another name for an offset bend in a pipe. For example, in a *rainwater pipe* a swan neck bend is required to clear the *fascia* and *soffit*.

swarf
The debris produced when cutting or grinding stone or metal.

swept entry
An equal branch junction used in *sanitary pipework* or *drainage system* that is 45° or less, or has a centre line radius less than the internal pipe diameter.

swept tee
A type of tee in which the branch has a relatively long radius curve where it joins the main pipeline. The swept tee ensures that the *fluid* flowing from the branch enters the main pipeline in a more streamlined fashion and minimises the restriction to the flow of the fluid.

swivel trap
See *Tubular swivel trap*

system commissioning
This is the procedures for making sure an installation is working safely and effectively. For a water installation, commissioning includes a visual inspection of the installation, testing for leaks, flushing and disinfection, and performance testing. See *Commissioning*

A
B
C
D
E
F
G
H
I
J
K
L
M
N
O
P
Q
R
S
T
U
V
W
X
Y
Z

A
B
C
D
E
F
G
H
I
J
K
L
M
N
O
P
Q
R
S
T
U
V
W
X
Y
Z

system decommissioning

Decommissioning domestic water systems involves either temporary decommissioning, in which the system is temporarily taken out of action in order that it may be extended or maintained, or permanent decommissioning, in which the system is completely removed, including the removal of all its connecting services. See *Decommissioning*

system disinfection

Water Regulations requires that, after *system flushing*, any newly installed or significantly altered hot-water system in any property, other than a single-family dwelling, should be subject to disinfection. See *Disinfection of water systems*

system flushing

The *Water Regulations* require that every water system is flushed out before it is first used. This should be done for new installations, alterations, extensions or maintenance to make sure that any debris is removed from the system.

tack

See *Lead tack*

tank

A rectangular-shaped storage vessel which is not open to atmosphere, that is, not open-topped. An *oil tank* is one example.

tap connector

A fitting used to connect copper or plastic pipework to a *pillar tap*. The tap connector can be angled or a straight pattern and consists of a union nut which is screwed on to the pillar tap tail and sealed with a fibre washer.

tap gap

A *backflow prevention device* based on the *air gap* created between a tap outlet and the *spill-over level* of a sanitary appliance. There are two types of tap gap:

* AUK2 – this protects against a *fluid risk category* 3, such as the contents of domestic baths and wash basins. Air gap requirements are:
  – G½" – 20 mm
  – G½" to G¾" – 25 mm
  – Exceeding G¾" – 70 mm

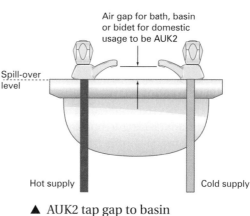

▲ AUK2 tap gap to basin

A
B
C
D
E
F
G
H
I
J
K
L
M
N
O
P
Q
R
S
T
U
V
W
X
Y
Z

- AUK3 – this protects against a fluid risk category 5 such as the contents of domestic sinks and medical equipment. Air gap requirements are a minimum of 20 mm, or twice the inlet diameter of the fitting, whichever is the greater.

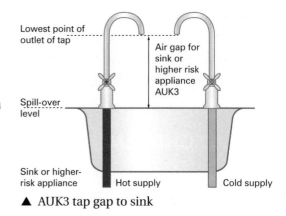

▲ AUK3 tap gap to sink

tap reseating tool

See *Reseating tool*

tapered thread

A *male* or *female thread* in which the thread cut becomes progressively shallow as the thread progresses on the pipe or into the fitting. A fitting therefore becomes progressively tighter as it is screwed on to the pipe with a tapered thread. Most *low-carbon steel* pipes and fittings are jointed using tapered threads. See *Parallel thread*

tappings

A connection built into an appliance, such as a radiator or boiler, and threaded to allow the attachment of pipes, or valves. For example, radiators usually have ½" BSP tappings, for connecting valves.

Tee

A fitting which has three pipe connections, the branch connection being for the purpose of connecting a branch pipe into the fluid flow of another pipe.

temper

The relative degree of hardness of a metal. A metal that has been *annealed* is softer than a metal that has been *work hardened* which is said to have a hard temper.

temperature

Temperature is the hotness or coldness of a substance, measured in degrees Celsius. See *Heat*

temperature control

See *Thermostats*

temperature-relief valve

A safety control valve fitted to an *unvented hot-water system* that is pre-set by the manufacturer to open at approximately 90–95°C. A probe filled with a temperature-sensitive liquid is immersed in the hottest section of the storage cylinder; this activates the valve when the temperature reaches the set level and water is discharged from the valve to a discharge pipe, thus reducing the water temperature in the system. This valve protects the system if the cylinder thermostat and high-limit thermostat fail.

▲ Temperature relief valve

tempering

The process of hardening or softening a metal.

temporary continuity bond

This is an essential part of maintenance work, ensuring that earth continuity is maintained when branching into existing pipework. A temporary bonding wire is securely fixed to connect the pipes which will remain in place while the section of pipework is removed to form the branch.

▲ Temporary continuity bond

temporary hard water

This is water which contains dissolved carbonates such as calcium carbonate which, if heated, will result in the precipitation of *scale* on the inside of plumbing components such as *boilers* and *cylinders*, resulting in a possible restriction in water flow, and in severe cases potential blockage.

tensile strength

The breaking strength of a material when subjected to stretching forces.

terminal

The point at which a flue discharges its *products of combustion* to atmosphere. There are many designs of flue terminal available. The *Building Regulations* and *British Standards* lay down strict requirements for flue terminal position in order to avoid the possibility of *down draught*, re-entry of the flue gas products into the building, and to ensure correct functioning of the combustion appliance that the flue serves. See *Ridge terminal*

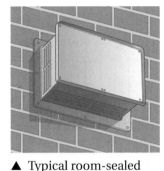

▲ Typical room-sealed flue terminal

▼ Typical open-flue terminals

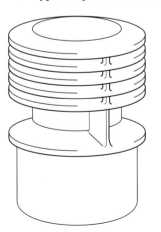

terminal fitting
> The outlet of a hot or cold fitting such as a *tap* or a *shower mixer valve*.

terminal guard
> A wire cage or similar device fitted to a *room-sealed flue* terminal to protect against burns by touching. A flue terminal guard must be fitted to a gas-fired room-sealed flue terminal when it is sited at 2 m or less above ground level, or at a point where it may be touched, such as from a balcony.

termination
> The end point of a wire or pipe.

test nipple
> A plumbing fitting designed for attaching a test instrument to take measurements and readings of the performance of a component or system.

test pressure
> This is used for testing water systems; an internal water pressure of at least 1.5 times the designed maximum pressure of the installation or part should be applied. See *Soundness test – water systems*

testing bag
> See *Inflatable stopper*

testing for soundness
> See *Soundness – water systems*

thermal
> Related to or associated with *heat*.

thermal conductivity
> The ability of a material to conduct heat. See *Conduction*

thermal envelope
> The thermally insulated space in a building enclosed by the walls, floor and roof. A laundry room, cellar or conservatory does not have to be included within the thermal envelope, according to the *Building Regulations*.

thermal insulation
> The use of materials to reduce *heat transfer*, for example to prevent water pipes from freezing or to retain the heat energy in water pipes. The recommended thickness of insulation for different pipe insulation materials is shown in the table.

Thermal insulation of insulation material at 0°C					
Watts per metre degrees Kelvin	0.02 W/(m.K)	0.025 W/(m.K)	0.03 W/(m.K)	0.035 W/(m.K)	0.04 W/(m.K)
15	20	30	25	25	32
22	15	15	19	19	25
28	15	15	13	19	22
25	15	15	9	9	13
42 & over	15	15	9	9	9

▲ Recommended insulation thickness (in mm) for different insulation materials

thermal insulators

Materials made from wood, ceramics and plastics which are poor conductors of heat.

thermal movement

The *expansion* and *contraction* of materials at different temperatures, usually expansion on heating and contraction on cooling. The *molecules* of a substance move further apart from each other and occupy more volume when heated. Linear expansion is the increase in length due to heating. Plumbing systems are constantly subjected to heating and cooling and allowances must be made for this to avoid potential noise or material breakdown. See *Coefficient of linear expansion*

thermal movement of gutter and rainwater systems

Between 6 mm and 8 mm should be left from the end of the pipe to the inside shoulder of each fitting to allow for thermal expansion of the pipes. See *Coefficient of linear expansion*

thermal movement of sheet lead

The *coefficient of linear expansion* for lead is quite high – 0.0000297 per °C. Regular *expansion joints* should be included in sheet-lead weatherings to allow for thermal movement, including where flashings are secured by lead wedges.

thermal transmission

Part L1 of the *Building Regulations* covers the requirements for standards of *thermal insulation* in domestic properties. The *thermal transmission* rate from the inside to the outside of a building is called the 'U value'. A home heated with an appliance conforming to the relevant SEDBUK rating should have a wall construction with a U value of $0.35 \text{ W/m}^2 \text{ K}$. In order to satisfy the Building Regulations, most wall constructions will require further insulation.

A
B
C
D
E
F
G
H
I
J
K
L
M
N
O
P
Q
R
S
T
U
V
W
X
Y
Z

thermal transmittance rate (U value)

The energy, in watts per square metre of construction (W/m^2), for each degree of temperature difference between the inside and outside of the building (W/m^2K). Building materials have a U value which identifies the rate at which they transmit heat through them; a low U value indicates high insulation properties for the material. U values are extensively used in the sizing of *heat emitters* for rooms as the emitter must be sized to overcome the rate of transmission through the fabric of the building.

thermistor

A thermistor is a type of resistor used to measure *temperature* changes, relying on the change in its *resistance* with changing temperature.

thermocouple (flame failure device)

See *Thermoelectric devices*

thermocouple interrupter

A special type of thermocouple which incorporates an interrupter circuit that causes the current flowing from the tip of the thermocouple to the thermoelectric valve to cease when energised. This type of thermocouple can be used in conjunction with *high-limit thermostats* or *atmosphere sensing devices*.

thermoelectric devices

A type of *flame supervision device* that operates by heat application to a *thermocouple*, producing a small electrical voltage. A thermocouple is a loop of two dissimilar metals joined at one end and heated by the *pilot light*. The opposite ends of the two metals connect to a magnet in a spring-loaded gas valve. As long as the pilot light is lit, and the thermocouple is producing a voltage, the valve will be held open. If the pilot light is extinguished and the thermocouple cools, the magnet is de-energised and the valve closes. The tip of the thermocouple must be positioned correctly to access heat from the pilot light.

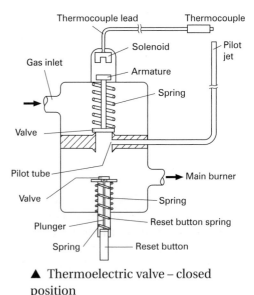

▲ Thermoelectric valve – closed position

thermometer

A device used to measure *temperature*. Typical thermometers used in plumbing include a standard thermometer for taking temperature readings at outlets such as taps, a clip-on thermometer for taking pipe temperature readings, and a differential digital thermometer, a multi-purpose device that can be used for taking water and pipe temperature readings. It can also take two pipe temperature readings simultaneously and is often used when *balancing* central-heating systems

thermoplastics

A type of plastic which can be softened by heat and which is used to manufacture pipework materials. Thermoplastics are usually resistant to *acids* and *alkalis*, have a low *specific heat capacity* and are poor conductors of heat. Thermoplastics exposed to sunlight can become brittle; this is also called degradation. *Polybutylene* used for hot and cold pipework is an example of a thermoplastic.

thermosetting plastics

These plastics soften when first heated then set hard to a fixed shape which cannot be altered by further heating. Thermosetting plastics are used for moulding components such as WC *cisterns*.

thermostat

This is a temperature-control device designed to control and maintain steady temperatures. Thermostats are manufactured for use in many different situations, for example for controlling the temperature of water in a boiler or the air in a room. Most thermostats have a simple on or off action; other types produce gradual change by adjusting the flow rate (of gas or water). Thermostats may be fixed or adjustable and are activated by using the different expansion rates of metals, by the expansion of liquids or gases (mechanical) or by electricity. See *Cylinder thermostat; Frost thermostat; Liquid-expansion thermostat; Room thermostat*

thermostatic mixing valve

A type of mixing valve that is installed close to hot-water outlets to provide hot water at a safe level which will not scald users. The thermostatic mixing valve takes both a hot- and cold-water supply and mixes the water to achieve a desired temperature, usually of around 43°C. They are used extensively in healthcare properties or other properties with young, elderly or infirm users. The valve must be installed at point of use in order to minimise the length of pipe run that otherwise may be subject to distributing water at a temperature that would promote the growth of *legionella bacteria*.

▲ Thermostatic mixing valve

thermostatic radiator valve (TRV)

These valves control the rate of water flowing through a *radiator* which in turn controls the heat output. The valve can be adjusted to maintain the desired

A
B
C
D
E
F
G
H
I
J
K
L
M
N
O
P
Q
R
S
T
U
V
W
X
Y
Z

A
B
C
D
E
F
G
H
I
J
K
L
M
N
O
P
Q
R
S
T
U
V
W
X
Y
Z

room temperature and automatically controls the radiator to produce the set heat requirement. TRVs have a built-in sensor which opens and closes the valve in response to room temperature. An *automatic bypass valve* must be fitted to prevent the boiler and pump working against a closed system if all the TRVs are closed and the water flow rate is very low.

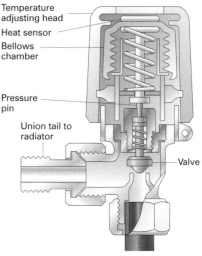

threaded pipe fittings
These may be manufactured from malleable iron to BS 1256 or from steel to BS 1740. Steel is more expensive but can withstand higher pressures. A very wide range of fittings are available, including bends, elbows, tees and unions.

▲ Section through a thermostatic radiator valve

threading machine
See *Pipe-threading machine*

three-port diverter valve
A valve which controls the flow of water in a *fully-pumped* central-heating and hot-water system to be controlled on a selective priority basis that is, the valve can only provide hot water and central heating at any one time – not both together. The domestic hot-water supply is usually selected as the top priority. This type of fully-pumped central-heating system control is not that widely used.

three-port mid-position valve
See *Mid-position valve*

▲ Three-port diverter valve

throat
A contraction located in a *flue* that is designed to accelerate the flue gases.

throating
The reduction in the diameter of a pipe at a bend caused by bending the pipe with the roller, guide and former of the *bending machine* incorrectly adjusted or too tight.

through-flow expansion vessel
A type of *expansion vessel* which has an inlet and outlet connection with the cold-water supply flowing through it. This type of expansion vessel is used to minimise the possibility of stagnation occurring at the diaphragm in the vessel.

thrust blocks

Blocks used to anchor and support pipes, fittings and appliances, preventing undue noise or vibration which could result in damage. Thrust blocks also ensure that thermal movement is not restricted.

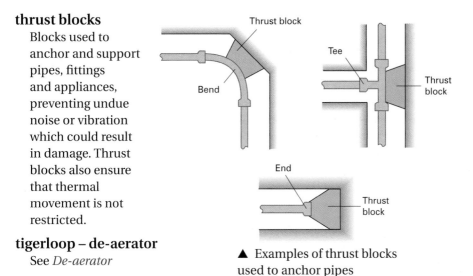

▲ Examples of thrust blocks used to anchor pipes

tigerloop – de-aerator

See *De-aerator*

tightness test

This is the process of testing gas pipework for leakage.

tightness testing procedure – for a low-pressure installation

The tightness testing procedure on new and existing systems is a four-stage process: the visual inspection; 'let by' test; pipework-only test; complete installation.

The visual inspection:
- Check the completed installation and ensure all sections to be tested are connected.
- Make a visual inspection of all pipework and joints to ensure they have been correctly made. Ensure all open ends have been properly capped off.
- Make sure that any appliances fitted are isolated, that is, turned off at the *isolation valve*.
- It is important that pipework only is tested as there is no allowable drop in pressure. This applies whether the pipework is new or existing.
- Connect a correctly zeroed *pressure gauge* to the system at the test point on the meter.
- Check the section of pipework between the *emergency control valve* and *governor* with *leak detection fluid*.

The 'let by' test is carried out to ensure that the emergency control valve is not passing gas (letting by):
- Slowly raise the pressure to 10 mbar and isolate the supply.
- If the pressure rises more than 0.5 mbar over a one-minute period, then the emergency control valve is passing gas in the closed position.
- If passing gas, then the gas emergency service provider must be contacted and the installation not put into use.

A
B
C
D
E
F
G
H
I
J
K
L
M
N
O
P
Q
R
S
T
U
V
W
X
Y
Z

A
B
C
D
E
F
G
H
I
J
K
L
M
N
O
P
Q
R
S
T
U
V
W
X
Y
Z

In the pipework-only test all appliances must be isolated, cookers removed from bayonets, etc.:

- Slowly raise the pressure to 20 mbar and turn off the supply (do not raise any higher as it may cause meter lock-up resulting in incorrect readings).
- Allow one minute for temperature stabilisation.
- Record any pressure loss in the next two minutes.
- If there is no perceptible pressure loss (i.e. below 0.5 mbar for a water gauge and 0.3 mbar for a digital gauge) and there is no smell of gas, then the installation has passed the test.
- If the test has failed, then the leak must be found or the installation sealed and made safe.

The complete installation is tested once it has been established that the pipework is sound and not leaking. For this the appliance isolation valves must be turned on and the full system tested. Remember, some cookers have fold-down lids that turn off the supply to the control valves, so with this type of cooker the test should be carried out with the lid in the open position:

- Slowly raise the pressure to 20 mbar and turn off the supply.
- Again, do not raise to higher pressures than 20 mbar, as this may cause the *meter regulator* to lock-up.
- Allow one minute for temperature stabilisation.
- Record any pressure loss in the next two minutes.

With new installations there is no allowable pressure drop for new appliances. For existing installations a pressure drop is allowed at the appliances provided that there is no smell of gas and the drop is not on the pipework:

- Installation with a U6/G4 meter – loss of up to 4 mbar acceptable, provided there is no smell of gas.
- Installation with an E6 meter – loss of up to 8 mbar acceptable, provided there is no smell of gas.
- Where no meter is fitted in the dwelling, such as a flat supplied by a communal meter, then up to 8 mbar loss is allowed.

If the test is failed then the leak must be found or the installation sealed and made safe.

tightness testing procedure – medium-pressure installation

This procedure differs from testing low-pressure gas pipework.

Stage 1 – Test *emergency control valve* (ECV):

- Turn off gas at the ECV and connect gauge.
- Carry out 'let by' test on ECV.
- Release pressure from installation and hold open release-mechanism lever on side of regulator.
- No more than 0.5 mbar rise should take place over the next one minute; if more than 0.5 mbar, then ECV is letting by, in which case contact emergency service provider.

Stage 2 – Test regulator:
- Allow release-mechanism lever on regulator to return to off position.
- Open ECV.
- No more than 0.5 mbar rise should take place over the next one minute; if more than 0.5 mbar then the regulator is letting by, in which case contact the emergency service provider.

Stage 3 – Tightness test:
- Following a successful let by test on both the ECV and the regulator, release all pressure from installation and switch off.
- Slowly raise pressure to 19 mbar (no higher to prevent regulator lock-up).
- Allow one minute for stabilisation.
- Check pressure loss over next two minutes.
- The following applies:
    - pipework only, no drop allowed
    - new appliances, no drop allowed
    - existing appliances fitted:
        (a) U6/G4 meter: 4 mbar drop with no smell of gas.
        (b) E6 meter: 8 mbar drop with no smell of gas.

tilting fillet
A triangular section of timber installed to support the tiles or slates near the edge of a sheet lead component such as a *back gutter*, and to prevent *capillary action* taking place between the tile/slate and the sheet lead.

time switch
An electrical switch in a heating system operated by a clock and controlling either space heating or hot water, or both together.

tin snips
A cutting device used to cut sheet metal such as sheet lead. There are a number of different styles of tin snips; those used by plumbers include straight (general purpose) snips, which may be used for cutting gas-fire *closure plates*, and curved snips, which are often used for cutting sheet lead.

▲ Straight and curved tin snips

tinning
The process of applying *solder* to the surface of a metal.

A
B
C
D
E
F
G
H
I
J
K
L
M
N
O
P
Q
R
S
T
U
V
W
X
Y
Z

toggle bolt
A type of device used for fixing plumbing equipment to plasterboard. The toggle bolt makes a fixing to the other side of the board which cannot be directly accessed.

toilet
A room containing a *water closet* or a *urinal*.

tongue and groove
A type of joining system for floorboards.

tool safety
See *Equipment – tool safety*

▲ Toggle bolt

top hat
A plastic spacer washer fitted to *pillar taps* when they are tightened on to thin materials such as *stainless steel* sink tops.

top-up bottle
An open-topped bottle that may be fitted to the high point of a *sealed heating system* for the purpose of making up water that may be lost from the system.

total hardness
Water which contains both sulphates *(permanent hardness)* and carbonates *(temporary hardness)*.

total heat
The total heat contained in a substance which may include *sensible heat* and *latent heat*.

total pressure
See *Water pressure*

towel rails
A combined radiator and towel rail is used in a bathroom and allows towels to be dried and warmed but does not prevent *convection* currents from the radiator from heating the room. Tubular towel rails are available with an electrical element option.

toxic agent
Any poisonous substance, liquid or gas.

trace heating
A frost protection strategy, mainly for industrial installations. A thermostat-controlled, low-temperature heating element is attached to the outside of a pipe. When the temperature drops towards freezing the heating element is turned on by the thermostat, preventing the pipe from freezing. Self-regulating trace heating is covered by BS6315, which also specifies the nominal thickness of pipe insulation required to protect the pipe if the trace-heating device fails.

tracking

A defect that occurs in a pipe when using a *pipe cutter* in which a number of additional cuts are made into the pipe. Tracking is usually associated with damaged cutting wheels or rollers.

tracpipe

Corrugated *stainless steel* pipe, manufactured to BS 7838, that is specially produced for use on gas-supply systems.

▲ Tracpipe joint

trade effluent

This is water discharged after industrial use and processes have taken place.

transformer

An electrical device consisting of a magnetic core and one or more windings, used to change the *voltage* of an a.c. circuit from one value to another. A transformer may be used on a construction site to change the voltage of the electricity, normally supplied at 240 V a.c. to 110 V a.c. required to use a power tool.

trap

A device that prevents the passage of foul air by means of a water seal.

trap seal depth

The depth of water that would have to be removed from a fully-charged trap before gases and odours at *atmospheric pressure* could pass through the trap, as shown in the diagram. The *Building Regulations* require that traps to waste appliances in a *sanitary pipework* system must retain a minimum trap seal depth of 25 mm under all operating conditions.

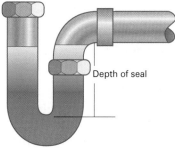

Depth of seal

▲ Trap seal depth

trap seal loss

There are a number of ways in which trap seals may be lost:

- *Evaporation* – this occurs in warm weather when the trap is not being used, with the water in the seal simply evaporating.
- Wavering – this is caused by excessive wind pressure across the top of the stack vent, creating a wave motion in the trap (usually WCs) and causing water to wash over the weir of the trap.
- Momentum – a large volume of water, such as flushing with a bucket, removes the seal of the trap.

A
B
C
D
E
F
G
H
I
J
K
L
M
N
O
P
Q
R
S
T
U
V
W
X
Y
Z

- Capillary action – in S traps this is caused by a thread of material overhanging into the trap seal and into the discharge pipe; water is then lost from the seal by capillary action.
- Self-siphonage – this commonly occurs in basins. A partial vacuum is created in the discharge pipe between the water plug and the basin. This negative pressure can *siphon* the water out of the trap, particularly if the water empties quickly. Self-siphonage can be avoided by ensuring that branch pipes are not too long and are laid to correct falls. If it occurs, it can be eliminated by fitting *ventilating pipework* to the appliance or, more commonly, by fitting a *resealing trap*.
- Induced siphonage – as the water plug flows past the second appliance connection, negative pressure is created between the pipe and appliance which can siphon the contents of the second trap. This is why care needs to be taken when connecting two appliances into a common discharge pipe with the *primary ventilated stack system*. The problem can be cured by installing ventilation pipework to the two appliances or fitting resealing traps.
- Compression – as water is discharged into a stack from upper-floor levels it creates a compression effect (*back pressure*) at the base of the stack which can be sufficient to remove a trap seal. This is why *long radius bends* must be used at the foot of the stack, and branch connections must not occur within 450 mm of the invert of the stack for buildings up to three storeys.

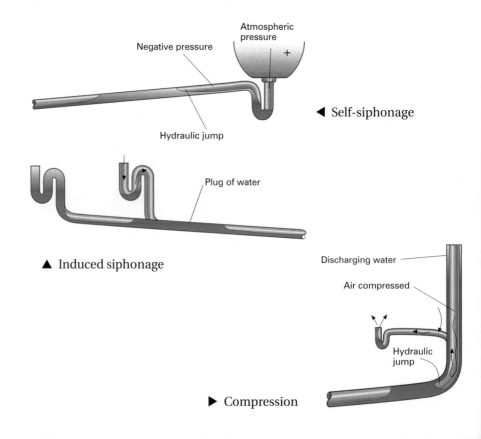

Atmospheric pressure

Negative pressure

◀ Self-siphonage

Hydraulic jump

Plug of water

▲ Induced siphonage

Discharging water

Air compressed

Hydraulic jump

▶ Compression

trapped gully

A type of *gully* that includes a *trap* which is usually connected to a *black water* drainage system as compared with an untrapped or trapless gully which is connected to a *surface water* drain. See *Gully*

trestles

If a task cannot be completed using a *ladder* or *stepladder*, a trestle scaffold can be used. Two trestles or 'A' frames are spanned using trestle scaffold boards to provide a safe working platform. Erect trestle scaffolds on a solid, level base with the trestles fully open and all the feet in full contact with the ground. Construct the platform using at least two boards of equal length and place these no higher than two-thirds of the way up the trestle. The overhang should not be less than four times the thickness of the board. A platform higher than 2 m must have toe boards, guardrails and a separate access ladder. A trestle can never be placed higher than 4.5 m.

trough urinal

A type of urinal comprising a long wall-mounted trough section, usually manufactured from *stainless steel*. There are no sections or dividers along the trough.

trunk main

The very large water mains that are used to supply water from the treatment works to the distribution mains and to supply water from town to town.

TRVs

See *Thermostatic radiator valves*

tube bending

See *Pipe bending*

tubular swivel trap

A type of *trap* that is useful when replacing components and connecting to an existing waste pipe; they are also commonly used on sinks with multiple bowls.

tubular trap

A type of trap formed from tubular sections of connecting pipework (e.g. a *P trap*).

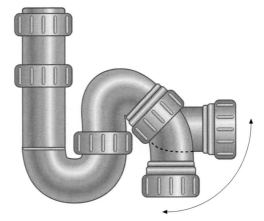

▲ Tubular swivel trap

A
B
C
D
E
F
G
H
I
J
K
L
M
N
O
P
Q
R
S
T
U
V
W
X
Y
Z

tundish

A component which provides an air break in a discharge pipe. A tundish can be used in a variety of systems, including an *unvented hot-water system*, where it provides visibility in the event of a discharge from the *pressure-* or *temperature-relief valves* and prevents pressurisation in the system should the discharge pipe become blocked.

twin-wall flue pipe

There are two types of flue pipe: one is fully insulated and one has an *air gap*. In *open-flue* gas systems the type with an air gap can only be used internally or for a maximum of 3 m externally. The fully-insulated twin-wall pipe should be used for all other installations.

twist drill

The type of drill bit used to make holes in wood or metal.

▲ Tundish

two-pipe central-heating system

A central-heating system which contains separate *flow* and *return pipework*. Each *heat emitter* is therefore supplied with water at the same *temperature*. The heat emitters usually require *balancing* to ensure that the correct water-flow rate is provided to each. See *One-pipe semi-gravity central-heating system; Two-pipe semi-gravity central-heating system*

two-pipe oil supply

See *Oil-supply system*

two-pipe reversed return

See *Reversed return*

two-pipe semi-gravity central-heating system

A type of central-heating system that was popular in the past, however under the *Building Regulations* it is only now suitable for use in *solid-fuel* heating systems as no *boiler control interlock* is provided – an essential feature of new systems fired by oil or gas. Key features of the system are: the heating circuit is a conventional pumped two-pipe circuit and the hot-water circuit operates by *gravity circulation*, in which there is usually no temperature control other than that provided by the boiler *thermostat*.

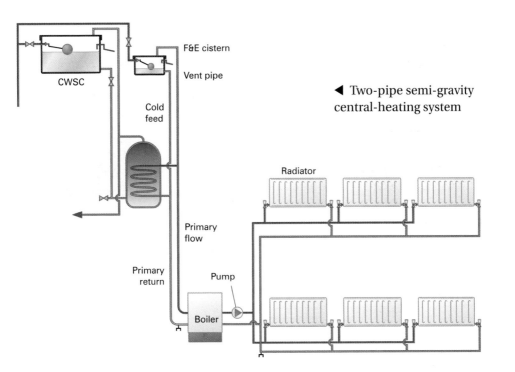

F&E cistern

Vent pipe

CWSC

Cold feed

◀ Two-pipe semi-gravity central-heating system

Radiator

Primary flow

Primary return

Pump

Boiler

A
B
C
D
E
F
G
H
I
J
K
L
M
N
O
P
Q
R
S
T
U
V
W
X
Y
Z

two-port valve (two-port motorised valve)

This valve is used on *fully-pumped systems* in domestic properties to give greater flexibility in system design. Extra valves may be added to the system to zone separate parts of the building and to provide separate temperature control for both heating and hot-water circuits. For two-port valves, the water must flow in the same direction as the arrow on the valve. See *Motorised valve; Types of fully-pumped central-heating system*

▲ Two-port motorised valve

types of central heating

Whole-house central heating is the simultaneous heating of all spaces in a domestic property so as to maintain specified temperatures based on calculated heat losses from the rooms. *Part-house central heating* is the simultaneous heating of some of the spaces in a domestic property so as to maintain specified temperatures based on calculated *heat losses* from the rooms. *Background central heating* is the simultaneous heating of all or some of the spaces in a domestic property to a temperature below that normally recommended in *British Standards* based upon calculated heat losses from the rooms.

types of drainage system

There are three types of *drainage system*:

- Combined system – a system in which the discharge from sanitary appliances *(black water)* and rainwater *(surface water)* all go into the one *sewer*.
- Separate system – a system in which black water is run into the one sewer and surface water to another. The surface water sewer will typically discharge into a nearby stream or river.
- Partially separate system – in this system there are two sewer connections but some of the surface water is discharged into a *soakaway*.

Plumbers clearly need to be able to recognise the type of drainage system to a property in order that they do not discharge black water, in particular, to a surface water sewer where it may present a health hazard. Surface-water-only pipework need not contain *trapped gullies* designed to prevent the spread of noxious smells. All black water systems and combination systems must contain gullies that are trapped.

svp = soil vent pipe
rwp = rainwater pipe
fwg = foulwater gully

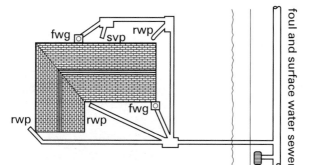

◀ Combined drainage system

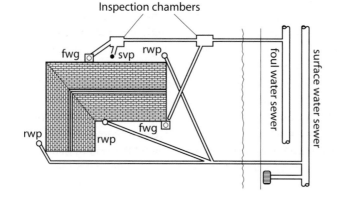

◀ Separate drainage system

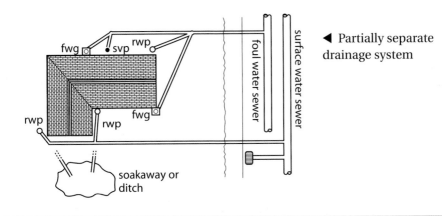

◀ Partially separate drainage system

System	Advantages	Disadvantages
Combined	• Cheap and easy to install • Gets a good flush-out during periods of heavy rain	• More costly to treat the water at the sewage works • At times of heavy rain, inadequately sized drains could overflow • All gullies have to be trapped
Separate	• No need for water treatment of surface water • No need for trapped gullies on surface water drains	• Danger of cross-connections – foul to surface water
Partially separate systems	• Greater flexibility with the system design	• Danger of cross-connection

▲ Advantages and disadvantages of different drainage systems

types of fully pumped central heating

A type of wet central-heating system in which both the heating and hot-water circuits are fully pumped. This system is mainly used with gas- and oil-fired installations and meets the requirements of the *Building Regulations* by having full *boiler control interlock*. There are essentially two types of control system that are used: two × *two-port valves* and a three-port *mid-position valve*. The system must include a *programmer*, providing time control to both the heating and hot-water circuits; the heating circuit is controlled by a *room thermostat*, whereas the hot-water circuit is controlled by a *cylinder thermostat*. The operation of the pump and boiler is based on demand from either circuit, with the last circuit to turn off isolating both the pump and boiler, thereby providing boiler control interlock.

A B C D E F G H I J K L M N O P Q R S T U V W X Y Z

A
B
C
D
E
F
G
H
I
J
K
L
M
N
O
P
Q
R
S
T
U
V
W
X
Y
Z

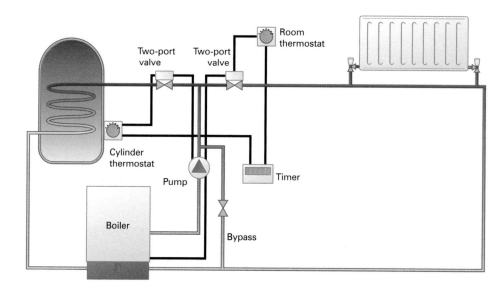

▲ Fully-pumped heating system with two × two-port motorised valves

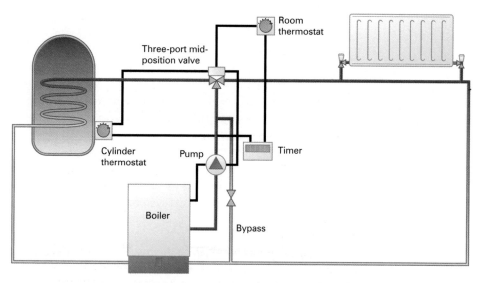

▲ Fully-pumped system with three-port mid-position valve

types of sanitary pipework system

There are three main types of sanitary pipework system:

- *Primary ventilated stack* system (previously known as the single-stack system) – this is used in situations where appliances are closely grouped around the stack and the stack is large enough to limit pressure fluctuations without the need for a separate *ventilating stack*.

- Secondary ventilated stack system (previously known as the modified stack system) – this system can be used where there are pressure fluctuations in the stack that could affect *trap* seals. All appliances must be closely grouped around the main stack, eliminating the need for *branch ventilating pipework*.
- Ventilated branch discharge system (previously known as the fully ventilated one-pipe system) – this type of system is used in circumstances where there may be large numbers of sanitary fittings in ranges or where appliances have to be dispersed at a distance from the main *discharge stack*. (See diagram overleaf.)

The discharge stack is connected to a *ventilating stack* in order to minimise pressure build-up in the system and provide ventilation to the drains. It may be possible in certain circumstances to use an *air admittance valve* as an alternative to the ventilating stack. There are key requirements laid down for the design of systems aimed at minimising the possibility of *trap seal loss*; these are covered in Approved Document H to the *Building Regulations*, which can be freely accessed at: www.communities.gov.uk

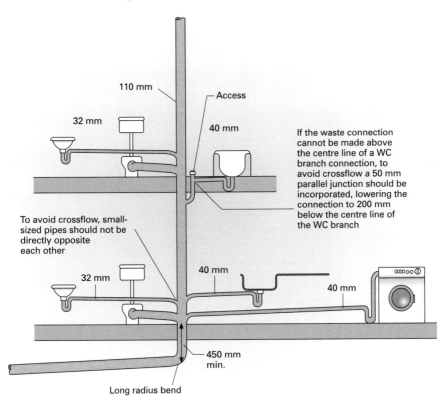

▲ Primary ventilated stack system

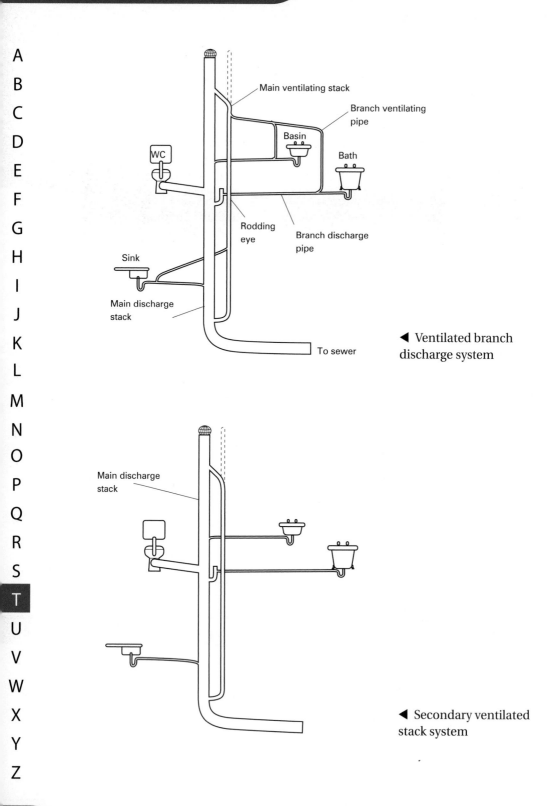

Main ventilating stack

Branch ventilating pipe

Basin

WC

Bath

Rodding eye

Branch discharge pipe

Sink

Main discharge stack

To sewer

◀ Ventilated branch discharge system

Main discharge stack

◀ Secondary ventilated stack system

U duct

A type of flue system used in multi-storey dwellings which contains a U-shaped vertical duct with openings at the roof. Fresh air is drawn through an inlet by the *convection* currents set up by the heated *products of combustion* in the other side of the U, that are discharged to atmosphere. A special type of *room-sealed flued appliance* must be fitted to the flue system; replacements must therefore be of that type.

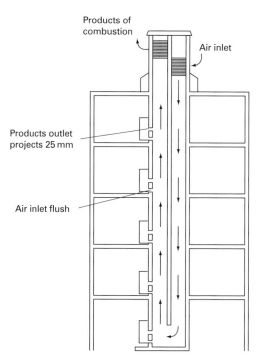

Products of combustion

Air inlet

Products outlet projects 25 mm

Air inlet flush

▲ U-duct flue system

A
B
C
D
E
F
G
H
I
J
K
L
M
N
O
P
Q
R
S
T
U
V
W
X
Y
Z

U gauge
> See *Manometer*

U value
> See *Thermal transmission rate*

unbalanced pressure
> The water supply to a sanitary appliance, such as a bath or wash basin, where the hot and cold supplies are at different pressures, hence the term 'unbalanced pressure'. See *Balanced pressure*

undercloak
> The undercloak is the piece of lead that fits underneath another piece of lead at the joint known as the *overcloak*. It is used in the jointing of *sheet weathering* components.

undercutting
> When *lead welding*, the thickness of lead sheet at the joint may be reduced if the flame is held for too long on the lead surface. This is called undercutting; it weakens the lead and may result in cracks on the weld line.

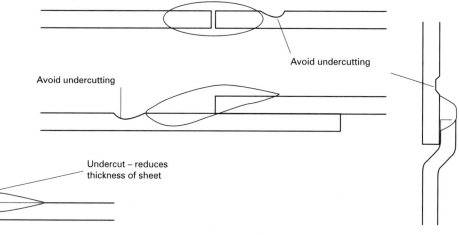

Avoid undercutting

Avoid undercutting

Undercut – reduces
thickness of sheet

▲ Undercutting

underfloor heating
> A type of wet *central-heating system* that employs loops of pipework that are laid under the flooring surface to heat the room. The underfloor heating system removes the need for *heat emitters* that some people may regard as unsightly. The design of the heating system tends to be different as the water temperature flowing through the system is less than with a conventional system – it is typically 43–55°C. Each individual room is piped back to a central manifold to control the pipe circuit to that room.

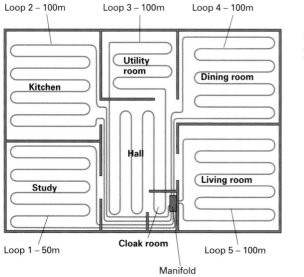

Loop 2 – 100m   Loop 3 – 100m   Loop 4 – 100m

Kitchen

Utility room

Dining room

Hall

Study

Living room

Cloak room

Loop 1 – 50m   Loop 5 – 100m

Manifold

◀ Typical underfloor heating pipe layout

A
B
C
D
E
F
G
H
I
J
K
L
M
N
O
P
Q
R
S
T
U
V
W
X
Y
Z

underground water pipes and fittings

Underground water pipes must be laid at least 750 mm deep. If the ground is uneven, the same rule applies and the pipe laying must be carefully planned. If the 750 mm depth proves impossible, the *water undertaker* must be notified and other protection measures may need to be applied, for example a load-bearing slab and waterproof insulation. Underground water fittings are subject to the same rule; the 750 mm depth also protects the pipe and fittings from ground movement, traffic vibrations and digging. Fittings should never be placed on pipework at a depth greater than 1350 mm as maintenance or repair work may prove difficult.

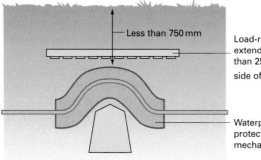

Less than 750 mm

Load-relieving slab extending not less than 250 mm either side of trench

Waterproof insulation protecting against mechanical damage

▲ Protecting underground pipes

A
B
C
D
E
F
G
H
I
J
K
L
M
N
O
P
Q
R
S
T
U
V
W
X
Y
Z

underlay

An underlay is laid underneath sheet roof coverings in order to:

- minimise noise from rain
- provide insulation against heat loss
- prevent condensate forming on the underside of the lead, which may lead to *electrolytic corrosion* between the lead and its fixing materials
- assist the lead in moving when heated or cooled (*thermal movement*) across the surface of the roof.

Underlays can be in the form of building paper or an inodorous felt.

unheated spaces – frost precautions

Water pipes and fittings should not be installed external to the building or in unheated parts of buildings. If it is unavoidable, and pipework and components have to be installed in unheated parts of the building, such as outbuildings and garages, they must be protected from frost. See *Insulation material thickness*

union connector

A type of *disconnecting joint* used on *low-carbon steel* pipework. The union connector comprises two *female threaded* pieces that are joined with a large nut. It is used extensively where the two pipe ends cannot easily be spread apart or to joint two long lengths of pipe that will normally require opposing clockwise and counter-clockwise insertion into the fittings.

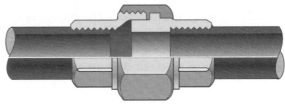

▲ Union connector

unplasticised polyvinyl chloride

A type of *polyvinyl chloride* in which no plasticiser has been added to reduce the brittleness of the plastic, known as UPVC or PVC-u. It is therefore susceptible to damage by a heavy blow. Most *plastics* used in sanitary and drainage pipework systems are unplasticised plastics.

unsafe situations procedure

A procedure agreed by the gas industry for categorising and dealing with gas faults in systems and components. There are three classifications of unsafe situation:

- Immediately dangerous – an installation that is an immediate danger to life or property if it is operated or left connected to the gas supply.
- At risk – an installation that could create a risk to life or property.

- Not to current standards – other situations that are not immediately dangerous or at risk, such as an older installation which does not meet the modifications laid down by a new *British Standard*.

The unsafe situations procedure lays down key actions to be taken by the plumbing operative on establishing an unsafe situation based on the categories shown above, including possible isolation, appliance labelling and issue of warning notices. Certain immediately dangerous situations are reportable to the Health and Safety Executive.

untrapped gully

A type of *gully* used on drainage systems receiving *surface water* only, that do not require a *trap*.

unvented hot-water system

A type of pressurised hot-water system that takes its cold-water supply straight from the *supply pipe*. The system is a type of closed system that does not have an *open vent pipe* to atmosphere, operating at higher pressures of typically 2 to 3.5 bar pressure. The system, in order to comply with *Building Regulations* and *Water Regulations,* requires a number of specific safety controls and functional

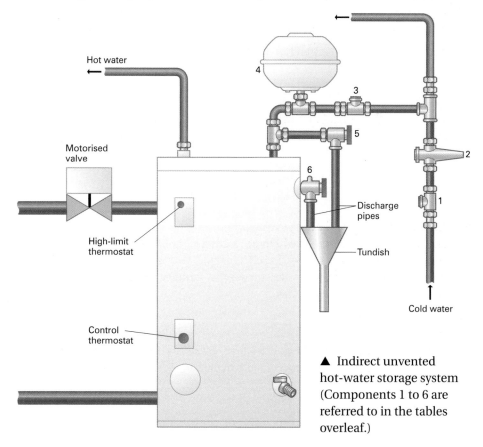

▲ Indirect unvented hot-water storage system (Components 1 to 6 are referred to in the tables overleaf.)

A
B
C
D
E
F
G
H
I
J
K
L
M
N
O
P
Q
R
S
T
U
V
W
X
Y
Z

controls. Water that discharges from the *temperature-relief valve* or the *expansion valve* must be safely discharged to waste by a correctly routed discharge pipe in order to prevent scalding of any passers-by. Under the *Building Regulations* this type of system must only be installed by a competent person and the installation must either be notified to the local building control department or the installation must be carried out by a member of a competent person's self-certification scheme.

Safety item 1	Control thermostat	Controls the water temperature in the cylinder to between 60 and 65°C
Safety item 2	High-limit thermostat (energy cut-out device)	A non-self-resetting device that isolates the heat source at a temperature of around 80–85°C
Safety item 3	Temperature-relief valve (Component 6)	Discharges water from the cylinder at a temperature of 90–95°C (water is dumped from the system and replaced by cooler water to prevent boiling)

▲ Safety devices in an unvented hot-water system

Line strainer (Component 1)	Prevents grit and debris entering the system from the water supply (causing the controls to malfunction)
Pressure-reducing valve (on older systems may be pressure-limiting valve) (Component 2)	Gives a fixed maximum water pressure
Single-check valve (Component 3)	Stops stored hot water entering the cold water supply pipe (a contamination risk)
Expansion vessel or cylinder air gap (Component 4)	Takes up the increased volume of water in the system from the heating process
Expansion valve (Component 5)	Operates if the pressure in the system rises above design limits of the expansion device (i.e. the cylinder air gap or expansion vessel fail)
Isolating (stop) valve	Isolates the water supply from the system (for maintenance)

▲ Functional devices in an unvented hot-water system

unwholesome water

Unwholesome water is not fit for drinking. Water suppliers are required to ensure that water is clean, free from impurities and fit for drinking. Plumbers are responsible for ensuring that water supplied is not contaminated by the installation and commissioning of water systems. Recycled water or other water supplies that are not fit for drinking must be clearly labelled to ensure that they are not cross-connected with *wholesome water* supplies.

upland surface water

Water sources in hills and mountains, such as *impounding reservoirs*, lakes and natural reservoirs. This is a relatively clean source of water as there is very little contact with pollutants.

upper flammability level (UFL)

See *Flammability level*

UPSO/OPSO valve

See *OPSO/UPSO valve*

upstream

A point in a pipeline before the component being considered, for example a *communication pipe* is upstream of the *supply pipe* in a cold-water system.

urinal

Non-domestic sanitary appliance for males. Most urinals are flushed by an *automatic flushing cistern* or a *pressure flushing valve*. The diagram shows a typical urinal setup with individual wall-fixed bowls. Slab urinals have a *flush pipe* mounted on the face. This is called a *sparge pipe*, which has a number of holes that emit water to wash the face of the slab and the channel. Trough urinals consisting of a long trough are also manufactured. Stall urinals were commonly manufactured in the past but do not now tend to be that popular; these are similar to slabs but there are individual sub-divisions between each urinal position.

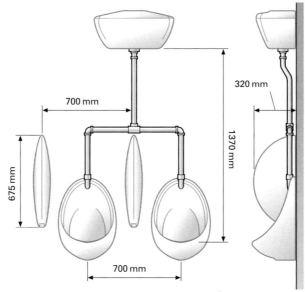

▲ Typical two-bowl urinal layout

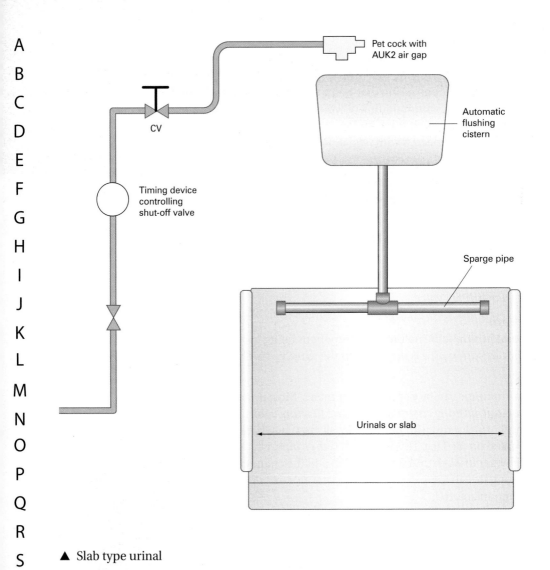

Pet cock with
AUK2 air gap

Automatic
flushing
cistern

CV

Timing device
controlling
shut-off valve

Sparge pipe

Urinals or slab

▲ Slab type urinal

ABCDEFGHIJKLMNOPQRSTU **V** WXYZ

vacuum

An enclosed space or container from which air has been removed; a space empty of all matter.

vacuum break

See *Anti-vacuum valve*

valley gutter

The sheet-lead weathering that is formed where two sloping roof surfaces meet. A valley gutter may be of the open type with exposed sheet lead or may be of a *secret gutter* type with minimal lead exposure.

▶ Valley gutter

Saddle

Two rows of head fixings

Mortar bedding on plain tile slips

Welt

valve

A component used to regulate the flow of fluid in a system. The valve may be of the direct on/off pattern or may place a restriction in the pipeline to the flow of the fluid. There are many examples of valves, for example *non-return valve*, *check valve*, *screwdown stop valve*, etc.

vanity basin

A type of *wash basin* fixed into a cabinet or a worktop.

vaporising burner

A type of oil-fired burner in which the oil is warmed to change its state, to a gas, where it is mixed with air and readily ignited. There are three types of vaporising burner: *natural draught burner*, *forced draught burner* (includes a fan) and *rotary vaporising burner*. The oil flow into a vaporising burner is controlled by a *solenoid valve* feeding into a *constant oil level control*. The solenoid valve is operated by a *thermostat* based on the heat requirements from the appliance. The oil is supplied at a constant fixed rate and level by the constant oil level control and is ignited by glowing igniters sited in the appliance. A vaporising burner is typically used with an oil-fired range cooker that may include a boiler.

vapour

The gaseous form of a substance that is normally a liquid, for example water vapour.

vapour barrier

An *impervious* membrane (usually a *plastic*) inserted into building components to prevent moisture penetration as a result of condensation from passing into components such as timber and causing rotting.

vapour-pressure flame failure device

A type of mechanical *flame failure device* used on room/water heaters and cooker ovens (see diagram opposite). Heated liquid eventually turns into vapour with a much greater volume. The increased volume creates a higher pressure which is used to operate the valve, either opening or closing it.

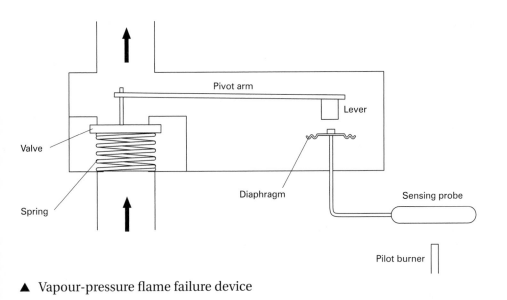

▲ Vapour-pressure flame failure device

velocity

The speed at which a fluid travels through a pipe or component.

vent pipe (water systems)

A pipe connecting a water system to the atmosphere. The vent pipe that is fitted at a high point in a system ensures that air is vented from the system on filling, and in an overheat situation, pressure in the system cannot build up because a safe route is provided for hot water and steam flow from the storage vessel or boiler into the cistern. A vent pipe from a *primary circuit* must not terminate over a wholesome water storage cistern used for domestic supply or for supplying water to a *secondary circuit*. Vent pipes from a secondary circuit must not terminate over any combined *feed-and-expansion cistern* connected to a primary circuit.

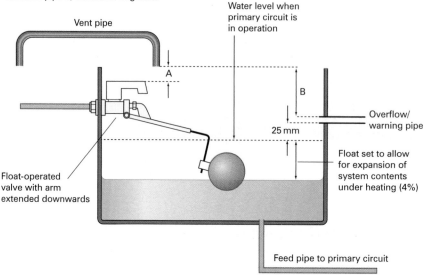

Vent pipe to terminate not less than twice the diameter of the vent pipe above the top of the float-operated valve A or the top of the overflow pipe B, whichever is greater

Vent pipe

Water level when primary circuit is in operation

A

B

25 mm

Overflow/warning pipe

Float set to allow for expansion of system contents under heating (4%)

Float-operated valve with arm extended downwards

Feed pipe to primary circuit

▲ Vent pipe requirements (primary system)

vent pipe (discharge systems)

See *Ventilating pipe*

vented hot-water system

A hot-water system which includes a *vent pipe* and where the *cold-water storage vessel* is connected by a cold-feed pipe to the *hot-water storage vessel*.

ventilated stack system

See *Types of sanitary pipework system*

ventilating pipe

A pipe provided to limit the pressure fluctuations in a *discharge pipework* system. See *Types of sanitary pipework system*

ventilating stack

A main *ventilating pipe* connected to a *discharge stack* to limit pressure fluctuations in the discharge stack.

ventilation

This is the process of supplying fresh air to an *open-flued* appliance for combustion purposes, or an air supply to an open-flued or room-sealed appliance sited in a *compartment* for the purpose of cooling the appliance. The

Building Regulations approved documents detail ventilation rates for specific types of appliance; they can be freely accessed at: www.communities.gov.uk

venturi

A device used in a gas-fired water heater to create a *differential* pressure in a water pipe which can then activate a diaphragm to control the gas flow to the appliance.

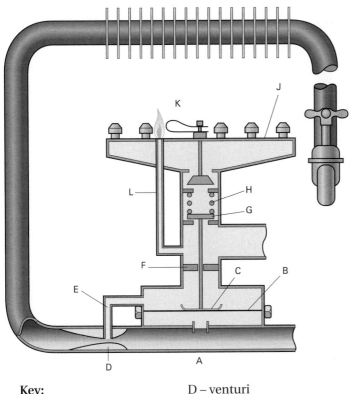

Key:

A – automatic valve/ diaphragm housing
B – rubber diaphragm
C – bearing plate
D – venturi
E – low-pressure side
F – gland for push rod
G – gas valve
H – gas-valve spring
J – burner
K – flame supervision (bi-metal strip)
L – pilot feed

▲ Heat exchanger operation – closed position, showing venturi

verdigris

A green coating which can form on *copper* pipework and components. Verdigris occurs when copper comes into contact with an *acidic* material such as a corrosive flux. Verdigris can slowly destroy the metal by *corrosion*, therefore contact with the acidic substance should be prevented.

vertex flues (type C7)

A type of *room-sealed flue* (not now commonly used) which takes the air supply for combustion from the roof/loft space. The secondary flue is connected to a *draught break* in the roof space which must be at least 300 mm above the level of any insulation. No bend should be made in the flue before 600 mm beyond the draught break.

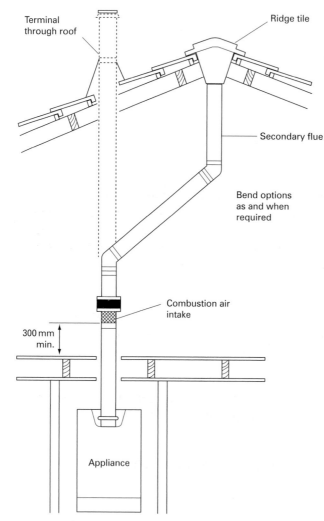

▲ Vertex flue

vessel charge pressure

The air or *nitrogen* charge pressure in an *expansion vessel*. The vessel is charged prior to system filling, or when the system is at *atmospheric pressure* to the design charge of the system. For an *unvented hot-water system* this will be the usual working pressure of the system set by the *pressure-reducing valve*.

viscosity

A measure of the internal friction or resistance of a fluid to flow. As the *temperature* of an oil is increased, its viscosity decreases and it is therefore able to flow more readily.

vitiated air

Air that has lower than normal levels of *oxygen*.

vitiation sensing device

See *Atmospheric sensing device (ASD)*

vitreous china

A *ceramic* material made by combining white burning clays and finely ground materials, and firing the mixture at high temperatures. The cooled china is then finished with a coat of impervious non-crazing vitreous (glassy) glaze. The final product is very hygienic, stain-proof, burn-proof, rot-proof, rust-free, non-fading and resistant to *acids* and *alkalis*.

vitreous enamel

A coating provided to *pressed steel* and *cast-iron* components, such as baths, to provide protection against *corrosion* and a cosmetic coating which is pleasing to the eye and easily cleaned.

vitreous-enamelled steel flues

A single-skin pipe with a cosmetic easy-clean coating, used to connect an appliance to the main *flue*, often with a *disconnecting joint*.

voltage

A measurement of electromotive force, expressed as volts.

A
B
C
D
E
F
G
H
I
J
K
L
M
N
O
P
Q
R
S
T
U
V
W
X
Y
Z

A
B
C
D
E
F
G
H
I
J
K
L
M
N
O
P
Q
R
S
T
U
V
W
X
Y
Z

voltage-indicating device

A device used to measure the presence of voltage in a circuit. The voltage-indicating device is used during an electrical safe isolation procedure to ensure that a circuit is dead and is therefore safe to work on. The device should be clearly marked to show the maximum voltage that can be tested and should be fitted with *current* protection, such as a *fuse* up to 500 mA or a current-limiting resistor and a fuse.

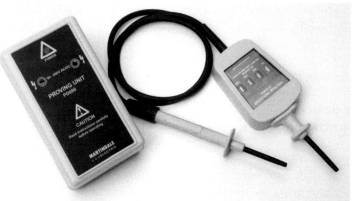

▲ An approved voltage indicating device

voltmeter

A device used to measure *voltage*, and to test batteries and electrical outlets.

volume

The amount of space occupied by a three-dimensional object as measured in cubic units. The volume of an object is calculated by the formula: length × breadth × height.

wall bolt

A strong masonry fixing, having a tapered end with segments which expand against the masonry when the nut is tightened. The wall bolt is used for making fixings to heavy plumbing components.

wall-mounted boiler

A type of boiler that is mounted on a wall surface rather than free standing on the floor.

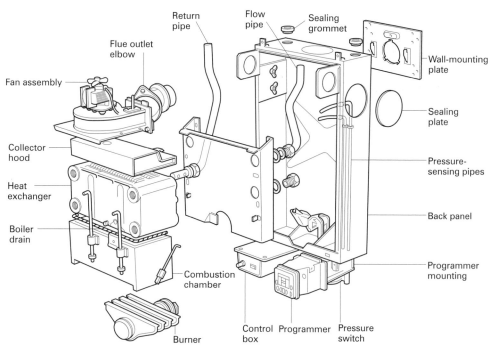

Return pipe · Flow pipe · Sealing grommet · Flue outlet elbow · Fan assembly · Wall-mounting plate · Collector hood · Sealing plate · Heat exchanger · Pressure-sensing pipes · Boiler drain · Back panel · Combustion chamber · Programmer mounting · Burner · Control box · Programmer · Pressure switch

▲ Typical wall-mounted gas boiler with fanned flue

A
B
C
D
E
F
G
H
I
J
K
L
M
N
O
P
Q
R
S
T
U
V
W
X
Y
Z

wallplate

This is timber placed for floors or ceiling joists to rest on. For example, a timber wallplate is used to spread the floor load evenly across a *honeycomb wall*. The floor joists are laid in the opposite direction.

warm air central-heating system

A type of dry *central-heating system* in which air is heated by a gas- or oil-fired burner via a ducted air heater which contains an air-to-air *heat exchanger*. The warm heated air is distributed throughout the building via a series of *ducts* which discharge warm air to the room via a series of air grilles. The air grilles must be carefully positioned in order that warm air reaches all parts of the room but does not cause excessive draughts. Cooler air is then returned via return air grilles and a further ducting system for reheating by the ducted air heater.

warning pipe

A warning pipe is used to alert the occupiers of a building to the fact that a *cistern* is overflowing and needs attention. Domestic cisterns of up to 1000 litres must have a warning pipe and no *overflow pipe*; a warning pipe for a small cistern should have a minimum internal diameter of 19 mm. Cisterns over 1000 litres should have a warning pipe and an overflow pipe. In domestic cisterns, the warning pipe should be installed with a minimum air gap of 25 mm between the invert level of the warning pipe and the normal water level, and have a continuous fall to the point of discharge. A *float-operated valve* should also be installed to ensure a minimum air gap between the valve outlet and the cistern spill-over level at the warning pipe.

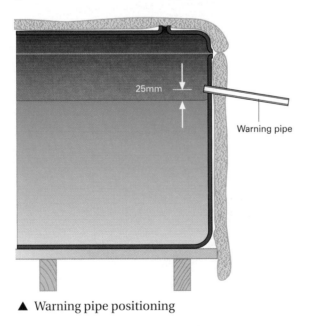

▲ Warning pipe positioning

wash basin

A sanitary appliance used for washing the upper parts of the body. There are essentially two types of wash basin: fixed-to-the-wall basins and countertop basins. Fixed-to-the-wall basins come in two types: pedestal-wash hand basins and wall-hung basins. Pedestal-wash hand basins tend to be more popular in domestic properties as they allow the connecting pipework to be easily hidden. There is a wide range of fixing devices available to mount wall-hung basins; manufacturer installation instructions should be referred to for greater detail. The *hand-rinse basin* is a type of small wall-mounted basin fitted in cloakrooms for the purposes of hand washing. There are three types of countertop basin: countertop, which sits proud of the work surface, semi-countertop, which is used to save space, and under countertop, in which the basin sits under the counter. Basins are usually manufactured from *vitreous china*, however countertops are available manufactured from acrylic (plastic); stainless-steel wall-hung basins are available for areas where damage may occur, such as in kitchens. Basins are available with 1, 2 or 3 tap-holes, dependent on the type of taps being used. A 1¼" waste is usually provided for normal domestic basins.

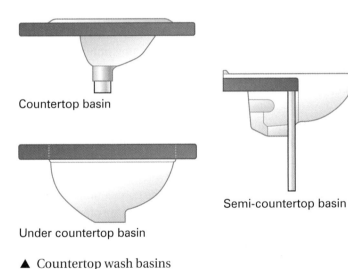

Countertop basin

Semi-countertop basin

Under countertop basin

▲ Countertop wash basins

washdown WC pan

A type of *WC pan* that removes the pan contents by the force of water created during flushing (See illustration overleaf).

A
B
C
D
E
F
G
H
I
J
K
L
M
N
O
P
Q
R
S
T
U
V
W
X
Y
Z

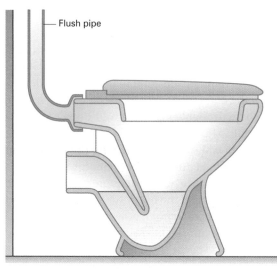

Flush pipe

▲ Washdown WC pan

washing fountain

A circular type hand-washing fountain, typically used in factories for a large number of people to be able to wash their hands at the same time.

washing-machine/dishwasher waste connections

There are two methods of making the waste connection to a washing machine or a dishwasher:

- 40 mm diameter washing-machine *trap* with *stand pipe* into which the U-shaped flexible hose from the washing machine is inserted
- 40 mm combined-sink trap with washing machine/dishwasher connection to which the flexible hose is directly connected and secured with a jubilee clip. The flexible hose must be routed so that, prior to the connection, it rises to above the height of the sink overflow; this is to eliminate the possibility of the sink contents being discharged into the washing machine/dishwasher.

Stand pipe

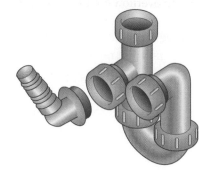

▲ Washing-machine trap and combined-sink trap

washing-machine tap

The *service valve* fitted to the hot- and cold-water connections to a washing machine or the cold water to a dishwasher. A *lever-operated spherical plug valve* is normally used for this purpose.

washing-machine trap

See *Washing-machine waste connections*

washout pipe

A pipe that is sometimes fitted to very large *storage cisterns* for the purpose of cleansing them and removing any deposits that have built up.

waste appliances

These are sanitary appliances that are used for washing and food production purposes, for example baths, basins, showers and sinks. See *Soil appliances*

waste disposal

There are regulations covering the disposal of certain waste materials and appliances, for example:

- Only certified tradespeople are allowed to remove and dispose of *asbestos*.
- Refrigerators must be taken to specialist sites.
- Plumbing companies must have a waste carrier's licence to move waste materials on the road.

waste-disposal unit

See *food waste disposal unit*

waste fitting

The fitting that makes a watertight seal between a waste appliance and the appliance *trap*. There are several types of waste fitting, including:

- *Slotted waste* – used with waste appliances that have overflows, such as wash basins. (See illustration overleaf.)
- Unslotted waste – used with waste appliances that do not have overflows, such as *shower trays*.
- *Combination waste fitting* – used with waste appliances to form a combined waste and overflow connection, for example at sinks and baths.
- *Pop-up wastes* – a luxury item that removes the need for a plug chain, with the waste plug operated by a lever mechanism.

Modern wastes may be made into the waste appliances with specially moulded seals provided with the waste fitting or using *silicone sealant* and plastic washers. On no account should putty or *jointing compound* be used with plastic waste appliances or plastic waste fittings as it degrades the *plastic* and causes breakdown.

▲ Making a slotted waste fitting to a wash basin

waste pipe
A pipe for carrying water from a *waste appliance*.

waste stack
A *discharge stack* which receives the discharge from *waste appliances* only. The minimum waste stack diameter is 50 mm.

waste water
This includes water which is contaminated by use and all water discharging into the *drainage system*, for example water containing faecal matter or urine, condensate water, and rainwater.

water
Water is liquid at standard *temperature* and *pressure*. It has the chemical formula H_2O, meaning that one molecule of water is composed of two hydrogen *atoms* and one oxygen atom. See *Hard water; pH value; Soft water*

water authority
See *Water undertaker*

water closet
A device used to convey waste products from the body – faecal matter and urine – to the *drainage system*. A water closet consists of two parts: a *WC pan*, into which the bodily waste is discharged, and a flushing mechanism, which is designed to flush the contents of the pan to the drainage system. The flushing mechanism can be either a *flushing valve*, where the pan is flushed direct from a supply or distributing pipe (this can only be used in non-domestic properties) or a *flushing cistern*. Water closets fed by flushing cisterns are available in the following patterns: *close-coupled WC suite*, in which the cistern and pan are joined together in one unit, a *low-level flushing cistern*, in which the cistern is no more than 1 m above the pan, and a *high-level flushing cistern*, in which the cistern is more than 1m above the pan and the flushing mechanism is usually operated by a chain.

water conditioner

A device designed to minimise the build-up of *scale* in water systems. The devices do not soften the water as in a *water softener*; they hold the calcium salts in suspension preventing them from precipitating out on to the surface of plumbing components. There are two main types of water conditioning device:

- Chemical conditioner (*scale reducer*), in which chemical additives are applied to the pipeline; these chemicals alter the *molecular* structure of the calcium salts, preventing them from bonding together; the scale reducer will need replenishing periodically.
- Magnetic or electronic water conditioner, where again the molecular structure of the salts is changed; electronic conditioners may be connected to the mains electricity supply by means of a *transformer*.

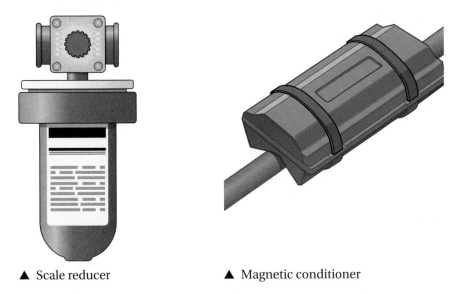

▲ Scale reducer   ▲ Magnetic conditioner

water expansion

Allowances for the expansion of water must be included in all water systems. Water expands when it cools below 0°C and turns to ice. If the water is in an enclosed space, for example a pipe, the pipe may break under the pressure. Water also expands when it is heated and hot-water systems need to have expansion allowances to prevent pressure build-up and potential damage to components. Up to 100°C, water expands by about 4 per cent of its original volume when heated; this expansion needs to be catered for in the system.

Water Fittings and Materials Directory

This directory lists chemicals, fittings and materials approved by *WRAS*. Always check that materials and fittings comply with relevant standards before using them. Manufacturers usually mark the product or its packing with a reference to the relevant quality standards. The Water Fittings and Materials Directory can be accessed online at: www.wras.co.uk

A B C D E F G H I J K L M N O P Q R S T U V W X Y Z

water gauge

See *Manometer*

water governor

Another name for a *pressure-reducing valve*, which is fitted to regulate water pressures.

water hammer

A loud noise caused by the sudden closure of a *valve* which sends shock waves along the pipework. Defective operation of *float-operated valves*, tap washers and unclipped pipework may cause this problem. Regular maintenance of these components may prevent water hammer altogether. The noise may be reduced by lowering the water-flow rate by installing a *pressure-reducing valve* and by clipping the pipework at regular intervals. Water hammer created by the quick closing of taps, such as *quarter-turn taps*, may require the installation of a *shock arrestor* which is a device designed to absorb the shock wave that has been set up in the pipeline.

water-jacketed tube heater

An appliance in which domestic hot water is heated inside a coil located within a large volume of stored primary hot water, that is, a reverse method of hot-water storage to an *indirect cylinder*.

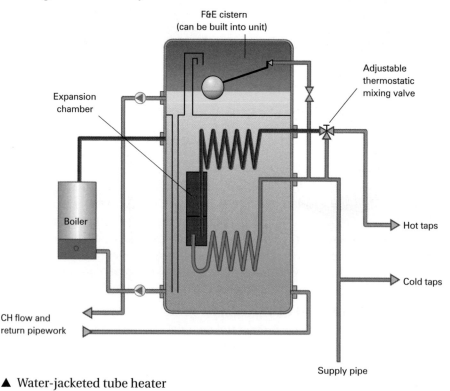

▲ Water-jacketed tube heater

water level

The finished water level in a storage vessel or cylinder when it is deemed to be full; for example the finished water level in a *cistern* is the level reached when the *float-operated valve* has closed.

water-level indicator

A device that can be used as an alternative to a *warning pipe* in a large *cistern*; the indicator gives off an audible alarm when the water reaches a pre-determined level identifying that the inlet control device needs attention.

water mains

The infrastructure network of water pipes that deliver a supply of *wholesome water* from large treatment works to domestic and commercial properties.

water meter

A device used to record the quantity of water that has been passed through it for the purpose of rendering an account to the customer. A new water meter to a domestic property is likely to be located with the supplier's *stop valve* in a chamber outside the property. Meters may also be sited inside a property.

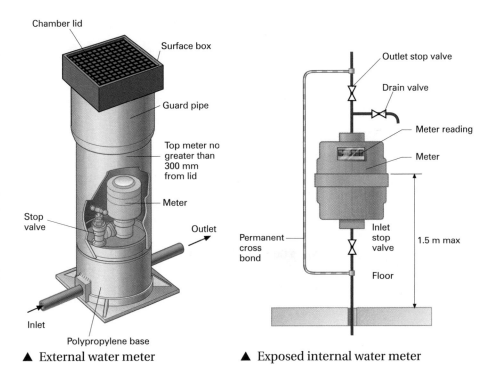

▲ External water meter   ▲ Exposed internal water meter

water pressure

The water pressure at an outlet that is not pumped is determined by the *head* of water over the outlet or *draw-off point*. There are two basic calculations that are used to determine the water pressure acting on components: intensity of pressure, which is the force acting on a component, and total pressure, which is the force acting over the total surface area of a component. The intensity of pressure of a column of water acting on a draw-off tap, if the water column is 6 metres high, is:

$6.0m \times 9.81 = 58.86 \text{ kN/m}^2$

The total pressure acting on a tank containing water with a head of 2.0 m and base dimensions of 2.0 m $\times$ 2.0 m is:

$2 \times 9.81 = 19.62 \text{ kN/m}^2$ - the intensity of pressure

Total pressure = $19.62 \times 2 \times 2 = 78.48$ kN

Water Regulations

The Water Supply (Water Fittings) Regulations 1999 apply to water installations in England and Wales. They provide a standardised approach to the installation of water fittings in England and Wales, replacing local bylaws that were in place previously and which applied to a local area.

Water Regulations Advisory Scheme (WRAS)

An independent organisation primarily supported by the *water undertakers* and industry bodies, which advises on the *Water Regulations*, approves fittings and materials, and produces a *Water Fittings and Materials Directory*.

▲ WRAS-approved product symbol

water softener

See *Base exchange water softener*

water table

The natural level of stationary underground water, below which the ground is waterlogged.

water test

A type of *soundness* test that can be undertaken on a new below ground *drainage system*. Key features of the test are:

- A *stand pipe* is erected at the high point of the drainage system.
- The lower ends of the system are capped using *drain plugs* or *inflatable stoppers*.
- The stand pipe is filled to a minimum height of 1.0 metres above the drain invert level and allowed to stand for a period of one hour to condition the pipe, topping up to the test water level at the end of this period as required.
- The test period is for a further 30 minutes during which time there should be no drop in water level greater than 0.15 litres/m^2 of pipework surface area or 0.2 litres/m^2 of pipework and *inspection chamber* surface area, if inspection chambers are included in the system.

Air testing of drainage systems is now more commonly used. See *Air test*

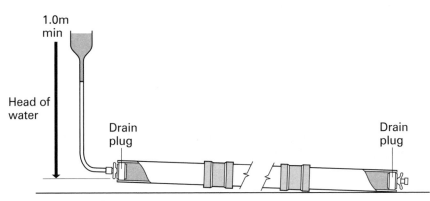

▲ Water test to drainage system

water undertaker
The correct legal term for the companies contracted by the government to supply wholesome water for domestic use and to ensure that systems and components are correctly installed.

waterline
The line in a *cistern* that indicates the finished water level. A *float-operated valve* should be adjusted so that it shuts off the supply of water when the waterline is reached.

waterway
The sections through a *heat exchanger* through which the water flows.

watt
A standard unit of power defined as one *joule* of energy transferred or dissipated in one second. Heating and electrical appliances are often rated in watts or kilowatts (1000 watts) related to their power consumption.

wavering out
See *Trap seal loss*

WC macerator
See *Macerator WC*

WC pan
A *soil appliance* designed to collect human waste in the form of faecal matter and urine and discharge it to the *drainage system*. There are many designs of WC pan, including floor-mounted and wall-mounted. There are two methods of WC pan operation: the *washdown WC pan* and the *siphonic WC pan*.

WC suite
See *Water closet*

A
B
C
D
E
F
G
H
I
J
K
L
M
N
O
P
Q
R
S
T
U
V
W
X
Y
Z

A
B
C
D
E
F
G
H
I
J
K
L
M
N
O
P
Q
R
S
T
U
V
W
X
Y
Z

weather compensator

In wet *central-heating systems* with *radiators*, a heating design engineer will calculate the size of the plant required (boilers, pumps, radiators, etc.) in order to achieve comfort conditions within the space with a boiler flow temperature of 82°C when the outside temperature is –1°C. It therefore follows that when the outside temperature is above –1°C, comfort conditions can be achieved with a boiler flow temperature of less than 82°C.

A compensator is commonly used in industrial/commercial situations where it measures the boiler flow temperature, the outside temperature and the room temperature, and adjusts the temperature of water to the flow pipe of the heating circuit through a mixing valve which is fed with hot water from the boiler flow pipe and cooler return water from the heating circuit. The compensator is essentially a sophisticated energy-saving device. See *Optimiser*

wedges

See *Lead wedges*

weight

See *Mass*

welding

The jointing of metals by heating, with or without the use of a filler rod. Welding can take place either using electricity or a gas flame.

welding blowpipe

The plumber may use three types of welding blowpipe when carrying out welding:

- Model O – used for *lead welding*.
- Model DH – used for heating activities such as *hard soldering*.
- Cutting blowpipe – used for cutting metal sheet and pipe by an injection of high pressure *oxygen*.

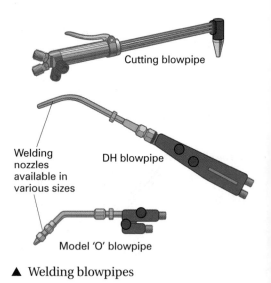

Cutting blowpipe

Welding nozzles available in various sizes

DH blowpipe

Model 'O' blowpipe

▲ Welding blowpipes

welding equipment

Key features of the use of lead welding equipment are:

- Lead welding is carried out using oxyacetylene as the heat source; oxygen cylinders are black, acetylene cylinders are maroon (lead welding can also take place using *LPG*).
- For general applications a lead welding torch is used with nozzle sizes 2 and 3 being used for sheet lead codes 4 and 5 respectively.
- Eye protection should be used (clear lenses) when lead welding in order to avoid molten lead splashing into the eyes.
- Flashback arrestors are needed to prevent flashback into the cylinders.
- The pressure gauges on both the oxygen and acetylene cylinders are set at 0.14 bar.
- When lighting, turn the acetylene on first, then light it, and then feed in the oxygen.
- A neutral flame will achieve the best results for lead welding.
- When turning off the welding torch, turn off the acetylene control first, then the oxygen control.

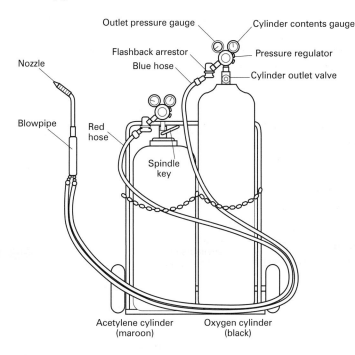

▲ Lead welding equipment

welding safety (lead welding)

The following is a safety checklist of the procedures that must be observed when lead welding:

1 Gas cylinders should be stored in a ventilated area on a firm base. If possible store *oxygen* and *acetylene* separately. Empty and full bottles should also be stored separately.
2 Acetylene gas bottles should be stored upright to prevent leakage of liquid.
3 Oxygen cylinders are highly pressurised. They should be stored and handled carefully to prevent falling. If the valve is sheared, the bottle will shoot forward with great force.
4 Keep the oxygen cylinder away from oil or grease as these materials will ignite in contact with oxygen under pressure.
5 Check the condition of the hoses and fittings. If they are punctured or damaged replace them. Do not try to repair or piece them together.
6 Do not allow acetylene to come into contact with *copper*. This produces an explosive compound.
7 Make sure the area where you are welding is well ventilated.
8 Erect signs or shields to warn and protect people from the process.
9 Always have fire-fighting equipment to hand.
10 Wear protective clothing: gloves, overalls, goggles (clear ones are suitable for lead welding).
11 Make sure that hose check valves are fitted to the blowpipe and *flashback* arrestors to the regulators.
12 Allow the acetylene to flow from the nozzle for a few seconds before lighting up.
13 In the event of a serious flashback or fire, plunge the nozzle into water, leaving the oxygen running to avoid water entering the blowpipe.

wells, shallow and deep

Shallow wells extend only into the top pervious layer of rock underground; water from this level has a greater risk of *contamination*. A shallow well may actually be 'longer' than a deep well. The term actually refers to the number of layers of rock the well travels through. Deep wells extend through the top pervious layer and the second impervious layer, down to the third layer of pervious rock. Water at this level is usually *wholesome* and may be used by a *water undertaker* as a back-up in case of drought.

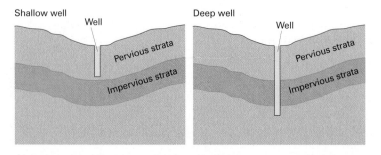

◄ A shallow well does not penetrat impervious strata. A deep wel penetrates throug impervious strata

wet-pipe sprinkler system

A type of sprinkler system which remains charged with water at all times. This system may be susceptible to freezing so additives in the form of anti-freeze may be required, or a dry-pipe sprinkler system may be considered as an alternative. See *Dry-pipe sprinkler system; Sprinkler systems – backflow prevention*

wet riser

A type of fire-fighting pipeline which includes *hydrants* to which the fire brigade may attach hoses. A wet-riser system is particularly suited to higher-rise buildings which may not be supplied by water from the mains, such as with the use of a *dry riser*. A wet-riser system is usually supplied with water from a low-level *break cistern* that contains a duplicate pump set. The pump set will normally require a back-up electrical supply in case of mains failure. See *Dry riser*

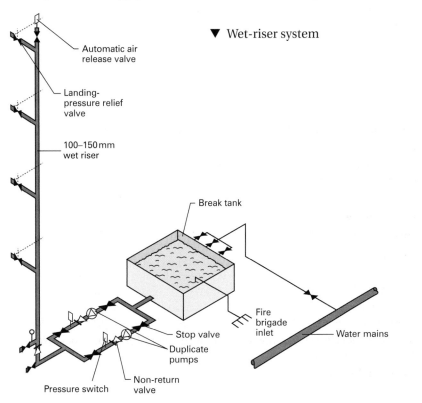

▼ Wet-riser system

wetted perimeter

The surface inside a pipe which has been wetted due to contact with water.

wheelhead radiator valve

A valve which may be used to manually turn on or off an individual radiator in a *central-heating* system. See *Radiator valves*

▲ Wheelhead radiator valve

A
B
C
D
E
F
G
H
I
J
K
L
M
N
O
P
Q
R
S
T
U
V
W
X
Y
Z

whole-house central heating
See *Types of central heating*

wholesome water
Water that is fit for human consumption with no danger to health; the water supplied through a *water undertaker's* main is regarded as wholesome water.

wind farms
An area of land used for the installation of large windmill-type structures that produce electrical power when the blades are rotated by the wind.

wire wool
See *Steel wool*

wobbe number
This identifies the amount of heat produced by a burner; it is found by dividing the *calorific value* of the gas by its *relative density*.

wood bits
These are drill attachments used for drilling holes in timber for pipes to pass through.

▲ Selection of wood bits

wood chisels
See *Chisels*

wood-cored roll
See *Solid roll*

work hardening
The process of working, hammering or bossing a metal so that its *molecules* are pushed tightly together. In this state the metal appears very hard and it can be brittle (subject to fracture). Work-hardened metals can be softened by *annealing* them. See *Tempering*

working head
The water pressure created by the *head* of water over a pipe or component and which it is designed to work to.

working pressure
See *Gas pressure*

workman-like manner
This describes good quality work which conforms to *British* and *European Standards* or to a specification approved by the Water Regulator as detailed in the *Water Regulations*.

WRAS

See *Water Regulations Advisory Scheme*

wrenches

These are *hand tools* used for holding or gripping pipes, or for loosening threaded fittings. Care for these tools is provided by ensuring that the teeth are cleaned free of *jointing compounds*; the tool should be replaced when the teeth are worn down. A *stillson* is an example of a wrench.

wrought iron

A metal that contains almost pure iron; it was used extensively in the past in building work but has now largely been replaced by *steel.*

ABCDEFGHIJKLMNOPQRSTUVW XYZ

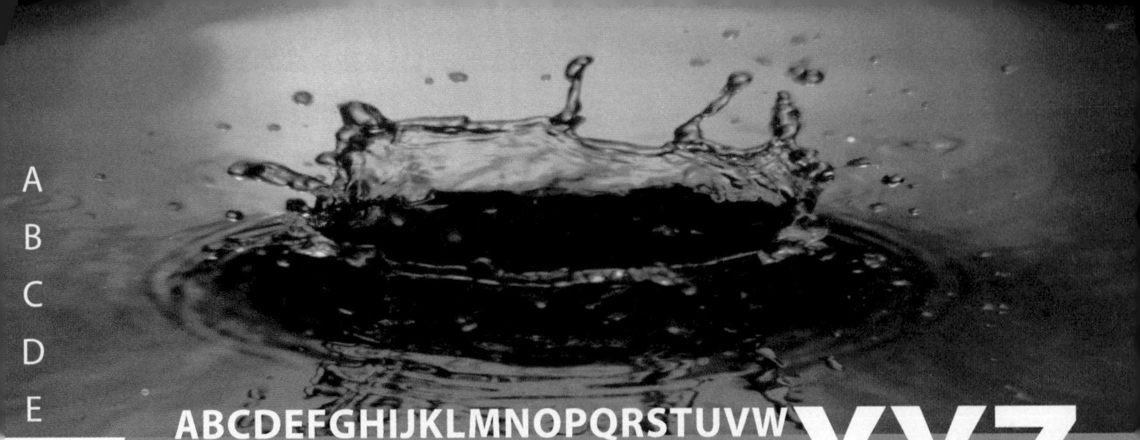

zeolites

A zeolite is a mineral with a unique interconnecting lattice structure that is used in a *base exchange water softener*. This lattice structure is arranged to form a honeycomb framework of consistent diameter interconnecting channels and pores. Negatively charged alumina and neutrally charged silica tetrahedral building blocks are stacked to produce the open three-dimensional honeycomb framework. Zeolites sieve the calcium carbonates and sulphates in *hard waters*, not letting them pass into the system. The softener needs regenerating periodically by backwashing (a process of drawing water through the zeolites to remove and drain away any calcium salts that have been collected).

zone backflow prevention devices

The *Water Regulations* require whole site or zone protection against *backflow* to be provided in addition to *point-of-use backflow prevention devices* in circumstances where water is supplied to two or more separately occupied premises from the same *supply pipe* and a supply pipe conveys water to a property which stores water for more than 24 hours ordinary use (see diagram opposite).

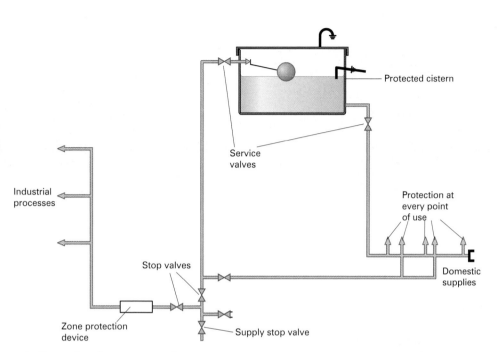

Protected cistern

Service
valves

Industrial
processes

Protection at
every point
of use

Stop valves

Domestic
supplies

Zone protection
device

Supply stop valve

▲ Example of zone protection

zone valve

See *Two-port valve*